SELECTED READINGS IN PHYSICS

General Editor: D. TER HAAR

THE QUINTESSENCE OF IRVING LANGMUIR

THE QUINTESSENCE OF IRVING LANGMUIR

by

ALBERT ROSENFELD
Science Editor 'LIFE' Magazine

PERGAMON PRESS

OXFORD · LONDON · EDINBURGH · NEW YORK
TORONTO · PARIS · FRANKFURT

Pergamon Press Ltd., Headington Hill Hall, Oxford
4 & 5 Fitzroy Square, London W.1
Pergamon Press (Scotland) Ltd., 2 & 3 Teviot Place, Edinburgh 1
Pergamon Press Inc., 44-01 21st Street, Long Island City, New York 11101
Pergamon of Canada, Ltd., 6 Adelaide Street East, Toronto, Ontario
Pergamon Press S.A.R.L., 24 rue des Écoles, Paris 5e
Pergamon Press GmbH, Kaiserstrasse 75, Frankfurt-am-Main

First edition 1966
Library of Congress Catalog Card No. 65-19839

(2119/66)

Contents

Foreword	8
Introduction	9
Chapter 1	13
Chapter 2	23
Chapter 3	34
Chapter 4	46
Chapter 5	59
Chapter 6	77
Chapter 7	93
Chapter 8	109
Chapter 9	121
Chapter 10	136
Chapter 11	147
Chapter 12	164
Chapter 13	176
Chapter 14	186
Chapter 15	197
Chapter 16	208

Chapter 17 224

Chapter 18 238

Chapter 19 250

Chapter 20 260

Chapter 21 273

Chapter 22 282

Chapter 23 295

Chapter 24 311

Chapter 25 324

List of Principal Sources 331

Appendix I 337

Appendix II 340

Index 357

"He pored intent
Upon a sea-anemone, like a flower
Opening its disk of blue and crimson rays
Under the lucid water.
He stretched his hand
And with a sea-gull's feather, touched its heart.
The bright disk shrank and closed, as though a flower
Turned instantly to fruit, ripe, soft, and round
As the pursed lips of a sea-god hiding there.
They fastened, sucking, on the quill and held it.
Young Aristotle laughed. He rose to his feet.
'Come and see this!' he called."

ALFRED NOYES

Foreword

THIS series of books, "Selected Readings in Physics", is compiled with the aim of showing "how physics is made". In most of the volumes this is done by reprinting the most important "classical" papers on a particular subject, these being accompanied by a carefully written outline of how the subject has developed since its inception and a review of its present status. Sometimes, however, it is instructive to show the progress of physics by considering, not the development of a subject, but the contribution made by some one outstanding physicist. Thus a division of the "Selected Readings in Physics" series is called "Men of Physics" and in these volumes the work of men such as Landau, Eddington and Kramers is discussed and some of their papers reprinted. It is hoped to include such a volume on Langmuir, but the present volume has a slightly different slant. It is the biography of Langmuir, written by A. Rosenfeld to whom I am exceedingly grateful for his agreement that this reproduction may be included in the series. Mr. Rosenfeld, the Science Editor of *Life,* makes the biography read like a novel but, at the same time, the text shows very clearly "how science is made" and I am certain that this volume, as much as, or perhaps even more than, any other volume in the series, will contribute to a development of a "feel" for physics in those who read it.

D. ter. Haar.

Introduction

THIS book, the first full-length biography of Langmuir, was written to accompany *The Collected Works of Irving Langmuir*, published by the Pergamon Press in 1961. It appeared as Volume 12 of the series, and has so far reached the public only in that form. This new paper-back edition is designed to introduce the biography — and the man — to a much wider audience.

The first eleven volumes of the collected works offered, through Langmuir's own technical papers and through evaluations of them written by other outstanding scientists, a well-rounded picture of Langmuir the scientist. The biography was to deal with Langmuir the man. But to write about Langmuir and omit science would be like printing his photograph with the head missing. So science permeates this biography just as it permeated his life.

Langmuir's greatness as a scientist has been insufficiently appreciated by laymen largely because of the esoteric nature of much of the subject matter in which he dealt. The author has attempted, therefore, to describe just enough of Langmuir's work, in just enough detail, to convey to the non-scientist the nature of his achievement — and to share some of the excitement of Langmuir's intellectual adventures.

Special attention has been paid to Langmuir's early life and family background, which are essential to any understanding of the forces that shaped his unique character and career.

In the performance of this task the author was fortunate in having access to persons and documents hitherto untapped, and in receiving the wholehearted co-operation of the two most important sources on Langmuir — the Langmuir family and the General Electric Company.

The author is especially grateful to C. G. Suits, vice-president and director of research for GE, whose invaluable suggestions and contributions were offered generously — and with no hint that the author should be anything but scrupulously honest about the role of the General Electric Company in Langmuir's life. (Actually, this role was so favourable that a Langmuir biography must, in a sense, be an extended "commercial" for GE.)

My gratitude is also due to Miles J. Martin, director of information for the GE research laboratory; to many of Langmuir's former colleagues in and out of the laboratory, notably Albert W. Hull, Kenneth H. Kingdon, Vincent J. Schaefer, E. J. Workman, and Edward Hennelly; and to Harold E. Way of Union College, executive editor of the Langmuir memorial volumes. Thanks are also in order for the assistance received from staff members of the General Electric research library, the New York Public Library, and the Library of Congress.

One of the great rewards of working on this biography was making the acquaintance of so many stimulating and delightful Langmuirs, who collectively constitute one of America's truly remarkable families. Among those who cheerfully permitted themselves to be imposed upon were Langmuir's nephews, Alexander, David, and Robert (and their families); his nieces, Mrs. Laura Langmuir, Mrs. Evelyn Harmon, and Mrs. Ruth Van de Water; his sister-in-law, Mrs. Edith Langmuir (widow of his brother Charles Herbert, and mother of Alexander and David); his son-in-law, Harry Summerhayes, Jr; his grandnephews, Bruce, Donald, and Allan; and his cousins, Mrs. Gertrude Collins and William C. White, who was also Langmuir's colleague at the GE laboratory. Many important family documents — letters, diaries, photograph albums, newspaper clippings, genealogical studies, etc. — were made available to the author by Bruce Langmuir, Mrs. Evelyn Harmon, and Mrs. Ruth Van de Water.

Most indispensable of all (if there are degrees of indispensability) was the help unstintingly given by Langmuir's widow, Mrs. Marion Langmuir, by his son Kenneth, and by his daughter Barbara (Mrs. Harry Summerhayes, Jr). Perhaps the most useful single contribution was made by Kenneth — who volunteered to excerpt his father's personal diaries (themselves unavailable to the author) running from 1910 to 1955.

A. R.
New Rochelle, N.Y.

Chapter 1

"Everything's incredible, if you can skin off the crust of obviousness our habits put on it."

Philip Quarles, in ALDOUS HUXLEY'S *Point Counterpoint*

"ALL THE boys seem greatly interested in gymnastics," wrote Irving Langmuir's mother from Paris on January 13, 1893, when Irving was almost twelve years old. "Irving thinks it is of much more importance than his studies, and I guess it is just as well, for his brain is too active, and I really think if he studied vigorously we could not send him to school. His brain is working like an engine all the time. . . ."

Irving Langmuir, descended from hardy Scots, never lost his enthusiasm for "gymnastics." Once he walked fifty-two miles in a single day. He climbed the Matterhorn for the first time when he was past forty, and did it with practically no preliminary hardening. Throughout his life he performed prodigies of physical endurance, just for the exuberant fun of it.

But neither did the Langmuir brain ever stop "working like an engine" — not, at least, until it stopped working altogether on August 16, 1957, the day he died. Langmuir's lifelong celebration of cerebration enriched all of mankind. It also, incidentally, paid off handsomely for his wisely undemanding employer, the General Electric Company. He left behind a monumental body of achievement which, for sheer quantity of quality, has nothing to equal it in the history of American science.

Langmuir's curiosity was all-embracing, his enthusiasms almost indiscriminate. He was like Browning's duchess who "liked whate'er she looked on and her looks went everywhere." When Langmuir — officially a chemist — looked on something with his trained scientist's eye, he did not stop to inspect the label to see whether it said "chemistry" or "physics" — or even "biology." He was, in fact, among the first to recognize and prophesy how dependent chemistry would become on physics, and how much biology would owe to both. The broad range of his scientific tastes, the passion with which he pursued them, and the durability of his ardor, all combined to make Langmuir anything but a typical scientist. He was not even a typical *great* scientist.

In reconstructing a scientist's life the biographer can ordinarily build his literary structure around a single dramatic highlight, the climactic achievement of the great man's career — the moment he made his historic discovery, or performed his classic experiment, or experienced the flash of insight that led to the theory which bears his name. But in Langmuir's case, so steady was his output and so high the level of its excellence, that one can, at best, imitate the biographers of artists — and write, say, of Langmuir's Surface Chemistry Period, as one would of Picasso's Blue Period.[1] It would not be stretching the truth to call Langmuir an artist. He certainly contemplated the world, in its multifarious detail, with the candid eye of an artist — not merely looking, but seeing. And to the ingenuousness of the artist's eye, he added the ingenuity of the scientist's intellect.

"Perhaps my most deeply rooted hobby," Langmuir once wrote, "is to understand the mechanism of simple and familiar phenomena." The phenomena of the moment might be anything from molecules to mountains; he was curious about whatever attracted his omnivorous attention. And what Langmuir was curious about, he investigated. And what he investigated, he thought about.

[1] Even at that, the periods would all overlap.

Though the thoughts often led down blind alleys, they also, with startling frequency, bore scientific fruit — such a rich and abundant variety of fruit, over the years, that it is difficult to catalogue the contents of the Langmuir-laden cornucopia without overlooking something of importance. Sir Hugh Taylor, for example, wrote a comprehensive article on Langmuir's life and work for the *Biographical Memoirs of Fellows of the Royal Society,* in which he enumerated Langmuir's outstanding accomplishments with seeming thoroughness. Yet there was at least one dissatisfied reader. Dennis Gabor, who has pursued Langmuir's trail-blazing researches into the nature of plasmas (a word Langmuir invented), complains goodnaturedly that, in Sir Hugh's account, full as it is, the word plasma does not even occur. "Irving Langmuir was such a great man," writes Gabor, "that one could leave out such a giant creation of his, and there still remains enough!"

Gabor is not the only scientist to point out that even a small piece of Langmuir's work might have justified a lifetime of research effort for a lesser man. Moreover, apart from the specific achievements which are directly and undeniably attributable to Langmuir, there *is* no way of calculating what he may have contributed to the work of others.

His incandescent intellect gave off ideas like sparks. He broadcast ideas, and others fertilized them. Even had he done no research of his own, Langmuir's very presence in the General Electric laboratory served as an invaluable catalyst for others. "It was impossible to be around him without coming under his stimulating influence," says Kenneth Kingdon. And Saul Dushman once commented, "Langmuir is a regular thinking machine. Put in facts, and you get out a theory."

Once, on a fishing trip with a GE group, Larry Hawkins was trying to remember the relationship between the height of a wave and its velocity. He questioned several of the GE scientists to no avail before he ran across Langmuir. Langmuir did not remember ever having seen the formula, but it looked quite simple to him. "The height represents energy," he said, "and energy is proportional to v^2, so the height should be proportional to the square of the velocity." Hawkins checked the formula in the laboratory's library when he got back, and Langmuir turned out to be exactly right. "Langmuir," says Albert W. Hull, "was always interested in everybody else's work, and always lavish with his suggestions. You could depend upon him to come up with a fresh approach to even the knottiest problem."

Nor was Langmuir's influence limited to the General Electric laboratory. He was equally unstinting in handing out advice and assistance to researchers from other laboratories whenever they exchanged visits.[1] To know about a scientific problem — anybody's — was, for Langmuir, to think about it and discuss it. There is no telling how many ideas he may have given to others in intense conversations on trains and planes, in desultory talk on some lakeside or ski slope, or at scientific conferences all over the world. "I can think of more than one instance," says Edward F. Hennelly, "where I have heard Langmuir make a suggestion which was later published as someone else's discovery. I am not suggesting that anyone *stole* his ideas. Just as Langmuir himself freely used the work of other people to build on, so he gave freely of himself to others." He could not have cared less who got credit for what. To him this free and constant interchange was the essence of science. And to have operated in any other fashion would have spoiled the fun.

Science as fun was one of Langmuir's cardinal tenets,[2] and it

---

[1] "As an example," writes Harry Sobotka, distinguished biologist of the Mount Sinai Hospital in New York, "I once showed Langmuir an article by Engström on the ultramicro determination of nitrogen by X-ray absorption spectroscopy, based on the sharp difference in absorbance at a wavelength slightly to the left (say: K−) and to the right (say: K+) of the K line in the X-ray spectrum of nitrogen. Having glanced through the paper, he conceived without a moment's hesitation the following method: Superimpose a positive photograph, taken with monochromatic K− light, and a negative photograph, taken with K+ light. This optical subtraction will eliminate absorption by all other elements and give at once a map of the distribution of nitrogen."

[2] When asked to give a series of five Hitchcock Lectures at the University of California in the spring of 1946, Langmuir chose as his general subject, "Science for the Fun of It."

helps explain his phenomenal productivity. In his later years he always insisted, "Everything I have ever done, I have done for the fun of it." Nor did he ever feel that, in so acting, he was cheating his employers. He and they both knew that his fun nearly always resulted in products and profits for them. Thus, even during his official working hours, Langmuir pursued only what pleased his fancy. It was natural that he should continue pleasing his fancy after hours by having still more fun with science.

During cloud-seeding experiments in New Mexico, Langmuir spent a good deal of off-hours time with his collaborator and good friend, E. J. Workman, president of the institution then known as the New Mexico School of Mines. Workman recalls the joy of going off in an automobile with Langmuir to tour the back roads of some remote area. The remoter the area the better he liked it. Even on a joyride, Langmuir would come fully equipped with slide-rule, notebook, Leica, binoculars, geological compass with directional level, thermometer for both wet-bulb and dry-bulb temperatures and a seatful of other instruments. "You could hardly drive a mile without Langmuir wanting to stop and examine something," says Workman. "It might be the odd-colored moss on the back of a tree, an ant colony on some rock, or a peculiar geological formation."

Once, on an Adirondack mountainside with his close associate, Vincent J. Schaefer, Langmuir grew fascinated with the galls on an oak tree, inspecting them with wonder and delight. "We lay awake in our bedrolls for hours watching the stars that night," says Schaefer, "while Langmuir tried to figure out the evolutionary pattern that accounted for those strange excrescences."

Langmuir's nephew, Alexander, now chief epidemiologist for the United States Public Health Service, remembers a visit with his Uncle Irving at Lake George back in 1931. On one occasion they lay flat on their stomachs on the ice watching, through a little hand lens Langmuir always carried, the formation of air bubbles on the surface. "I was about fifteen at the time, and even though his interest communicated itself to me, that ice was mighty cold to lie on. But he was seemingly impervious to the cold, or too absorbed to notice it, and he just lay there watching those bubbles until he was all watched out."

Another time, on a camping trip, Alexander and his Uncle Irving were looking at the sunset, and somehow got talking about how the sun was gradually cooling off to the point where some day it would no longer be able to warm the earth. "But that doesn't worry me much," Uncle Irving said.

"You mean because it's so far in the future?"

"Oh, no. I mean that we'll keep civilization going on earth even without the sun's help."

"But how? Surely not with coal?"

"Of course not, Stupid. With atomic enegy.'

He then proceeded to calculate, mostly in his head, using Einstein's formula for mass-energy equivalence, how much energy it would take to maintain the earth's atmosphere at a livable temperature. Then he figured out roughly how much matter would be available for conversion into energy and decided that mankind could still keep things going for another few hundred thousand years after the sun had cooled.

"This was all in fun, of course," says Alex Langmuir. "Yet he was quite serious about using atomic energy. And this was back around 1931, remember, long before the atomic bomb, long before Hahn and Strassman ever observed uranium fission in the laboratory, even before Chadwick had discovered the neutron."

In brief, Irving Langmuir did not merely practice science. He lived it. It was part of his daily sustenance. One need follow no convoluted threads of Freudian analysis to understand Langmuir. He needed science as he needed proteins and vitamins. He observed and measured and analyzed and philosophized as naturally as a child builds a snowman or throws a rock into the water. Langmuir never lost his childlike sense of wonder. Wondering was something he simply did, like breathing. And he was seldom content to say, "I wonder —" and let it go at that. He usually managed to find some straightforward way of satisfying his curiosity.

One summer afternoon, fishing from the deck of Langdon Gibson's sloop, *The Virginian,* in Penobscot Bay, Langmuir was watching the antics of a few seals romping nearby. "I wonder," he said, "how close a well-camouflaged man could come to them without frightening them off?"

"No way of telling," said one of his fishing companions. "Not very close, probably."

Langmuir went to look for his heavy black poncho — which he used more as a makeshift darkroom for developing film than for keeping off the rain. He draped it over his head carefully for fit, then cut two small eye-holes and a nose-hole in the poncho. Then he tied a black canvas strip around his neck, arranged so he could see out of the eye-holes. Then, stripping off everything but the poncho, he went over the side and dogpaddled slowly over to the seals. After a few initial grunts of caution, they permitted him to join the party.

That was when Langmuir was a young bachelor, still in his twenties. But he never changed. His niece, Mrs. Evelyn Harmon, remembers one of the last times her Uncle Irving came to visit them at their home in Connecticut. He was past seventy-five. He rough-housed with the boys, did some experiments with floating bodies, explained to them how satellites are held in orbit by gravitational force and illustrated it by swinging a bucketful of water over his head in the back yard. Later, at the beach, he challenged them to a diving contest and showed them how to swim like a porpoise. Then they all went to the Stamford zoo, where Uncle Irving sat in rapt fascination observing the behavior of a little red fox long after even the children were bored. "Uncle Irving lived every minute," says Mrs. Harmon, "and usually with a notebook in hand." Langmuir's sensibilities never grew jaded. His outlook was as fresh at seventy as most scientists' are at twenty.

In an era when scientists over thirty-five seem increasingly inclined to start leaving the laboratory for the administrator's office, Langmuir was a living refutation of the stereotyped notion that great ideas in the physical sciences come only from young men. It is true that they generally come from young *minds.* Langmuir

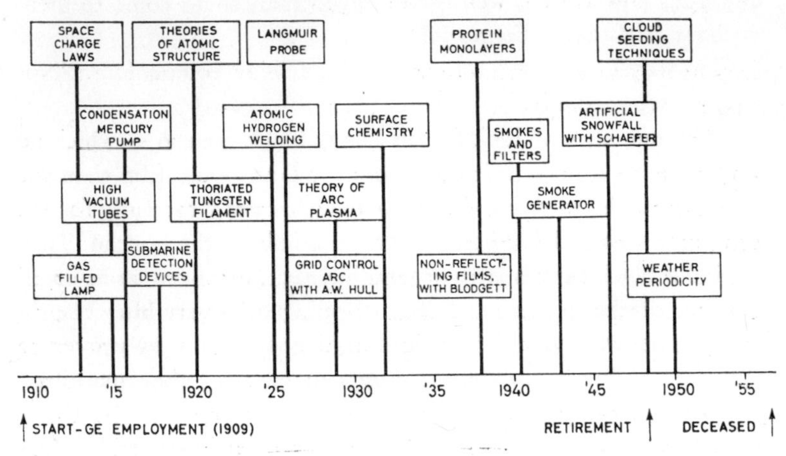
IRVING LANGMUIR'S CREATIVE OUTPUT
BOTH SCIENTIFIC AND APPLIED – THROUGHOUT HIS RESEARCH CAREER WITH GENERAL ELECTRIC
SPACE CHARGE LAWS
THEORIES OF ATOMIC STRUCTURE
LANGMUIR PROBE
PROTEIN MONOLAYERS
CLOUD SEEDING TECHNIQUES
CONDENSATION MERCURY PUMP
ATOMIC HYDROGEN WELDING
SURFACE CHEMISTRY
SMOKES AND FILTERS
ARTIFICIAL SNOWFALL WITH SCHAEFER
HIGH VACUUM TUBES
THORIATED TUNGSTEN FILAMENT
THEORY OF ARC PLASMA
SMOKE GENERATOR
GAS FILLED LAMP
SUBMARINE DETECTION DEVICES
GRID CONTROL ARC WITH A.W. HULL
NON-REFLECTING FILMS, WITH BLODGETT
WEATHER PERIODICITY
1910 '15 1920 '25 1930 '35 1940 '45 1950 '55
START-GE EMPLOYMENT (1909)
RETIREMENT
DECEASED

FIG. 1.

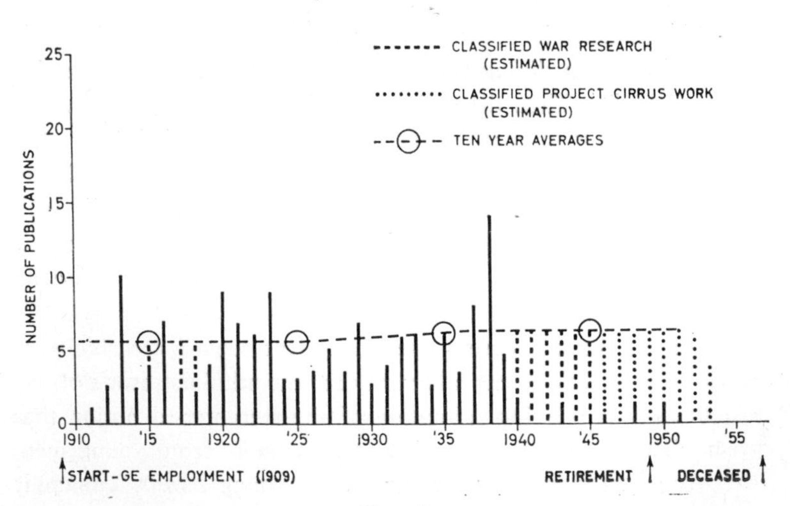
IRVING LANGMUIR'S SCIENTIFIC PUBLICATIONS
INCLUDING ESTIMATED EQUIVALENT CLASSIFIED WORK
CLASSIFIED WAR RESEARCH (ESTIMATED)
CLASSIFIED PROJECT CIRRUS WORK (ESTIMATED)
TEN YEAR AVERAGES
NUMBER OF PUBLICATIONS
0
5
10
15
20
25
1910 '15 1920 '25 1930 '35 1940 '45 1950 '55
START-GE EMPLOYMENT (1909)
RETIREMENT
DECEASED

FIG. 2.

was one of those rare minds that knew how to keep itself young. He was never content to bask in his prestige as a Nobel laureate and as a senior statesman of American science. He not only remained on the frontiers of science; he made it a practice to open up a new frontier of his own now and then. His sense of intellectual adventure remained undiminished to the end.

(The charts on page 20, prepared by the General Electric Research Laboratory, graphically make the point that Langmuir had no isolated "creative periods." His entire working life was one continuous creative period.)

It was this perpetual ebullience, inexhaustible yet running in controlled channels under the guidance of a disciplined intelligence, that impelled Dennis Gabor to call Langmuir "the most harmonious of human spirits." When Gabor first met him in Berlin in the early thirties, he could not help noting that Langmuir possessed, behind those spectacles, the clearest blue eyes he had ever seen — and that, while they flashed with energy, yet they somehow reflected a great inner serenity.

"I have written about morbid inventors like Rudolf Diesel, W. H. Carothers, and Edwin Armstrong," says Gabor, "all of whom worried themselves into committing suicide. And I think of troubled geniuses like Oppenheimer and Teller and Szilard as being representative of our troubled time. Langmuir," says Gabor, "was obviously not of our time. He was the sanest and most well-adjusted genius I have ever heard of."

The very harmony of Langmuir's life presents yet another problem for the biographer. Because of it Langmuir will always remain a frustration and a disappointment to the novelist or playwright wishing to exploit him literarily. Though Langmuir's life was replete with incident, it had no dramatic structure, and though his work was often controversial, there was virtually no emotional conflict on a personal level. He had no formidable obstacles to surmount, no parental opposition to the attainment of his career. There were no traumatic sibling rivalries, no tempestuous extracurricular romances.

He did not have to bear the mark of a visible physical handicap, as did Steinmetz and Toulouse-Lautrec, for example. He did not work frantically against the approach of an early death, as did Keats and Mozart. He did not have to contend with Beethoven's deafness or Milton's blindness.

Once he had gone to work for the General Electric Research Laboratory, which gave him complete freedom, and once he had married Marion Mersereau, who wanted nothing more out of life than to be the wife of Irving Langmuir, he had the perfect job and the perfect mate. Against this backdrop of financial and emotional security, he simply spent the rest of his vigorous life on a smooth plateau of uninhibited scientific self-indulgence.

It is no wonder that, approaching his official retirement age, he was able to tell his younger brother, Dean, "I have never spent a really unhappy day in my life."

Well, if Langmuir took maximum advantage of every American's declared right to the pursuit of happiness, we can all be grateful. For we have all eaten the fruit thereof.

Chapter 2

"What we love and revere generally is determined by early associations."

OLIVER WENDELL HOLMES Jr.

IRVING LANGMUIR was the third of four Langmuir children, all boys. He was born, a lustily bawling seven-pounder, on January 31, 1881, at 120 Lafayette Street in Brooklyn, New York — not Thomas Wolfe's teeming, subway-tunneled Brooklyn that "only the dead know," but a quiet, pastoral Brooklyn which Mitchell Wilson describes as "a meadow of small, tree-lined, church steepled towns," none of whose residents had yet heard of the Brooklyn Dodgers or experienced the esthetic thrill of throwing a pop bottle at an umpire.

The only thing he could later remember about those first years on Lafayette Street was being sick in bed, probably with the measles, along with one of his older brothers—he could not be sure whether it had been Arthur or Herbert. When Irving was only four years old, the family moved to Elmsford, New York, to a spacious house which sat on a five-acre tract of land. "In front of the house," he noted in a later diary, "was a pond about seven hundred feet long and a couple of little waterfalls." Langmuir's cousin, "Ducie," who later became Mrs. Gertrude Collins, retained a vivid recollection of being shoved into that pond by Irving at a very early age.

At Elmsford, Dean, the last of the Langmuir boys, was born. Arthur, the first-born, was nine years older than Irving; Charles Herbert (called simply Herbert) was five years older; and Dean was six years younger.

Irving was not old enough to go to school in Elmsford days, but when Arthur and Herbert went off to their school — coincidentally named the Irving Institute — in Tarrytown, Irving was glad to see them go. Irving was both volatile and sensitive, a combination that made him irresistibly teasable, and his older brothers took full advantage of his vulnerability. When they ran out of specific things to tease him about, they would hold him down on the floor while they invented weird, polysyllabic nonsense words which, while not insulting in themselves, would infuriate him. Or they would take some perfectly familiar word like oranges and distort it into "Oh-*ran*-gees," and shout it at him with satanic vigor until he wept with rage. Then, giving themselves time to get off to a gleeful, running head start, they would let him go, and he would go tearing after them, screaming threats of maximal mayhem. They usually managed to bait their little brother when Mama was out of earshot, so she was at a loss to understand why Irving, a reasonably well-behaved boy elsewhere, was getting to be such a terrible-tempered brat around the house.

Irving was not, however, unique in serving as the butt of juvenile misbehavior in the Langmuir household — nor did the badgering he got from Arthur and Herbert chasten him sufficiently to refrain from giving his own younger brother a hard time in his turn. In a letter to their Aunt Fanny from Paris in 1895, Herbert, writing with all the detached maturity of his nineteen years, enclosed "one of Dean's letters to Papa complaining bitterly of ill-treatment by Irving." Herbert went on to reminisce about the cudgelings he himself used to get from Arthur (known as "A.C."). "I remember a great many such occurrences with great vividness because of the terrible vows of vengeance which each offense of 'A.C.' caused to rise in my heart. For instance, during lunch 'A.C.' would be just as likely as not to feel a sudden longing to empty the pitcher over my head. I was generally opposed to such proceedings and a race around the table often ensued. If there happened to be two pitchers, things grew very lively, and frequently two heads or two pitchers got cracked in the fight. Now all these things don't appear so dreadful after some years have elapsed, but at the time of their occurrence they are often very tragical. For instance Dean's accusation of Irving is quite an awful event in Dean's history and we fully appreciated its gravity. Last night we had a mock trial over it and Irving was warned against such occurrences in future and was condemned to the costs of the procedure."

No wonder their mother always wished for a daughter.

The four Langmuir boys were four distinct and different personalities. They fought as children, though never seriously; and as adults they frequently disagreed violently and argued vociferously, addressing each other in acid tones as "My Dear Sir." Yet they always remained close. They were fond of one another and proud of one another. And they all had reason to be proud.

Arthur became a first-rate chemist and an international authority on shellacs, made a great deal of money, and was able to retire as a relatively young man to a comfortable estate in Hastings-on-Hudson, New York.

Herbert became a vice-president of the New York Life Insurance Company, and raised four successful sons of his own, three of them scientists.

Dean became an investment counselor whose financial advice was much sought after, and who made his opinions heard in lecture halls, on radio programs, and via magazine articles.

And terrible-tempered little Irving grew up to become Irving Langmuir.

In 1888, after three years at Elmsford, the Langmuirs moved back to Brooklyn, this time to 296 St. James Place. Irving, now seven, was enrolled in Public School No. 11, where "I did pretty well... but never behaved very well in class. I was never left back but was once allowed to skip a class because of good work."

While Irving went to P.S. No. 11, Herbert attended Pratt Institute in Brooklyn, and Arthur, already scientifically inclined, was studying at Columbia. Their father, Charles, a successful insurance man, was probably one of those leisurely commuters who Mitchell Wilson says "rode to offices in the city across the river on horse cars and steam trains." Brooklyn Bridge, the masterpiece of American engineering up to that point, had just been opened to traffic in 1883.

Charles Langmuir and his wife, Sadie, instilled in all four of their sons a strong sense of family. When the adult Irving visited the University of Edinburgh, he managed to take time off for a side excursion to look up a bit of Langmuir lore. Dean did some genealogical spadework and informed his children in writing that, by virtue of his mother's ancestry, "we can belong to any of those societies whose membership is confined to descendants of those who came over on the *Mayflower*."

A special opportunity for solemn family soul-searching arose when Irving Langmuir was awarded the Nobel Prize for chemistry in 1932. At a big reunion on November 27 of that year at Herbert's place in Englewood, New Jersey, the host addressed the assembled Langmuirs. "Among all the families of the United States," he pointed out, "there are only eight who now have a Nobel Prize winner. The honor which has come to Irving Langmuir is therefore an extraordinary one which entitles us to our day of congratulation to him and of celebration for all.

"Now, how does it happen," Herbert asked, "that our family scales this peak, and having done so, can we in future generations maintain the impulse and the energy?

"This much I believe can be truly said: that each of the three generations of our family since we came from Scotland has been a better generation than its predecessor, and that the fourth generation, many of whom are with us today, is the most promising of all. We are an ascending family.

"In England there are many families whose sons and daughters distinguish themselves as a matter of course, and it is evident that there is no greater or better influence than that which comes from the tradition, character and success of a family.

"The United States is a comparatively new country in which

material and human foundations are inclined to change too rapidly to become established, and yet this country is already developing families of the highest value to the nation and to the world, and there will be many more to come.

"In our family, is there a distinguishing type of mind and character? Perhaps we cannot yet answer that question, but I believe it is at least evident:

"(1) That we are gifted with the inclination and the courage to ask the reason why, accompanied by the ability to think things through for ourselves. There are no mental rubber stamps in our family; and

"(2) That we are naturally of clean and sound personal character and thought. There are no wastrels, no mere parlor ornaments among us.

"It is apparently through simple virtues such as these, but raised to their highest power, that Irving Langmuir has won the Nobel Prize."

Herbert's speech was only one of eight that were made that evening in Englewood — all by Langmuirs about the Langmuirs.

Arthur, to prepare for an address he was scheduled to give two nights later at the Chemists' Club in New York, did a lot of boning up on the family background. The occasion was a dinner honoring Irving on the eve of his departure for Stockholm to accept the Nobel Prize. Arthur's speech was carried in the News Edition of *Industrial and Engineering Chemistry* for December 20, 1932, but that portion of the speech dealing with the family was omitted entirely, and has never been published anywhere. Which is just as well, since further research done by Arthur in the ensuing years with the help of his Canadian cousin, Winifred, turned up a number of inaccuracies in his earlier account.

"Lang and Muir," Arthur told the members of the Chemists' Club that night, "are rather common Scottish names, but the combination, Langmuir, is quite rare. There are no Langmuirs in the New York telephone directory, and I found only one in the Glasgow and Edinburgh directories of the year 1932."

Arthur's — and Irving's — grandfather, Charles Langmuir, was the son of a Glasgow brickmaker named Matthew, who, according to an obituary sketch, "consecrated his heart and life to Christ in Glasgow" in 1828 when the "First Primitive Methodist Missionary entered Glasgow." Charles, who learned the printing trade before leaving Scotland, came to Montreal in 1842, when he was about twenty-two years old. After three years in Montreal, where his oldest son was born in late 1843, Charles moved his family to New Haven, Connecticut. There another son, also named Charles, was born on May 21, 1846. While the second Charles — who was to become Irving Langmuir's father — was still a baby, his father decided to give up the printing business in favor of life on the frontier.

The family went back to Canada on an Erie Canal boat and settled in a tiny Ontario lakeside village on an Indian reservation north of Toronto, where the Langmuirs were the only white family. As winter came on, earlier and more severely than expected, and food and money began to run out, the Langmuirs — with three small sons to care for now — grew panicky. But they were saved by a lucky circumstance. A missionary to the Indians named Horace Dean, who lived in a village across the lake, heard rumors of a white family in the neighborhood, and went out to look for them. When he found the Langmuirs they were on the verge of starvation. The Deans took them in and fed them, while Charles Langmuir worked hard through the winter, clearing his land for cultivation.

When spring came, he learned to his dismay that, because of a surveyor's error, he had been clearing a piece of land that was not his own. He had spent his savings and a year of his life, had exhausted his energies, and had endangered the lives of his wife and children on this frontier venture. Now he had not the heart to begin again. He went back to Toronto and the printing business. By winter he had saved enough money again to send for his family, and they returned to Toronto by sleigh.

In Toronto, where two more Langmuir boys were born, the younger Charles spent his boyhood working as a clerk in a bookstore. In his spare time, he taught himself stenography, then started a shorthand class of his own. Later he moved to Hamilton, Ontario, where he worked for a railroad attorney named Amellius Irving, after whom Irving Langmuir may have been named. Charles was still in his early twenties when he came to the United States to go into the insurance business.

"Except for our father's fatal infection with pneumonia," Arthur told the Chemists' Club in 1932, "both of our parents were of rugged health and never had a serious sickness. They have bequeathed to their four sons the same good health and sound bodies that they enjoyed . . . .

"Our father was a practical man of sound judgment and common sense with the ability to make a subject crystal clear to his listeners, and Irving has all of these qualities to an even greater degree.

"Our mother, who is still living at the age of eighty-four in excellent health and of good mind, is a woman with an intense interest in the world around her, looking forward rather than backward and a great reader of biography, history and travel. After her sons were educated and married, her insatiable curiosity took her to nearly every corner of the world. She went around the world three times and on her last trip at the age of seventy-six circled South America."

Irving's father, a self-taught and self-made man and a great advocate of self-discipline, was a rather reserved individual, somewhat formal even in his family relationships. When his wife wrote to her sisters, even in later years, she usually referred to her husband not as Charles but as Mr. Langmuir. And though she had quite a reputation for being a strong-willed, even a domineering, woman, there was no doubt that it was he who controlled the family pursestrings. His wife was unable to wangle a regular allowance out of him until after they had been married for over twenty years; and then she managed it only by threatening to take a job with a Parisian corsetière. As a result of this lack of independence in financial matters, she drummed into all her sons the notion that they must give their wives a proper allowance.

Charles Langmuir's penny-watching should not be misconstrued as penny-pinching. He was a tightwad not by nature but out of necessity. He had gone to work at fourteen and amassed a comfortable fortune by the time he was thirty-five. But, shortly after Dean was born, he lost it all in a gold mining venture. Even worse, many of his friends and relatives who had invested in the venture on his advice lost their money too. Charles's strict ethical code made him feel personally responsible for their losses. Though he had no legal obligation to do so, he felt he had a moral one, and he spent the rest of his life paying back the money. He only finished paying the last of it just before he died in 1898. Thus, though his sons were given the advantage of European travels and cosmopolitan educations, everyone in the family had to keep careful accounts every step of the way in order to achieve it.

The need for frugality hovered constantly in the background of all Langmuir activities. Charles Langmuir's letters to his sons were full of cautionary advice about money. His close scrutiny and questioning of expenses must have made him seem, at times, a bit unsympathetic.

There was the matter of Irving's eye trouble, for example, which was occasionally costly in terms of spectacles and oculists. There was no doubt that Irving did have trouble with his eyes, though it took everyone an unconscionably long time to find out about it. The revelatory incident took place on a boat trip down the Rhine when Irving was about eleven years old. Everyone was exclaiming on the beauty of an old castle they were passing. Irving's mother, disappointed at his seeming lack of appreciation, pointed it out and asked what he thought of the castle. "Castle?" said Irving. "What castle?"

When his eyes were examined in Paris, they were found to be atrociously myopic. After getting his first pair of glasses, properly fitted with sufficiently concave lenses, Irving was beside himself with excitement at the discovery of the world. He was "astonished", for example, to learn that the vague green blurs called trees were made up of thousands of leaves with fascinating shapes, each individually distinguishable. Irving had already become interested in laboratory science by then — but his lifelong delight in observing the minutiae of nature may very well date from his sudden awareness of how much more there was to see than he had ever imagined.

A defect – even one so small as nearsightedness – costs money. And Irving's father was a man, like Clarence Day's father, whose own robust health and iron energy made him a bit impatient with the physical failings of others.

"I am sorry to hear that you have had more trouble with your eyes," he wrote Irving from Paris in 1896. Irving, at the time, was fifteen, and attending Chestnut Hill Academy in Philadelphia. His father went on to say that he was "still more sorry to learn that you have had to go again to an oculist, and not only once, but three times. I don't take much stock in this oculist who cannot decide on the second interview, and it looks to me as if he was anxious to have as many visits as possible at the price of $5 a visit, which is an extraordinarily high price. It is all right for the first visit and examination, but for the following visits it is entirely too much, and I hope three visits covered the whole business."

Earlier that same year, just before his fifteenth birthday, Irving had written to Paris that he had broken his glasses and had to have them replaced. His father wrote back promptly: "I think if we make a rule that you will have to pay the expense of repairs, you won't break them so often. I hope you will find that you will be able to do without them, because I think it must be a nuisance to have to wear spectacles all through one's life. I have got up to age 50 without having to wear any yet, and if you take care of your eyes I think they will come round all right and you won't have any further trouble."

Actually Irving's eyes got worse instead of better, and later in life he had to have cataracts removed from both of them.

And yet Charles Langmuir was no skinflint. To be sure, he kept a sharp eye on all budgetary matters. But for a man who had seen his own parents near starvation and who had lived through a boyhood of penury, he was surprisingly indulgent with his children. He watched small expenditures so that he would not have to deny them things which other, freer-spending parents might have considered luxuries. For example, when Irving was only sixteen, his father let him take a summer trip through Belgium, Holland, Germany, and Switzerland. He sent Irving detailed instructions on how he was to travel, where he was to stay, how much everything was to cost in American dollars as well as in the local currency. He recommended places to visit and eat, interesting side trips to take, and sent along maps and rates of exchange for all the countries he was to visit.

"It is rather a risky thing to have a youth of your age take such a trip," he wrote, "but I guess we can risk it if you will keep your wits about you, not go into the uncivilized parts of the cities you visit and not be out too much after dark."

In preparing Irving's itinerary and getting advance reservations he must have gone to a great deal of trouble. He was no more miserly with his time than he was, really, with his money. He uncomplainingly took young Dean sightseeing all over Paris, for example — even taking him, against his better judgment, to the Paris morgue, were he was happy to report that "there were only three dead bodies exposed."

When Irving was still quite a small boy, his father often took him along on business trips — including several to Canada. In 1889, when Irving was only eight, his father was sent to Johnstown, Pennsylvania as claim adjuster for the New York Life Insurance Company. (The company later ran a picture of him in Johnstown, working on claims, in their newspaper advertisements.) The devastation of the city and its environs after the great flood that took more than two thousand lives left on Irving's impressionable mind a series of vivid scenes that he never forgot.

Though Charles Langmuir could be the sternest of parents, he also knew how to be gentle. His essential kindness came through to the children, and no one ever doubted that he loved his sons and cared a great deal about what happened to them. One of his close friends Dr. Oscar H. Rogers once told Herbert, years after his father's death at the age of fifty-four, "Your father I recall as the man among all I have ever known who was most absorbed in plans and dreams for his children. He never stopped talking about his boys."

Chapter 3

"Family spirit — accuracy re facts — no lies or half truths — Feet on the ground always, yet imagination . . . Influence of mother — always dissatisfied with accomplishments . . ."

Rough notes for a book planned,
but never written, by DEAN LANGMUIR

IT WAS a surprise to all when Sadie Comings, whose mother was one of the socially prestigious Lunts of Evanston, Illinois, took it into her head to marry one Charles Langmuir, an upstart with no formal education, of immigrant stock recently arrived from Scotland. The Lunts were descended from one of the original *Mayflower* passengers, and Sadie's mother, Sarah Ann Lunt, was only three generations separated from Major General Joseph Vose who, during the Revolutionary War, joined the main colonial forces under Washington in New Jersey, participated in the siege of Yorktown and the surrender of Cornwallis, had two horses shot under him, was made a general by brevet and later corresponded with the Marquis de Lafayette.

Actually, Charles Langmuir, though self-educated and raised in poverty, did not suffer from any feelings of family inferiority. On the contrary, he was pridefully aware that he was descended, on his mother's side, from a brother of John Knox, and on his father's side from Mary Seaton, Lady-in-Waiting to Mary Queen of Scots. And Charles, though an immigrant from Canada, had been born during his parents' brief stay in New Haven, Connecticut. Thus he qualified as a full-fledged native American citizen.

Irving Langmuir was blessed with an abundance of aunts and uncles by virtue of the fact that his father, who had four brothers, chose to marry a girl who had four sisters. Sadie was the most spirited of the five daughters of Dr. Isaac Miller Comings, himself from a pioneer family of Freedom, Maine. A graduate first of Colby, then of the Reform Medical College in Georgia, Isaac Comings became a physician, surgeon, professor of anatomy, editor of a medical journal and author of several medical textbooks. Sadie was born in 1848, while her father was a member of the faculty at Worcester College in Worcester, Massachusetts. While she was still a baby, Dr. Comings accepted a position at a small college in Macon, Georgia, and the family moved South. We learn from Sadie's memory book that, as a little girl, before being sent North to school, she spent a great deal of time on the slave-serviced plantation of her Aunt Dolly Burge.

Life in Macon was never serene for the Comings family. Dr. Comings was not only a thoroughgoing Yankee in attitude and speech; but he was not a man to keep his anti-slavery sentiments to himself. The family underwent an especially wrenching experience when their hired cook, a girl named Seely, had to watch in helpless grief as her husband was sold into slavery and sent to another state. After that Dr. Comings was so outspokenly critical of the slave system that his life was threatened, and there was open talk of having him tarred and feathered. In 1859, he decided his situation had grown too perilous for his family's safety, and, with his six women, moved from Georgia to New York.

In 1870, when Sadie was twenty-two, she went to visit one of her sisters in Clinton, Iowa. There, soon after her arrival, on the croquet field at Revere House, she met Charles Langmuir whom she "liked extremely from the first meeting." By September of that year they were exchanging photographs rather formally. Charles, writing from Madison, Wisconsin (he was even then a traveling man), addressed her as "Dear Friend" and signed himself "Your friend, C. Langmuir." By January of 1871 he was addressing her as "My dear Sadie," and the closing salutation was "Ever your happy Charley."

In the period between the two letters they had become engaged, but not before Charles had officially asked her father's consent. In a letter dated October 19, 1870, from Clinton, Iowa, Charles stated his case:

"I became acquainted with your daughter Sadie about the time she arrived in this city," he wrote Dr. Comings, "and since then we have met frequently. Our acquaintance has not been of very long duration, but sufficiently long to mature a sincere love for each other, which has resulted in my asking her to become my wife and I am happy to say she has consented. I now have the pleasure of asking your consent to a union which we are certain will give you satisfaction.

"I am a stranger to yourself and family and therefore you will desire to know something concerning me. My place of business is Chicago and at present I fill the position of Auditor of Agency Accounts in The Mutual Life Insurance Company. I have been connected with the company for three years and a half, and for a year ending last June 1 was Cashier. My present duties require me to travel from one agency to another about half my time, but I have the assurance of the officers that in January or April next they will give me the position of Actuary, for which I have been studying. Mr. Leadbetter who represents the Company here has known me for nearly three years and will be able to give you any information you may desire in reference to my reputation and Character in Chicago. I have resided at Evanston for the past year, and own a pleasant house there. We will make that our home. My income is amply sufficient to support us comfortably.

"I know it will grieve you to part with Sadie and you may hesitate in granting your consent, owing to never having met me, but I trust the favorable opinion entertained by Mr. and Mrs. Leadbetter will induce you to acquiesce. Were it possible I would go to New York and make the request personally.

"I will do my utmost to prove myself a worthy husband to Sadie . . ."

Sadie's father gave his consent, and they were married on April 25, 1871. Their life was eventful and apparently quite happy. They moved their residence frequently, and did a lot of traveling between moves. Each of the four boys was born in a different city.

Early in 1892, John A. McCall, the new president of the New York Life Insurance Company, decided to enlarge the company's European operations. To scout the largely untapped insurance potential of Europe, McCall selected Charles Langmuir. First, Charles and Sadie were taken on a tour of the United States agencies. Then, in April, they went to Europe, where they were treated royally everywhere by the European agency directors and their wives. During their six months of travel, Sadie wrote home indefatigably, describing in detail people, places, incidents, prices, customs and living conditions.

"Is it not fortunate," she wrote her sister Mamie when they arrived back in London in September, "that we finished our trip before cholera became epidemic in Europe? We did not have to give up any country except Denmark" (where they would have been quarantined for ten days).

At that point, though she considered Europeans "so much ahead of Americans in hospitality," she seemed glad the tour was ended. "I hear that Arthur and Herbert have returned from their summering," she wrote Mamie, "and the house is opened by Mary for the season, and I am commencing to think of home. Dean will stay at Bay Head with Mrs. Dean until my return, and Irving will board with Aunt Tilly so as to have good care, and the two big boys will be taken care of at 296 by Mary, so I feel that all will go on smoothly now that the school season has opened, but I don't want my family scattered very long and I think we will be able to start about the 20th of October."

There was one last visit to make to Paris before their departure. Almost as soon as they got there, Charles received a call from McCall in London offering him a job as director of all New York

Life's European agencies, with headquarters in Paris. It was a tempting job with excellent pay, and they were both charmed with Paris. Charles said Yes. Sadie wanted to go home to settle household affairs, pack up, and bring the boys back. But Charles opposed it and "gradually persuaded me to remain with him and let the boys and the cook, with the help of Aunt Fannie, do the whole job." Another six months went by before the boys arrived in Paris.

The nineties in Paris were full and exciting years, with the Langmuirs maintaining their tradition of maximum mobility by traveling all over the continent. Arthur finished his studies at Columbia, then went to Germany to get his doctorate at Heidelberg. Herbert went to work for the New York Life Insurance Company, first in Paris, then in London. After attending some French schools, Irving went back to the States to study first in Philadelphia, then in New York. Everyone wandered around Europe, sometimes in a party, sometimes each going off separately and meeting the others now and then at some prearranged spot — often at some Swiss resort, where there were nearby mountains to climb. The boys camped, skated, hiked, and climbed mountains in the meanest weather.

Their father made frequent trips, some on business, some on vacation, meeting his wife and sons — together or separately — wherever he could. The children were farmed out whenever necessary — though never cavalierly or carelessly. Through it all, Charles and Sadie kept track of each other and their family through voluminous correspondence, reporting to one another in detail all that they saw and did.

One of Sadie's 1894 letters to Mamie is indicative of the pattern: "Mr. Langmuir had to leave me in Cairo after traveling with me for two months, and I took the Nile trip with friends and returned alone after visiting Naples for a month on my way home . . . I found everything so beautiful there and the boys seemed to be getting along so nicely without me that I made quite a long visit and returned by the way of Genoa . . ."

In November of 1898, when Irving was back in Brooklyn

going to Pratt Institute and living with Arthur, now married, his mother wrote that they were coming home for Christmas, bringing Dean with them. They left in December, and the rest of the story is best told in a series of three moving letters to Herbert — who remained in London — from his mother.

The first, written from the Manhattan Hotel in New York City, is dated December 23, 1898: "Here we are in this great country after a remarkably smooth passage across the ocean and a quick one as far as Sandy Hook where we encountered a dense fog and had to anchor for twelve or fifteen hours and arrived Wednesday afternoon at the wharf. But, Herbert, although we had smooth sailing and good weather, never did I or your father have such a terrible six days. Papa had a very severe cold when he left Paris and could hardly talk above a whisper. For five days before we started he had been ailing and I tried to persuade him to give up the trip but he did not think the trouble serious and would not think of it. He had a dry hacking cough and was feverish and had no appetite but he *would* go and when we had spent the day on the cars going to Cherbourg he was a sick man and had to go to bed in the stateroom as soon as we boarded the *Kaiser Wilhelm.*

"He grew rapidly worse and for four days and nights I had more anguish than I ever had in my life. He had fever and was flighty and suffered so with his throat that I would not have been surprised to have had him die. He had laryngitis and a nervous affection of the stomach and the irritation in his throat and the dry tongue was terrifying to me. Of course I was among the best of friends and everything was done that could be, but the doctor was a poor one and did not understand the case and it was a fearful strain on me. All the party were as kind as kind could be and when we arrived every attention was given and we got him in a carriage and up to this hotel as soon as possible and in the hands of the N.Y. Life's best doctor. He commenced to get better the day before we arrived or we never could have got him here without a litter. He is very weak but the trouble is over. He sleeps peacefully and the cough irritation is gone. He will be up next week, and there is no danger of any complication now. The doctor thinks that he has had a touch of pneumonia and pleurisy with the acute laryngitis and it is the greatest wonder it didn't kill him. Dean had a fine time on the ship and enjoyed himself for the whole family. I did not see even the deck of the ship and never may I have such another six days. I am feeling all right however...

"... Our Christmas will be spent in the sick room but it will be a happy one with the assurance that your Papa is on the road to recovery... Dean is spending the time with Alice and is greatly enjoying being with Irving..."

The next letter is dated simply "Friday morning" and begins: "Papa has been losing ground for some days and last night there was a consultation of three doctors and it is heart breaking to tell you that they felt there was little hope for him. He has been sick so long that there is great danger of heart failure and they say if he was not such a strong and temperate man he would have passed away twenty-four hours ago.

"He has to have a doctor with him every moment and trained nurses day and night and he is breathing oxygen from a tank night and day at intervals to relieve the heart action, and they hope to pull him through by constant watching but dear Herbert they think he has but a poor chance. He is conscious and breathing hard for life. He does not know he is so dangerously sick but still realizes a little about it. Mr. Perkins, Willy, Jimmy, the three doctors and myself were up all last night for we felt that the crisis had been reached and we could not do ought but wait the outcome. This morning he is a shade better but the doctors do not dare hope much yet but in twenty-four hours they think there will be a change one way or another and a cable will be sent you if necessary but I do not want to warn you of what may come unless necessary but of course you will have a cable before this reaches you telling of his condition."

Here Mrs. Langmuir was interrupted, and she took up the letter again in the afternoon: "The doctors are again here in consultation and they think he is holding his own and that is encouraging. I send this off and I know the letter would affect you terribly if you were not going to get a cable before it reaches you. We are among the dearest... friends and all the New York Life people are kindness itself. Mr. Perkins spending much of his precious time with us. Arthur is with me and a great comfort. You see this is not an acute case and there is no pain. He has been sick for over three weeks and growing weaker but his lung inflammation does not extend to the right lung except at the base of it and if it had not been so long drawn out with a relapse on Tuesday he would not have this heart weakness but his left lung is first inflamed in one spot and then another until the whole thing has been affected and there is danger of the right lung. He has just seen Arthur for a few minutes and talks as rationally as possible, and his voice has much improved since yesterday. We feel brighter about him, and pray and hope..."

We do not know what the cable to Herbert said, but the next letter is dated January 2, 1899, and sent from 42 Mann Street, Brooklyn, New York. "Arthur was to write you a long letter last night," she began, "and tell you all about Papa's death and funeral. My darling Herbert we have had a terrible affliction and your cables have been a great comfort to me. My heart too has gone out to you in your loneliness way off in London alone and I am so anxious to see you and tell you of this sad sickness and all the details that I know you are longing for. I have been so tenderly cared for since Papa died that I am doing all I can to restrain my grief and be worthy of the kindness and care that is bestowed by being self controlled and resigned to the inevitable.

"Everybody shows such consideration and did so much for Papa in his sickness that I appreciate as I never did before the preciousness of friends and relatives. Willy has just given up all his time to us and Fanny and Lilly and Jimmy have been devotion itself. Mr. Perkins has been like a brother and the doctors have watched day and night by Charles bedside and shown the most loving sympathy. He was certainly greatly beloved in the office and all the skill and care that the best doctors could give has been tried on our dear one. The letters and cards and cables received show how dear he was to very many and it has been a great shock for Papa was the personification of health and strength.

"Papa executed a will two days before he died and Mr. Perkins was made executor and so we shall confer together as soon as I feel equal to it and learn his wishes and arrangements. He tried to talk to me about his affairs but he was too weak and did not accomplish it, but he had a plain and long talk with Mr. Perkins that I shall learn of soon. I don't know whether I shall have to go to Paris or not. Perhaps you will be able to take charge of things but all these things will be talked over with Mr. Perkins in a few days. We slipped out of our apartment leaving everything as if we were going to enter the next day and the girls were allowed to stay in their rooms and were to receive their wages while we were absent.

"I cannot as yet realize the terrible change but I am not sick and with the loving family and friends about me I am sure I shall soon recover my strength and will power to take up life as it is left to me and live for you and the other dear boys. I hope Arthur told you of the smooth death and beautiful face of Papa. He looked so natural and lifelike that I wanted to be with him just as much as possible until he was put away in the vault and I took great comfort in it. Today I am keeping on the sofa and getting my nerves back but by tomorrow I shall be all right, I am sure... My boys are my comfort and salvation. Thank you for those precious cables dear Herbert...

"All Papa's friends sent beautiful flowers and he was just banked up with lovely things. We put the white roses that you boys sent on each side of his dear face just as the cover was screwed down. I closed the glass and saw him last. The dearest sweetest body to me in the whole world."

It was after her husband's death — and after she had, for the first time in years, set up a New York home for the boys — that a thoughtful and momentarily tranquil Sadie Comings Langmuir made the entries in her memory book. "My life with my dear husband is over," she wrote, with overtones of having very little time left herself, "and now I shall exist without him as happy as it is possible until I go too to meet him in the unknown world."

The known world was destined, for a good many years longer, to serve as the theater of Mrs. Langmuir's activities. And her activities, as it turned out, hardly had to be curtailed at all. Once the shock of grief had worn off, Sadie's irrepressible wanderlust reasserted itself and, especially after the boys were grown, she became an inveterate habitué of planes, trains and steamers. Even after her writing hand had become painfully arthritic, she remained as prolific — and as prolix — a letterwriter as ever.

For a while after her husband's death, it began to look as though financial straits alone would force her to become a stay-at-home. Charles Langmuir, it is true, had made a lot of money, in investments as well as in salary. And he had always practiced the strictest thrift. Even so his determination to pay back every cent of the money his friends and relatives had lost in that ill-fated gold mine took care of any spare cash that might otherwise have landed in the bank. As a consequence, the estate he left was alarmingly small. Happily for the family, Charles Langmuir had good friends in the financial world, who invested the money so well that the Langmuir standard of living — especially with the older boys now on their own — could be maintained at the old level.

So the widow Langmuir went round and round the world. She hardly missed a country, and got just as excited about crossing the Andes at seventy-eight as she had about crossing buffalo country as a young girl. Yet she managed to keep track by letter of all the details of the lives of all the Langmuirs — even those who by now were named De Silva and Van de Water, Leadbetter and Leverenz — and she returned frequently to the United States. She especially made it a point to be home on her birthday, October 5, when the clan would gather at Arthur's in Hastings-on-Hudson, or at Herbert's in Englewood, and she would bring them up to date on her travels.

Like an absentee landlord, she kept a strong advisory hand in the affairs of her sons, and was not a bit bashful about bluntly criticizing the habits of their wives or their children. One of her grandchildren today says flatly, "Grandma was an old battle-axe." Yet she was so obviously and overtly fond of her family that its members could not help being fond of her in return — any more than they could help appreciating the fine qualities that made her the charming, irritating, stern and stimulating Supreme Matriarch that she was.

Though the Langmuir boys, whose father had resisted every suggestion to have them baptized, were non-churchgoers by upbringing and tradition, they had been inculcated with a strict code of ethical principles. They could not have been more upright and clean-living had they been raised in a rigidly Fundamentalist household. The boys were all grown men before any of them dared override their mother's imperious opposition to habits she considered immoral, if not downright wicked — smoking and drinking, for example. Irving was nearly forty before he smoked his first cigarette.

Mother Langmuir usually kept an apartment of her own in either New York City or Englewood, but she did not hesitate to move into anyone's house with a certain regal possessiveness, assuming herself welcome — which she usually was, though some resented the assumption. She even helped herself to other people's food, if it happened to intrigue her, without bothering about by-your-leaves. One granddaughter remembers eating with her parents and grandmother in a restaurant. She ordered steak, while Grandma ordered chicken. "My, yours looks so good," said Grandma. And though — for all she knew — her granddaughter may have hated chicken, she simply swapped dinners on the spot.

In brief, she was a tyrant, albeit a benevolent one. In certain areas, she was so insensitive as to seem quite inconsiderate of the wants and feelings of others. Yet her sheer vitality, bubbling even when it was bullying, called for admiration. She was as generous as she was demanding, and as free with her love as with her criticism — and, ultimately, Grandmother Sadie Comings Langmuir somehow managed to come through as a thoroughly endearing personality.

She died on February 11, 1936, in her eighty-eighth year, at home in the Hotel Windermere, New York City, after returning from a vacation in Palm Beach, Florida. Her obituary was carried prominently in the Lincoln's Birthday edition of the Englewood *Press.* A headline in the Yonkers *Herald-Statesman* that same day read: "World Traveler Dies at 87; Mother of Famous Chemists."

The funeral was held on February 13, in the chantry of Grace Church. Her husband had steadfastly avoided the practice of formal religion (there is no record to tell where, along the line, Grandfather Matthew's consecration to Christ in Glasgow was lost), but Sadie had remained an Episcopalian to the end. The rector of her church in Englewood came over to conduct the service, and she was buried in Greenwood Cemetery, Brooklyn. Irving, scheduled to give a talk at the dedication of New York's new Museum of Science and Industry, canceled his participation, and made one of his rare trips to church for the funeral service.

Thus, outliving her husband by thirty-six years and leaving behind four sons, eleven grandchildren, and four great-grandchildren, Sadie Comings Langmuir died, full of years, with her generations gathered around her.

Chapter 4

"Did you ask any good questions today?"

I. I. RABI'S mother to young
Isidor, returning from school

IT HAS often been pointed out — e.g., by Bernard Jaffe in *Crucibles* — that Irving Langmuir had no scientific forebears. His brother Arthur glibly gave all the credit for Irving's scientific leanings to his mother's father, Dr. Isaac Miller Comings. However, that esteemed (outside the South) gentleman had little opportunity to impart any direct instruction — medical or otherwise — to his itinerant grandsons before he himself died of Bright's Disease at the age of seventy-eight. Arthur's explanation is hardly acceptable, then, unless one is willing to go along with the likes of Lamarck and Lysenko on the transmissibility via the genes of an acquired talent.

A more reasonable explanation is simply that Irving Langmuir, with his natural brightness and enthusiasm, learned to be a scientist right at home. His mother and father, it is true, knew no science, and had no thought of teaching him any. But they taught him things far more valuable for a potential scientist than any specific information about atoms and galaxies that they might have passed on had they possessed it.

Charles Langmuir was a methodical man who kept complete

diaries — including, for example, not only the hotels he stopped at while traveling, but the room numbers as well. He kept strict account of all his expenditures, down to the last penny he spent for a newspaper. His wife was an equally diligent diarist, and she encouraged the habit in her sons. She also encouraged them to make notes of their interesting experiences, and to write out detailed descriptions — with emphasis on their own honest impressions — of whatever they saw that impressed them. Irving's parents constantly solicited — nay, demanded — from the boys a complete and articulate accounting of all their activities. They were intent listeners (when they were around) to the boys' critical comments on the movies or plays they saw, the music they heard, the books they read, the people they met. They supervised their sons' financial bookkeeping, and criticized their writing style, their spelling, and their penmanship.

"I enclose a letter to you from Dean," wrote Papa to Irving, who had just turned fifteen early in 1896. "I think you will find that he writes English very well, and that he does not strike out so many words as you do in your letters. You write an excellent letter, but I think you should not be in such a hurry when you write. I notice you begin a great many words, and you misspell them or something else happens, and you draw your pen through them. It would be well for you to be a little more careful and don't start to write a word until you are sure of what you are going to write and know how to spell it." He ends the letter with: "Dean came home yesterday with the red badge and medal, showing that he stood highest in his class. Do you make any such record as that?"

The Langmuir boys often felt, later in life, that despite the high standards of excellence their parents had set for them, their social training had been sadly neglected. Papa and Mama were often away when the boys went through crucial stages of development, and their sons often missed the kind of explicit instruction in proper dress and demeanor that most children get automatically. The boys could never predict when the straightforward honesty they had been taught might turn out to be offensive to someone, or even be taken for outright rudeness. They never learned to pass the time of day with smalltalk; they always felt gauche and ill-at-ease in unfamiliar company; and they passed many an uncomfortable hour for lack of the everyday graces which — it seemed to them — everyone else took for granted.

But from the standpoint of Irving's future as a scientist, the training he received could hardly have been better. He was taught to combine imagination with a scrupulous regard for accuracy. Among the priceless gifts he acquired directly from his parents were a restless curiosity, keenly-honed powers of observation, and a lifelong propensity for keeping detailed records. These characteristics made all the difference between casual interest and fresh-eyed fascination, between dilletantism and dedication.

To stack the deck even more neatly in favor of Irving's destiny, his older brother Arthur early became a serious student of chemistry. Even Herbert dabbled in chemistry, though he never followed it as a career. And both were on hand to shepherd Irving through his first scientific experiments.

In retrospect, Irving's career in science seemed inevitable from the very beginning. Yet, despite the boy's preoccupation with science, no one seemed to recognize the bent as lasting. No one except Mama. Writing from Paris around 1894, she flatly told her sister Mamie: "Irving is a born scientist, I can assure you, and he certainly ought to make his mark in the world."

It is curious that no one else was as prophetic — not even Arthur. Going through his old correspondence — from the 1890s — in 1932, Arthur noted: "I must have talked about my chemical work with Irving, for I was full of it, and it is strange that I said nothing to Alice in any of these letters ... making no reference to Irving's studies or scientific interests. I evidently had no particular idea that he would become a scientist."

Yet, Irving's cousin "Ducie" – the same little girl he pushed into the lake at Elmsford — who spent entire days with Irving when they were children in Brooklyn, recalls that Irving was full of science even then. He was always showing her tricks with magnets and iron filings. He talked incessantly about whatever he was building — or taking apart — at the moment, and would wonder aloud as they watched Herbert play tennis at the Pratt Institute about the force that made the ball go and why it bounced the way it did.

Like all children, Irving asked a lot of questions. But in Irving's case, he would not be put off with slipshod answers. His curiosity was as intense as it was insistent. What really makes it rain — *really,* now? Why does water boil? And *how* does it boil? And why does the boiling produce steam? And what *is* steam, exactly? And ice? Irving burned to learn, and what he learned he could not resist rushing to teach someone. A chronic victim of Irving's compulsive pedantry was his younger brother, Dean. When Dean was only three, Irving was already trying to cram arithmetic down his unwilling throat. And later, in Paris, Irving would talk chemistry to Dean until — backed miserably against the wall by his doggedly expository older brother — he would literally holler for help. Irving never lost his passion for pedagogy, but his later audiences were more appreciative.

In 1887, when Irving was only six, Arthur was already taking advantage of his special privileges to make free use of the small but well-appointed chemistry laboratory at the Irving Institute in Tarrytown, New York, where he performed — perhaps without realizing it at the time — some quite dangerous experiments. He was particularly fascinated with chlorine gas, and he loved to titillate his olfactory senses with tiny, clandestine sniffs out of a four-ounce stoppered bottle he sometimes carried around with him. One day he brought the bottle home to Elmsford and offered Irving a smell. Irving, never a cautious type, inhaled uninhibitedly, started gasping, and nearly strangled on the spot.

Several days passed before he could breathe normally again. During those anxious, choking days, his parents and a chastened Arthur worried about the possible onset of pneumonia and death. After that close brush with tragedy, Papa laid down strict orders: No more chemistry outside the classroom.

But the experience did nothing to diminish Irving's interest in all things mechanical and scientific. He pestered everyone for information, pored through technical books, skipping the sections too advanced for him, and stored all the data carefully in his retentive memory. He enjoyed playing around with both things and ideas. In his untutored, inchoate fashion, he was already beginning to associate theory with application — an association some scientists disdain to their dying day.

Irving's attention in those days was drawn to any gadget in the house, and parents as well as brothers soon learned to speak up in forceful, explicit terms if there was something they did *not* want taken apart.

Irving firmly believed there was a scientific explanation for everything, and he would have no truck with the supernatural. One can imagine Mama's sisters, in their piety, raising their eyebrows and clucking their tongues at Irving's irreverent attitude; one can also imagine them, in their kindness, excusing the precocious brashness of the poor, unbaptized child of a benighted father. Irving, when he was barely nine, scandalized one of his aunts — a former cook his uncle married after the death of his first wife — by being skeptical of the mysterious antics of her Ouija board. When she challenged him to "explain it if you're so smart," he replied that he wasn't old enough to know enough — but added that even if no one knew *now*, someone would one day find out.

By the time Irving was nine, even the proscription against chemistry was forgotten, and Papa gave him permission to set up a small workshop in the cellar of their Brooklyn home, under the guidance of an older and wiser Arthur. Though Arthur, with the chlorine incident still in mind, eschewed the really dangerous experiments, he still favored the spectacular ones. One of their favorite play chemicals was iodide of nitrogen, which they concocted out of iodine and household ammonia. Though the stuff was virtually harmless, it would explode instantly on any but the gentlest contact. The noise was mighty, the stench impressive, and the smoke blinding. "We astonished many a cat by dropping wood smeared with iodide in his vicinity," Arthur later reminisced. "In fact, in those days almost anywhere in the house one was liable to run into nitrogen iodide, as our baby brother Dean discovered one day, while running his hand along the window sill."

The cellar workshop was where Irving's main interest lay while he was attending Public School No. 11. But though he had little to do with the games of his neighborhood playmates — especially those of his own age — he was fond of vigorous outdoor exercise. Happily, his parents provided him plenty of opportunity to indulge his penchant, particularly during the summer months. When Papa's business kept him and Mama from accompanying the boys, they still arranged for relatives or close friends to take them along to some rugged bit of countryside — along the Delaware River, perhaps, or the woods near Bay Head, New Jersey, or at Muscoka Lakes in Canada — where the boys did a lot of hiking, rowing, canoeing, and camping out.

In the spring of 1892, when Charles and Sadie Langmuir sailed off on the European trip they believed would last only a few months, Arthur and Herbert were sent to the Adirondacks while Irving and Dean stayed with the Deans — the same Deans whose father had saved Papa's father from starvation in Canada — at Bay Head, where Irving's special friend was Emery Katzenbach, the son of a New York physician. Irving rated that summer an important one because it was toward the end of it that he finally learned to feel at home in the water and swim with real confidence.

In September Irving went back to Brooklyn to live with his Aunt Tilly and enroll once more at P.S. No. 11. "I am building a wind mill," Irving wrote Mama on the 30th of that month, "which is going to be about 3 feet high and 1 foot wide at the bottom and 6 inches wide at the top. The wheel is going to be like this." (A sketch was enclosed.) "The wheel's axil is going to be made out of wood with pieces of tin this shape, each one being about 3½ inches long. The whole wheel's diameter will be about 8 inches. I have two sides all done and the other two sides half done of the tower part."

In the same letter he told Mama: "Aunt Fannie makes me do three examples every night and is trying to make me quicker in arithmetic. She says the only trouble with me is that I am too slow." Definitely dissenting from Aunt Fannie on the point of Irving's slowness was Herbert. Writing to Mama at about the same time, he said: "I have come to the conclusion that Irving is the smartest of the family. I think he is inventive and he certainly knows a lot. He sticks me on a lot of things. I avoid entirely electricity. He is making a wind mill now and is doing it first rate. He will want to take it to Paris with him."

Irving's letter must have crossed in the mails with one Papa had just written from Paris announcing the news that he had been appointed general director of European agencies for the New York Life Insurance Company and that their home would henceforth be Paris. On October 22 Herbert herded his two younger brothers aboard the steamer *La Bourgogne.* Papa met them at Le Havre and took them to Paris. "I remember perfectly," Irving wrote years later, "going upstairs in the Hôtel de l'Athenée and seeing Mama. Everything seemed so magnificent. I had never seen anything so beautiful as the rooms of the hotel."

That winter at the hotel, Herbert renewed Irving's interest in chemistry, showing him how to make ammonia from lime and ammonium chloride. Before long Irving was exchanging letters with Arthur about his new experiments, spending nearly all his spare money buying chemicals and apparatus at Poulenc Frères on the Boulevard St. Germain,[1] and beginning to build up a well-rounded home laboratory.

"The boys have been here six weeks now," Mama wrote her sister Mamie — after congratulating her on the birth of a daughter and confessing she had always wanted a girl of her own. "While Herbert and I struggle along with French, Irving and Dean pick it up so quickly that it is marvelous . . .

"Everybody thinks Dean is very smart and cunning . . . and he

---

[1] On one of his chemical-shopping expeditions, Irving was caught in the midst of a mob of Socialist students, rioting wildly in celebration of May Day.

is very much thought of everywhere... Irving is thought to be very intelligent and interesting. I don't feel ashamed of my American boys by any means, and I do hope they will keep their characteristics and not get too Frenchy. I expect Herbert will go off to Heidelberg with Arthur next fall."

"It is wonderful to hear him [Irving] talk with Herbert on scientific subjects," she wrote in another letter, this one to Mrs. Horace Dean. "Herbert says he fairly has to shun electricity, for the child gets beside himself with enthusiasm and shows such intelligence on the subject that it fairly scares him."

In Paris, too, thanks to Herbert's keen interest, Irving became addicted to the opera — and especially to Wagner. During the season, Herbert and Irving hardly missed a performance. Though the only tickets they could afford were in the standing-room-only gallery up against the ceiling, they overcame the handicap of distance by a clever stratagem. They would climb up over the staircase and lie on their bellies for cramped hours at a time, armed with score, libretto and high-powered binoculars. In this manner they acquired a liberal operatic education, learning virtually every note of every opera by heart. In the Langmuir's Paris apartment, a likely accompaniment to the clinking of test tubes was "The Ride of the Valkyries", whistled spiritedly.

Much as Irving loved Paris, fascinated as he was by his extracurricular experiments, rapidly as he took to the nuances of the French language, his existence in France was rendered acutely unhappy by enforced attendance at a series of boys' schools on the outskirts of Paris. These were the schools which French novelists from Balzac to Gide have described and complained about, with their discipline that Langmuir later described as "absurdly rigorous," where narrow-minded and underpaid instructors taught strictly by rote, where pupils were supposed to sit in absolute silence and not ask foolish questions, where the plumbing and heating facilities were hopelessly inadequate.

The first of these schools, which he and Herbert started attending soon after their arrival in Paris, was the École Alsacienne, a long morning walk from the hotel. "The school," an older Irving wrote, "was in the Latin quarter near the observatory at the end of the avenue leading from the Jardins du Luxembourg. At this school I got acquainted with Charlie McLeod." The school day at the École Alsacienne was so long and exhausting that the boys were permitted to ride home in the evening.

About six months after the boys got to Paris, the family left the elegance of the Hôtel de l'Athenée for a more modest apartment on the Rue Galilée. They spent the summer of 1893 in Switzerland, where Arthur, who had just completed his studies at Columbia and was preparing to go to Heidelberg for graduate work, joined them. Papa and Mama took off in their own preferred directions, leaving the boys — minus Herbert, who had decided to take a job in Paris — at the Hôtel Bellevue at Bonigen, on Lake Brienz.

Here Arthur took twelve-year-old Irving on his first mountain-climbing expeditions, which he found immensely exhilarating. But later, at Montreux on Lake Geneva, Irving came down with neuralgia. They all believed he must have caught it on the first trip up Rochers de Naye, whose steep snowy slopes Irving had climbed wearing only light summer clothes while the temperature hovered around the freezing point. When he showed no improvement after four or five days spent mostly in bed, the boys, perplexed, decided to move to Bex, on the theory that the lake air was bad for Irving. Whether the theory had any medical basis or not, there, at the Hôtel des Salines, Irving made a rapid recovery.

Just as Irving had continued his boyish scientific investigations after the near-fatal chlorine incident, so he now started climbing again as soon as he was out of bed. After Arthur had gone on to Heidelberg, Mama and Herbert joined the party briefly. In September, writing from Rochers de Naye, Herbert reported to Papa: "Mama went up the funiculaire with Dean, while Irving and myself mounted on foot. That mountain is about 7000 feet high and it took us almost four hours to reach the top. We made the descent, however, in two hours. Irving makes a famous walker."

Irving saw no reason why he should not continue to climb

mountains even after Arthur and Herbert had gone. But Mama did not dare let him follow this perilous sport alone. Irving pleaded with Papa, who reluctantly gave his permission, as long as Irving would promise to follow strictly certain rules. He was to climb only where there was a clearly marked trail, he was to stick to the trail, and to use the same trail going and returning. He was always to be back by 6:00 p.m., and to insure this by allowing as much time for coming down as for going up. To be sure he knew what he was doing he had to make sketches, maps and trail notes before he set foot on the mountain. In this manner Irving, as a boy of twelve, climbed a number of mountains about the height of Rochers de Naye, and sometimes had to go back several days in a row before he could find a trail going all the way to the top. This superb self-training, directed long-distance by his father, turned Irving Langmuir into an expert mountaineer, as sure-footed as he was safety-conscious.

That winter the family moved to 57 Rue Ampère, and Irving switched to Dean's school, the École Mange, which he liked no better than the École Alsacienne. The ink froze in the inkwells, and he complained that he had to study Latin for three hours every day of the school year, while he got only two hours of arithmetic all week. The bleak school season was somewhat lightened by his chemistry experiments at home, and by a new friendship with the Dufresne brothers from California.

During the summer of 1894 the Langmuirs spent a month at Barbizon, where they ran into the McLeods, the parents of Irving's school friend, Charlie. They enjoyed long walks in the Forest of Fontainebleau, visited St. Malo, where Irving was fascinated by the tide which rose from forty to sixty feet. Later they went on to tour the Channel Islands with another set of family friends, the Fergusons.

That winter Irving and Dean were transferred to a boarding school, the École Jeanne d'Arc at Aulnay les Bondy, on the recommendation of a man named Anderson whom they had met that summer at Barbizon. This was in some ways the worst school of all. Describing it in a letter to Aunt Fanny, Herbert wrote:

"The boys' school is atrociously cold. In many rooms they make no attempt at all to heat. The boys all had chilblains and half of them couldn't write from their swollen hands. Of course the weather was particularly cold this year, but that does not excuse no heating at all. Irving says water froze in the schoolroom."

Commenting on the school in a later diary, Irving wrote: "I was very unhappy there and probably would hardly have consented to remain if it were not for Mr. Anderson who was our (Dean and I) friend and helped us out of many difficulties with the teachers. Here I began studying algebra. I also studied geometry and learned how to use logarithms with ease. I spent one to two hours a day in the chemical laboratory by myself. Mr. Viguer was the teacher I had most to do with. He was a disgustingly dressed and behaved man and very much disliked by the French boys, but as he respected Mr. Anderson he also respected me and we got along very well...

"We went home generally every second Sunday. On Thursday afternoons we went out walking in the woods. This was a privilege Mr. Anderson obtained for us . . .

"At École Jeanne d'Arc I did a good deal of experimenting with explosives such as crude gunpowder and a mixture of $KClO_3$ and Sb_2O_3 which later worked out very successfully. I was always very careful, and no accidents happened. I made $N_2H_3I_3$ etc. I made bombs and arrows tipped with a mixture of $KClO_3$ and Sb_2O_3 with powdered glass."

Dean recalled that Irving would sometimes bring home explosive arrows (tipped, he believed, with fulminate of mercury) and toss them against the apartment wall with highly satisfying results. "Both at home and at school," Mama wrote Mamie, "he is busy with experiments and he assists the chemists in the class and is looked upon as a prodigy. Arthur says that as soon as he gets settled in America he wants Irving with him."

After a year at the École Jeanne d'Arc, Irving and Dean were more than happy to return to Paris and go off on their summer vacation. The family went first to Brighton, then moved on to the Isle of Wight. There, at Shanklin on the east coast, they were forced to change boarding houses when they all came down with food poisoning. But Irving was too pleased at having just learned to ride a bicycle to mind very much.

From the Isle of Wight, they went on to London, then back to France and the beach at St. Nazaire. "Good bathing," Irving noted. "The coast was sandy in most places but rocky in others. A great deal of salt is obtained by evaporation of the sea water by the sun." The trip back to Paris was leisurely, with many stops along the way for rubbernecking at castles and cathedrals.

Soon after checking in at the Hôtel Belmont, near the Arc de Triomphe, there was a long discussion about schools. The Dufresne boys, who had become Irving's friends at the École Mange, had been enrolled at the Lycée Carnot which, though located in the same building, was reputed to be far superior in every way. Irving, remembering Mr. Anderson's high recommendation of the École Mange, remained skeptical. Nevertheless, Papa and Mama decided that they would try the Lycée Carnot that year.

Irving was not keen on going to any French school. He pleaded to be sent back to the States instead. According to one story, Mama said, "I couldn't think of sending such a terrible-tempered boy back to America alone." At which Irving promised on the spot never to lose his temper again. And — the same story goes — he never did.

In any case, just two days before the opening day at the lycée, Papa came into the boys' room in the morning and said, "The first boy dressed goes to America." The boys were sure Papa was teasing, but Irving was taking no chances. He always got into his clothes more rapidly than Dean — as Papa well knew — but that morning he set a new speed record. And as it turned out, Papa had not been teasing at all. He had decided to send Irving to a new school, the Chestnut Hill Academy, being started by a Dr. Frederick Reed in Philadelphia.

"I was so happy," Irving remembered, "I could hardly wait. I was to leave in one week. Mama bought me an outfit of French clothes . . . I left Paris about Oct. 7, 1895, by a 6:00 p.m. train. Papa, Mama, Dean and Herbert saw me off. Herbert was then in business in the New York Life Insurance Company and had been ever since he left École Alsacienne ... Before leaving Paris, Papa had given me a $22.00 watch, with stop-watch, compass, etc."

Thus, as the family saw him off to Dieppe, en route to Southampton, Irving Langmuir, fourteen, ended his residence in France. Had he left Paris a few days earlier, he might have missed an experience which made a profound and lasting impression on him. The experience was merely being present among the crowds that lined the sidewalks stretching from the Pasteur Institute to the Cathedral of Notre Dame on the morning of October fifth as the mile-long funeral cortège of Louis Pasteur passed by. All the officials of France, including President Félix Faure, were present for the elaborate ceremonies. So were representatives from every foreign embassy in Paris. So were the Grand Duke Constantine of Russia and Prince Nicholas of Greece. And so were the thronging masses of Paris.

Pasteur had brought to the common people, as no savant before him had done, an awareness of the worth of science; and he died acclaimed universally as a benefactor of humanity, and as one of the great men of all time.

It was gratifying to young Irving Langmuir to learn that Louis Pasteur, one of his private heroes, was also a public hero. The pomp and grandeur of the funeral rites, and the hushed reverence of the Parisian populace as the Minister of Public Education delivered the eulogy in the great cathedral square, enabled Irving to assure himself that science was not only more fun than anything, but also the highest and noblest calling of them all.

Chapter 5

"Tis the custom of pedagogues to be eternally thundering in their pupil's ears, as they were pouring into a funnel, whilst the business of the pupil is only to repeat what the others have said: now I would have a tutor to correct this error, and, that at the very first, he should, according to the capacity he has to deal with, put it to the test, permitting his pupil himself to taste things, and of himself to discern and choose them, sometimes opening the way to him, and sometimes leaving him to open it for himself; that is, I would not have him alone to invent and speak, but that he should also hear his pupil speak in turn. Socrates, and since him Arcesilaus, made first their scholars speak, and then they spoke to them."

MICHEL DE MONTAIGNE

WITH eager anticipation, and with a heady new sense of independence, Irving sailed from Southampton on the *St. Louis* of the American Line. On board was Mr. McCall, the head of Papa's company, with his wife and daughter. The McCalls kept an eye on fourteen-year-old Irving throughout the trip, but they took care to do it unobtrusively.

"The passage was a quick one," wrote Irving, in retrospect, "and generally smooth although we had one tremendous storm which was one of the grandest sights imaginable from the port-hole of the McCalls' cabin. The bow of the steamer would be way up in the air and would come down with great velocity right into the next enormous wave. There would be a big noise and the ship would quiver all over and make a lurch and the wave would be divided and two big masses of water could be seen piled up 15 or 20 feet above the bow on each side of it. Then some of this would fall on the deck and would come tearing along the deck and cover up the portholes I was looking through. It was a sight I could not tire of."

It was a sight Irving never did tire of. All his life he loved weather, the stormier the better. He exulted in what other people quailed at. That is why Arthur, addressing the Chemists' Club before Irving left on his Nobel Prize voyage, ended his speech by wishing his brother a rough trip.

Only a few weeks before Irving Langmuir died, he stood on a hillside at Bolton's Landing, New York, near Lake George, watching the progress of a summer storm — glorying in the flash of lightning, the clap of thunder, the lash of rain, his face glowing with excitement and satisfaction as he explained it all, in scientific terms, to a young relative. Langmuir never let his scientific understanding interfere with his emotional, almost mystical, response to the weather. It was no accident that Richard Wagner — who knew so well how to translate his own pagan worship of Thor into the stormiest music ever orchestrated — remained Langmuir's favorite composer. And it was no wonder that Langmuir became the first creator of manmade storms.

When the *St. Louis* docked in New York, Arthur was waiting to meet Irving. So were his Uncle Will and Aunt Tillie, who took Irving to their home in Brooklyn. "I was astounded by the change I saw in Brooklyn," wrote the returning world-traveler. "Trolleys everywhere and lots of electric lights and the tall buildings in New York all so changed in three years. When I left Brooklyn, trolleys were curiosities."

After a few days as a tourist-in-reverse in Brooklyn, Irving went with Arthur to Philadelphia, where he was to spend one of the happiest years of his life. There, for the first time, he stopped hating school. Though he already knew all the science which the tiny new Chestnut Hill Academy had to offer, he was able to catch up on other subjects in which he had fallen behind —

English grammar, for example, and geography. At school in Paris it had been a cardinal sin, an unforgivable breach of discipline, for a mere pupil — forgetfully carried away by curiosity — to interrupt the droning voice of the instructor by impudently asking a question. Here questions were not only permitted; they were encouraged.

And here the formal school day ended promptly at 1:00 p.m., leaving a young man lots of spare time to pursue his own inclinations. In one six-week stretch, Irving went through a calculus textbook and — Arthur later agreed — easily mastered the subject.

During his year at Frederick Reed's academy, Irving lived with the Reeds at their lovely cottage in Wissahickon Heights. He was not only enchanted with the surroundings, but he found the Reeds kind, indulgent, and delightfully stimulating. They seemed to recognize a mind of unusual capacity, and they enjoyed stretching it to the limit. Their long, rambling conversations covered a great variety of topics. They even succeeded in getting Irving interested in theology for a while — an interest to which he returned now and then throughout his life, though he never found a theology which his analytical mind would permit him to accept.

In Philadelphia he made a number of good friends — among them the Faught brothers, Francis and Albert. With Francis, who was also electrically inclined, Irving designed and installed a complicated system of bells in the school buildings — a system the school found most useful and whose ingenuity Dr. Reed applauded. With the Faught boys, Irving took long hikes through Fairmount Park, along Wissahickon Creek and the Schuylkill River. There, too, he learned to ice-skate, and became expert at it before the winter was over. "I bubbled over with joy," he wrote, "at the liberty I was allowed."

If the year in Philadelphia had been a wonderful year for Irving, it had also been a memorable one for his head master, Frederick Reed. Every real teacher lives for a pupil like Irving Langmuir—and Reed got him when his mind was in full flower. Irving, like any bright adolescent, looked forward to what came next, and probably gave little thought to the Reeds. But they never forgot Irving Langmuir, and they followed his later doings with great satisfaction.

After Langmuir had won the Nobel Prize, Frederick Reed, then in retirement in Fall Brook, California, wrote to his former pupil:

"We have read eagerly what we could find in the current news papers and magazines anent this signal honor bestowed upon our Irving. It goes without saying that we are happy and proud beyond words over your success, so richly deserved, a happiness and pride which we hope your dear mother is still living to enjoy. We know that your father passed away many years ago but we have had no word of your mother for years.

"How often have I reverted, in memory, to the tiny laboratory I had set up for you in the rear of the Chestnut Hill Academy in Wissahickon Heights... And to the slight built boy in knee trousers, who came to us from Paris, to begin his American education. In all my pedagogical experience, I can recall no pupil so overflowing with vital hunger to know why and how and where as was our Irving in those days now long gone. No wonder the deep secrets of science have yielded a rich harvest to such an insistent quest."

When the school year in Philadelphia ended, Irving was invited to spend the summer vacation with the family of Uncle Matt — his father's oldest brother — in Canada. Most of July and August passed quietly at Sparrow Lake, but Irving got back to Toronto in time to see the Exposition of 1896. Then he was taken on a week's bicycle tour with his cousin Winnie, and Mr. and Mrs. Corbett Whiton. One morning during the tour, after visiting Fort Niagara on Lake Ontario with Mr. Whiton, they bicycled the fifty-two miles back to Hamilton that same day — "the longest ride I had ever taken," he noted in his diary. He was to take many more like it.

Back in Brooklyn in the fall, Irving again moved in with Aunt Tillie. He now felt ready to tackle the Manual Training High School at Pratt Institute, whose curriculum Arthur — now a successful, practicing chemist — thought would be ideal for Irving. After a few weeks of intensive review work under the tutelage of Aunt Fanny — herself a high school principal — he passed the Pratt examinations painlessly, and was soon at the top of his class. He knew too much chemistry even for Pratt, and was permitted to skip all chemistry classes. But he continued with advanced studies in his own time, including more of the calculus. Arthur came frequently to visit and tirelessly talked science with his younger brother, who never seemed to get enough of it. Whenever Arthur heard about a new discovery or read an interesting technical paper, Irving wanted to know about it.

One evening in November of 1896, Arthur came to Aunt Tillie's house on one of his regular visits. He had just become engaged to Alice Dean, a young lady Irving was very fond of. He knew how excited Irving would be when he heard the news, but he decided not to tell anyone about the engagement until the wedding plans were a little more definite. Meanwhile he began telling Irving about the results, just published, of an experiment in which Lord Rayleigh and Sir William Ramsay had succeeded in isolating from ordinary air a strangely inert gas, the element argon, which was odorless and colorless, and seemed incapable of combining with even the most active of the other elements in the periodic table.

Arthur did not really find this inert gas very interesting, and found his mind wandering away from Irving's eager questions back to Alice and his engagement. On the spur of the moment he decided it was unfair to keep the secret from Irving.

"Irving," he said, pausing portentously before making the announcement. "Do you know that I'm going to marry Alice Dean?"

"Oh," said Irving. "But you were telling me about argon —"

Around November 1, Mama came back to Brooklyn to fit out an apartment on the fourth floor of 157 Halsey Street as a wedding present for Arthur and Alice. The wedding took place on December 17. While they took off on their honeymoon to Washington, Mama sent Irving down to Philadelphia for a few days.

He stayed with the Faughts in Wissahickon Heights, where the boys spent most of the daylight hours skating. "Then Mama came & met Mrs. Faught & we went on to Baltimore where we spent Christmas with the Habighursts. And a most doleful Xmas it was," Irving complained. "No presents & nothing to show it was Xmas...

"Then we spent a 5 or 6 days at Washington & had a thoroughly good time. Saw the Capitol, Congressional Library, Patent Office, Monuments, etc., saw Mt. Vernon, Washington's house & saw a house afire. Heard Bohemian Girl & Robin Hood & saw Keller's tricks."

From Washington Mama went South to visit her sister Mamie in Pensacola, while Irving returned to Brooklyn to live with Arthur and Alice. Judging from Arthur's correspondence at the time, their fourth-floor flat on Halsey Street was a crowded place. It accommodated not only Arthur and Alice, but also Irving, a Finnish servant named Mary, and Dr. and Mrs. Horace Dean.

It was only fitting that the Deans should be living with the Langmuirs, just as the Langmuirs had once lived with the Deans back in that Canadian frontier village. The families had been out of touch for many years when one day someone noticed in a Brooklyn newspaper the name Horace Dean listed as a witness in a lawsuit. Irving's father knew it could not be the same Horace Dean, the missionary to the Indians, who had saved their lives that ghastly winter. He must long since be dead. But could it be his son? It was. And once the lines of communication were reestablished, the two families became close friends again. It was Mrs. Dean to whom Sadie Langmuir wrote frequently from Paris. It was the Deans with whom Irving stayed at Bay Head, New Jersey. And it was their daughter, Alice, whom Arthur had married.

And now, Dr. Dean, a dentist by profession, had apparently run into hard times, and was living with Arthur and Alice. While he went from door to door trying to market a mutton-fat product he had invented — a cosmetic called Ovistra — Mrs.

Dean helped make ends meet by keeping house for a lady doctor named Upham in Asbury Park, New Jersey.

Even in this overflowing household Irving managed, in his cluttered-up little room, to build a first-class work bench and desk. There Arthur taught him qualitative analysis. "Other experiments still continued." Arthur later remembered, "and one evening a strontium nitrate red fire which we set off on the window sill brought rattling up on the cobblestones to our great surprise two fire engines, a hook and ladder, and a salvage corps." Arthur also recalled that "just for the fun of it and during his winter courses, he [Irving] spent several months all told working out the mathematics of third degree curves, refusing to spoil the game by referring to any mathematical works where other men had possibly preceded him."

Irving's interest in chemistry extended to the kitchen. He started concocting recipes in 1898, while Alice was on a tour of Europe with Mama, and cooking remained a lifelong hobby. "Everything is prospering with us," Arthur wrote to Alice in January of that year. "Irving now prepares the desserts and he has made two or three very successful dishes from our cookbook." About a week later he reported: "Irving is making us excellent desserts now, and Dr. Dean is in his glory. It is remarkable how easily Irving succeeds in anything he undertakes."

But if Arthur thought considerably more of Irving's culinary talents than those of the Finnish housekeeper, he thought considerably less of his housekeeping habits. On January 12, 1898, he wrote Alice: "Irving returned from Canada on Sunday, Jan. 2. He opened his bag on the floor and took out what was necessary for his immediate needs and has left the open bag in the same place since. It still contains articles of clothing. This bag must have proved a great discomfort to him as it lies right in front of his bureau and he has to stumble over it to get in and out of his room. His room and desk are in a condition of frightful disorder. Whenever he takes a book or anything which he requires he leaves it anywhere after he is through with it and never by any chance returns it to its place."

The next day he wrote again: "How Irving can put up with the constant inconvenience of the bag in that place and never think of putting it away is incomprehensible and amusing to Dr. Dean and me. It still lies open on the floor full of cuffs and collars, neckties, etc. It took him only a few moments to pack when he left for Canada but it is now eleven days since he returned. I am not going to say anything more on the subject, as I have already spoken twice, but will clean it up myself on Sunday if it has not been done by that time."

On January 22, Irving's twentieth day back home, Arthur was finally able to report that Irving had straightened out his room. "Whenever it gets untidy I will warn him, but wish I could impose some fine system such as papa adopted with his correspondence."

Irving more than made up for his neglect of his room by being useful in so many other ways. Aside from making desserts, he taught Mary how to whip up a number of entrées that were new to her. He even sought to cheer her out of her occasional gloomy moods by trying to teach her solitaire — "but without success. She could not seem to understand what it was for."

With Alice away, the men of the house apparently had a hard time getting up in the morning. Arthur wrote Alice how Irving solved the problem. "Irving fixed up an electric bell behind my bed. There are two batteries under the bed to work the bell. The clock is on the telephone bracket in the library and is placed on a box which contains an arrangement for making a connection at the right time. The bell rings until I get up and go to the library to stop it. It works splendidly. Every morning at exactly quarter to seven I have to get up. The bell is so boisterous that Irving is generally awakened at the same time."

Arthur seldom passed up a chance to brag about his kid brother. After Irving had given a lecture at Pratt, exhibiting lantern slides of his European pictures, Arthur wrote proudly: "Irving himself proposed to Mr. McAndrews that he should do this and of course Mr. McAndrews assented. Irving spent most of Sunday writing out his lecture without any assistance whatever. His talk lasted twenty minutes. Before he was on the platform he felt a little nervous, but was perfectly self possessed during his lecture. Herbert and I would have been overwhelmed if we had been called on at his age to deliver a lecture and would have never dreamed of suggesting it."

All in all, Arthur and Alice found Irving a joy to have around.

Naturally, Papa helped pay for Irving's board. Though the amount he sent was only $375.00 for the year, that was no piddling sum in those days following the Panic of 1893–1897. Arthur's grocery bill for four people, while Alice was away, amounted to $6.50 per week, not counting milk and rolls. Mary's total monthly salary was $10.00, and the rent was only $33.00 a month. Thus Papa's contribution paid nearly all the year's rent.

Irving lived happily with Arthur and Alice until he was almost finished with his studies at Pratt. Then, late in 1898, his parents made the ill-fated voyage home on the *Kaiser Wilhelm* where his father contracted his final illness.

After Papa's death and funeral, early in 1899, Mama remained in the United States and set up an apartment for her three unmarried sons in uptown New York. Arthur had already been contemplating a move from Brooklyn to Manhattan so that Irving would be near Columbia University when he began his studies there. Now the move would be unnecessary. Irving simply moved in with Mama. Dean, who had been with his parents all along, was already there. And now Herbert moved back from London to join them.

Later in 1899 Irving was graduated from Pratt and entered Columbia's School of Mines, where he enrolled in the metallurgical engineering course. One story has it that Langmuir took up metallurgy because his father, who had been bilked in a phony mining venture, wanted at least one of his sons to know something about the mining industry. But Langmuir's own stated reasons for his choice do not indicate that he ever had mining in mind at all. "The course was strong in chemistry," he explained. "It had more physics than the chemical course, and more mathematics than the course in physics — and I wanted all three."

Langmuir seems to have made singularly little impact on Columbia during his three years there. Certainly he made no effort to become a Big-Man-on-the-Campus. He was virtually unknown to his fellow students other than those who attended the same classes and laboratory sessions; and even to them he must have seemed forbiddingly bookish. He joined no clubs, went out for no teams (he never cared for competitive sports), edited no campus publications, never ran for class office or served on a class committee, and was never invited to join a fraternity. He participated in not a single campus-bound extracurricular activity.

Surely, then, this intense, unsocial scholar, so wrapped up in his studies — the pupil whose qualities had been noted by instructors at the Pratt Institute, at the Chestnut Hill Academy, and even at the École Jeanne d'Arc — surely this young man was at least the favorite of his doting professors? Not so. They gave him good grades (his average at Columbia was 94), but that was all. Only a few professors took any notice of him, and only one, Dr. R. S. Woodward, seemed to spot a rare scientific talent.

One day during Irving's junior year, Dr. Woodward asked his class in mechanics, "If you could do what you most want to do, what career would you choose?" When Irving's turn to answer came, he said, "I'd like to be situated like Lord Kelvin — free to do research as I wish."

The answer pleased Woodward, and thereafter he took a special interest in Irving, often suggesting challenging problems "which I loved to work out," Langmuir later recalled, "just for the fun of it."

Among the other things Irving was doing just for the fun of it was attending an evening class in organic chemistry which Arthur conducted for Pratt Institute alumni in downtown New York. "On Saturdays," Arthur remembered, "he worked on research toward the improvement in analytical methods at my laboratory with Ricketts and Banks and later in Brooklyn did some excellent work on the specific gravity of pure glycerol. And all of this work was done during the time he had to spare from a strenuous engineering course."

In summer school at Camp Columbia, near Morris, Connecticut, Irving learned surveying methods. Applying his new knowledge in the fall, he and Dean made a map of their 135th Street apartment, using the most elaborate techniques known to modern engineering, meticulously measuring and remeasuring, and making every possible allowance for error. "This," said Arthur, "was probably the most accurate and complete map of an apartment ever made in the history of man."

During his days as a Columbia undergraduate, Langmuir sought his recreation, as always, outdoors. His summers were as packed as ever with overland excursions. In the summer of 1900, for example, he went on a bicycle trek through Eastern Pennsylvania and the Catskill Mountains with Arthur and his Canadian cousin, Leighton. During the rugged vacation, they climbed many of the Pocono peaks — which seemed tame after the Swiss Alps — and sometimes bicycled more than fifty meandering mountain miles in a single day.

They visited not only museums, seminaries, college campuses, and all the standard historical sites, but made a special point of going through silk mills and shoe factories, pipe foundries and coal mines. Irving, endlessly curious about industrial Pennsylvania, complained because they could not get into the wire works in Allentown, and because the guide who took them through the iron works at Bethlehem could not properly explain the smelting and refining processes. Tours like these helped Irving appreciate how even the most abstract scientific principles were applied toward the fulfillment of man's manifold needs. His conscious awareness of these human needs helped him, in later years, keep one eye constantly on the lookout for practical applications of his own discoveries.

Thus, even Irving's vacations often contributed to his life work — largely, perhaps, because he took them so seriously. He was known to expend the same methodical care preparing for a vacation as he lavished on preparations for an experiment. In the summer of 1902, for example, he traced an intricate pattern of travels across the continent, going from New York to Washington to Chicago to Minneapolis to Banff to Lake Louise to Tacoma to Portland to San Francisco to Yosemite to Salt Lake City to Colorado Springs to Pittsburgh, with stops and side journeys en route. Before departing, he mapped out his itinerary in great detail, listing modes of transportation, and estimated costs — also in great detail — along the way. He took care to write down the addresses of people he intended to visit, noting their exact degree of relationship to himself. And the voluminous catalogue of items he planned to carry along included winter underwear, garters for socks, eighteen collars, a dozen pairs of cuffs, a corduroy bicycle suit, a cutaway, a pair of striped trousers, a suit of overalls, climbing shoes, suspenders, safety pins, needles and thread, a pair of smoked glasses for snow, telefoto and wide angle lenses for his camera, a developing outfit, a thermometer, a telescope, a set of mounted United States Geological Survey maps, a compass, a bottle of matches, Baedekers of the United States and Canada, prospector's hammers, and Byerly's *Calculus.*

Even during the school year Irving took his outdoor recreation seriously. On New Year's morning, 1902, Dean noted in his diary that he had got up at 11:00, then awakened Irving. Irving "complained bitterly" to Mama for not waking him earlier "because a postal was waiting for him telling him that the Fresh Air Club would go skating at Rockland Lake." The Fresh Air Club was an informal, loosely organized group whose members got together for a variety of weekend sorties into the surrounding countryside, mostly on foot. Irving especially enjoyed their skating excursions, and was irked that morning to have missed the trip to Rockland Lake. However, he was determined to try out his new $3.50 skates, and, with Dean in tow, he set out.

First they took the elevated to 155th Street, intending to skate at Van Cortlandt Park, but they were told it would be an hour before another train left for the park. So they walked there, only to find, on arrival, that skating was prohibited. They went next to Woodlawn, where Irving judged the pond fit for skating. They got in about two hours of skating before a policeman chased them off. The two hours had satisfied Dean. Besides, the admonishing finger of the law made it seem fruitless to hunt further for a good skating place so late in the day. But for Irving the skating day was yet young. Dean returned home alone, with twilight coming on. Irving, when last seen, was hunting for another pond.

About ten days later, Irving did get out with the Fresh Air Club on another skating trip to Rockland Lake. And it almost ended his career. Dean's diary, beginning on January 12, tells the curious and alarming story.

"Irving went to the Fresh Air Club," Dean wrote. "At about six he was brought home by a Mr. Murray who said that he had been found unconscious on the ice with a severe bruise on the right cheekbone. Irving had a good appetite and could think well of present circumstances but could not remember anything of the last week. Had great difficulty in making him believe it was not in the Christmas holidays.

"Irving asked what day it was and what month. When he was told what he did during the last week he would not believe it. He also seemed to have lost all present power of memory and he asked fully eight or nine times what day it was.

"Mama read to him in the evening. He went to bed at half-past nine very cheerful but not knowing what he had done during the day or during the last week. He did not know at all how he had been hurt. The wound is not painful. He had been skating alone on Rockland Lake as the other members of the Fresh Air Club had gone for a walk. He was found unconscious on the ice by the watchman of a hotel."

The next day's entry reported that Irving was still in bad shape. A Mr. Louis of the Fresh Air Club had come visiting, and was able to tell them more about the incident. The watchman at the nearby ice works had come upon Irving lying on the frozen lake, semi-conscious, with a little pool of blood around his head and a bad bruise on his right cheek.

"I'm tired," was all he could tell the watchman, who said that the ice all around the spot where Irving had apparently fallen seemed perfectly smooth, though there was a bit of snow on the surface.

Irving was brought to the hotel, and a doctor was called. But the doctor was slow in coming, and the Fresh Air Club had a train to catch. Since Irving seemed to be coming around and medical help was on its way, they decided not to miss their train. They had no way of knowing, at that point, that Irving had lost his memory. He was not able to tell anyone where he lived, and it is still not clear how the man who brought him home finally found his address. In any case, Irving was having so much trouble concentrating on his books the day after the accident that he decided not to try to attend classes for the rest of the week. "He is cheerful," Dean wrote, "and his memory is very much better than last night. He is now able to get vague impressions of past things by slowly thinking them out. We sent for Dr. Cassel to come in this evening, but he failed to come."

On Tuesday Dean reported that Irving was much better. Mama had called another doctor, who diagnosed Irving's case as "a slight concussion of the brain, probably caused by vertigo... Irving denies this as absurd..." On Wednesday Irving was "entirely out of danger," and on the following Monday "Irving went to college... and is able to study again as usual."

It had been a bad scare for everyone, but, as the world knows, the fall had no lasting effects.

That same year, 1902, apparently marked Irving's first awakening of interest in the opposite sex. Such scattered comments as had appeared earlier in family correspondence regarding Irvings' attitude toward girls indicated mainly that his attitude was negative. As recently as the summer of 1900, he had written Herbert from Camp Columbia, "You know that I am going to the Catskills next week, I suppose. I expect to do a lot of climbing and not waste any time talking to the girls..." But now Irving, just past twenty-one, was finally growing a bit more social, and Dean was making entries like: "Irving went to Lucy's reception and really enjoyed it. A year ago he would have hated it."

Irving did not yet begin liking girls to the point of getting romantic about any of them. He was still too full of his studies, in and out of class — and on weekends he still preferred his own masculine pursuits, which invariably involved some sort of locomotion out of doors. When he did not go alone or with the Fresh Air Club, he usually went with one of his brothers.

In those years — and even more frequently in later years, after he had completed his graduate studies in Germany — Irving used to take long Sunday hikes with Dean — into the New Jersey Palisades or the highlands along the Hudson. He never had quite shaken the habit of explaining science to his younger brother, and during those long walks he indulged himself uninhibitedly. The difference was that Dean no longer had to be backed up against an apartment wall to be made to listen, and he no longer hollered for help. He now listened with rapt attention to Irving's explanations of the familiar phenomena of nature until they became as fascinating to him as they were to Irving. He later counted those peripatetic talks with Irving among his most treasured memories.

But Dean, during Irving's Columbia days, was getting to be the family's problem child. In France everyone had made a fuss over Dean, the cute and cunning baby of the family, the bright youngster who picked up French so facilely, and who was held up even to Irving as a model student who led his class. But somehow he had eased into the age of awkward puberty, and was no longer considered either cute or bright, and he simply did not know how to cope with the changed circumstances.

Dean's troubled states was as much the fault of the family — its members insensitive to the sensitivities of adolescence — as it was his own. All the normal insecurities of teen-age existence were emphasized by the constant demands of Mama, by her critical scrutiny of all his activities, and by the standards of excellence set for him by the example of his three older brothers. At the age when Irving was feeling his powers come most alive, Dean was sinking into a despondent slough of self-castigating inadequacy.

Here are some sample entries from Dean's 1902 diaries, when he was not yet sixteen:

"Mama scolded me for not telling her more about what I see at the theatres, as I have not even spoken to her about either 'Quality Street' or 'Tosca'."

"Much against my will, Mama forced me to go to church." (Mama was now forcing him to do what Papa had all but forbidden.)

"Arthur, Herbert and Mama talked about how successful the boys are. It is now taken as a matter of course that I will not be anywhere near as successful as any of my brothers."

One is grateful not to see Irving's name mentioned as one of those involved in the discussion. However, Irving, for a long time, was just as hard on Dean as anyone. "Rode to school," Dean wrote one day, "and was sat upon by Irving all during dinner for not having a hustle about me because I rode to school."

"I think that the chief reason for my discouraging state of mind during the last $2\frac{1}{2}$ years," Dean wrote, "is that I am asleep. I am not wide awake, quick, and always on the go doing something important."

"Since Dec. 31, 1901," another entry reads, "I have had a little more self-confidence but I am not successful and when I see the small amount of respect they show for my abilities it is very discouraging. If I make a statement in the family, no one believes it or pays any attention to it. If I ask a question very often no one takes the trouble to answer it."

It might have comforted Dean to know that he was not the only one in the household plagued with feelings of inadequacy. Herbert felt the same way, but for different reasons. In Herbert's case, of course, the feelings were not apparent. Superficially he was a success — he was doing well with the New York Life Insurance Company, and his career seemed assured. But in his own mind he had cheated himself (he blamed no one else) by choosing to take a job instead of continuing his education. He had been interested in science as well as literature, but now, irrevocably caught up in the business world, he knew he would never pursue them. He envied the broader intellectual horizons opening up for both Arthur and Irving. He was a success, but not in the way he wanted to be.

In Paris and London Herbert had worked hard, barely supporting himself on his own earnings, with no extra money left over to enjoy what those capitals of culture and entertainment had to offer an inquisitive and experience-hungry young man. He had wistfully watched the rest of the family go off on European vacations while he worked away in his office. And he had come back to the States feeling that he had somehow missed the years when most American youths have the most fun of their lives. He would have liked to feel well-dressed, well-read, urbane, witty and charming. Instead he felt gauche and pedestrian, and somehow left out of the mainstream of educated American life.

But Dean had no way of knowing any of this. In his eyes, Herbert was as impossibly successful as his other two brothers. And Herbert, wrapped up in his own problems, had no time to take special thought of Dean, except to criticize him now and then as the others did. And the constant criticism made Dean do foolish things. Not wanting to be accused of malingering, he once went off to take his violin lesson in spite of the most severe pains in the stomach. He threw up violently during the lesson and, feeling throughly humiliated, had to come home.

On April 3, 1902, Dean, weighing 151 pounds, noted that he was already taller and heavier than Irving. But the superiority in physical measurements did not do much for his morale. "It is my unhappiness," he wrote a few days later, "to have three successful brothers and they are constantly calling me fool and stupid and I think that this is the principal reason of my condition. I have *absolutely* no self-confidence." That same month he was in disgrace for having failed German.

But at last Irving managed to take his mind off himself and his studies long enough to recognize the spot his kid brother was in. He became much gentler with Dean. And later that year Dean noted: "Irving is doing his best to help me get out of the rut."

Soon Dean's spirits were better, and he no longer needed Irving's help. This was fortunate, since Irving would not be around much longer to offer it. In June of 1903, Columbia University's School of Mines conferred upon Irving Langmuir the degree of Metallurgical Engineer, "equivalent to Bachelor of Science." The next stop now would be Germany.

Chapter 6

"... I think of those Companions true
Who studied with me at the U-
NIVERSITY OF GÖTTINGEN,
NIVERSITY OF GÖTTINGEN."

Song by GEORGE CANNING

IRVING had followed Arthur at the Pratt Institute and at Columbia, and now, like Arthur, he planned to do his graduate work in Germany. But, unlike Arthur, he was not going to Heidelberg. It would be either Leipzig or Göttingen, and he was going to get a chance to visit both during the summer of 1903 to help make up his mind.

On June 10, a week after Irving got his degree from Columbia, he and Dean boarded the S.S. *Noordam.* What we know of that summer comes from Dean's diary, and from a few letters written by Irving from Göttingen, Leipzig and Berchtesgaden.

On the day they boarded the *Noordam,* Dean wrote: "Both Irving and I are very much pleased with the ship... It is very large and we noticed in leaving the harbor that our boat deck was higher than that on any other ship — higher than even that of the *Kaiser Wilhelm* and the *St. Paul.*" If the presence of the *Kaiser Wilhelm* gave them a momentary twinge in reminder of their father, Dean made no mention of it.

Dean and Irving played a lot of chess on the way over, with Irving always the winner. Another favorite game was whist. One day they played whist with "the best player on board" — a Professor Stieglitz. This must have been — not the celebrated photographer Alfred Stieglitz — but Julius Oscar Stieglitz, then professor of analytical chemistry and soon to be head of the chemistry department at the University of Chicago.

A casual conversation with a chance traveling companion can often have a lasting influence, and one cannot resist speculating on what Julius Stieglitz and young Irving Langmuir may have talked about. Stieglitz had been born in Hoboken, New Jersey, home of the Stevens Institute of Technology, where Irving would, before long, be teaching chemistry himself. Might Stieglitz have talked about that thriving young institution? And might Stieglitz, himself an alumnus of Göttingen, have been influential in getting Irving even more interested in what was finally to become his own German alma mater? And did they have long, exciting talks about chemistry? They may have just quietly played whist, of course. Well, we shall never know — unless one of Langmuir's own diaries of the period turns up to enlighten us. We do know that the adult Irving Langmuir was invited to lecture to Professor Stieglitz's classes. And Stieglitz was one of the principal speakers on the occasion of the award of the Willard Gibbs Medal to Irving Langmuir. But there is no record of whether either of them recalled the early meeting on the *Noordam*.

Dean had a birthday — his seventeenth — on the way over, and there was a storm, though not as impressive as the one Irving had encountered coming back on the *St. Louis*. They both complained because the captain refused to let them go up in the bow when the weather was bad—which was, of course, the only time they were interested in going up there.

The incident that affected them most during the voyage occurred one quiet day when the ship's engines loudly called attention to themselves by their sudden silence, and the cry went up, "Man overboard!" A man from "the immigrant part of the ship" had apparently flung himself over the side. Irving and Dean ran to see.

"They were most inexcusably slow in lowering the boat," Dean wrote. "But about ten minutes after the man had thrown himself into the sea they gave orders not to lower the boat and to wait until the officers had found out where the man was with their glasses from the bridge. We circled slowly three or four times. . . . After about a half hour from the time the man reached the water we started up again and left him to drown if he was not already dead. He was with all the other immigrants in the stern of the boat.

"No one seemed to think much of the incident and it was soon forgotten. There was even joking about the subject."

On Saturday, June 20, they arrived at Boulogne, then went on to Rotterdam. "After leaving Boulogne," Dean wrote, "we bought from the steward for 30 cents all the editions of the *Paris Herald* since the day we left. The only piece of news of importance is that the Servian king and queen have been butchered."

They landed at the Hook of Holland and proceeded to Rotterdam by train. From the Hotel Weimar they telegraphed Mama, who was in Munich. After a bit of sightseeing in Rotterdam, they took a train for Cologne. There the brothers parted, Dean going on to meet Mama while Irving headed for Göttingen.

About a week later Mama and Dean got a letter from Irving, who told them he was comfortably settled in a pension and was saving money. When he first arrived, "I felt totally lost. I found I couldn't speak German at all and I knew nothing about the university or any of the pensions. There are no signs on any houses to show that they take boarders. So I wandered aimlessly around all morning not plucking up enough courage to find out anything at the hotel where no English was spoken (Gebhard Hotel). At last I went into a book store and found a Universitäts-Kalendar which straightened things out entirely. After studying that over for some while, I found out where all the university buildings were and who gave lectures and where they were and at what time, in fact it told everything I most wanted to know about the university."

Irving went out in the afternoon of that first day to see the physics and chemistry laboratories, where he met two American students. One of them, John Clement, he particularly liked, and the approval was apparently mutual. Clement first helped him find a place to stay, then took him to hear a lecture by Dr. Walther Nernst, in whom Irving was particularly interested. "I was surprised to find out how much I could understand," Irving wrote Mama. "It is probably because Nernst speaks rather slowly and very distinctly. He certainly seems to be a splendid professor." Irving was to revise his opinion downward after Nernst became his major professor. For the moment, though, he was charmed.

After the lecture, Irving went with Clement to his boarding house, was invited to stay for supper, and met the landlady and her two daughters, who succeeded in getting him to try to converse in German. Irving planned to stay in Göttingen until July 15, then go on to Leipzig. "I should think," he said, "that Leipzig is a better place than Göttingen for chemistry but that Göttingen is better for physics and mathematics."

Göttingen, in those days, was famous as the mathematical center where Karl Friedrich Gauss had taught until the middle of the nineteenth century. And Gauss's chair was now filled — and had been since 1886 — by another giant, Felix Klein, who had brought other leading lights of mathematics to Göttingen—men like Runge, Hilbert, and Minkowski. Even in chemistry, Irving was impressed by the presence of professors like Nernst, Wallach, and Kötz. Perhaps the strongest favorable impression made on Irving was by the picturesque town itself, its wonderfully peaceful atmosphere and pastoral surroundings.

Writing to Arthur and Herbert from Leipzig on July 26, Irving told them he planned to spend some time in Berchtesgaden learning German, then go back to Göttingen for one semester, then probably back to Leipzig for a while. So he was still undecided. But his letter made it obvious that he was leaning more and more toward Göttingen. He was pleased with the laboratories and library at Leipzig. But "I think it is impossible to learn German in Leipzig for there are about 1000 Americans here and in the laboratory there are actually more foreigners than there are Germans. Besides I find the lectures are very poor compared to those in Göttingen, and there are only about 1/3 the number of lectures in Leipzig on scientific subjects that there are in Göttingen . . .

"Ostwald does not lecture at all and has practically retired for two years so as to write books. Luther is a brilliant man taking Ostwald's place, but unfortunately has an exceedingly poor delivery."

On July 29, Mama and Dean arrived in Leipzig. Irving met them at the station, and they talked through the evening. He proposed that, from Leipzig, they should join him for two weeks in Berchtesgaden instead of going on to Berlin, as they planned. Dean was all in favor of it, but Mama was set on Berlin. They were all together for a few days, at least, and seemed to have a genuinely good time poking around Leipzig.

Dean, in his diary, described Irving's living quarters. "He lives on the top floor and his windows overlook a kind of garden. It is an old place and there is a rather musty odor. His bed is in a small, dark alcove at the back of the room. He has an old piano in the room on which he is learning to play the Wagner motives quite well."

They went one day to the museum to see Klinger's statue of Beethoven — Irving's favorite composer after Wagner — then looked through the picture gallery. Afterward, Dean wrote, "we went to an optical instrument shop where Irving bought a twenty dollar (80 marks) pocket barometer. The graduations are in meters. It took him a long time to decide whether to get a $13 or $20 barometer . . . In going up stairs on the way home he could estimate by the barometer the height of the house."

The next evening they ate at the open-air Palm Garten restaurant, listened to a band concert, then went home and talked and read the Bible. On another afternoon they spent hours poring over an exhibition showing the progress of book printing since the fifteenth century; then, on the way home, stopped to watch a less static exhibition. A horse had fallen, then, deciding he preferred the prone position, refused so stubbornly to get up that his exasperated owner had to call the fire department for help. It took six sweating men from the fire wagon, working with a chain and hoist, to get the recalcitrant animal on its feet again.

And so their time together in Leipzig ran out.

On August 4, Irving still had a few days left but would be entertaining an American college friend scheduled to arrive that day. It was true Mama and Dean would not now see Irving again for another year. But they had seen all they wanted to see of Leipzig, and Irving was going to be occupied with his guest, so they went on to Berlin. Irving and Dean were not to meet again until almost exactly one year later, in Lucerne, where they promptly climbed the Vitznanerstock.

From Berchtesgaden, Irving wrote mostly about his mountain climbing and his progress with the German language — which, once he learned it, he spoke with almost unaccented fluency throughout his life. But his letters indicated that he was by no means oblivious to the human spectacle around him. "There are only two boarders in the pension now," he wrote Mama, "and they are an old married couple. The wife is actually the most cowardly person I ever saw or heard of. She is thrown into a wild panic by distant thunder and is continually afraid of this, that, and five hundred other things. It took her all day to gather courage to go on the Königsee by boat and then she was deathly afraid that they would shoot of the pistol. The husband is not bad.

"The cousin of the landlady is here too. He is actually insane, I believe, but quite harmless. He doesn't talk much, and he only becomes obnoxious when he plays on the piano and *snorts* and *snores* with the music (?), unconsciously, I think. He never strikes a false note, but no one can ever tell what he plays and it is most weird and jerky music."

On October 18 he wrote Mama — from Göttingen — that he

had finally settled on Göttingen. He assured her that despite the expensive summer trips and the barometer he had bought in Leipzig he had saved thirty-two dollars. He was delighted to have run into a man named Tufts, an assistant in physics at Columbia while Irving was there, and — more important — a fellow member of the Fresh Air Club. Now he would have someone to tramp around the countryside with.

In this same letter, Irving told his mother about a mountain climbing expedition he had proposed while on a trip to Garmisch. The incident not only illustrates Langmuir's vigor and determination, and his appreciation of natural beauties, but it foreshadows his later distrust of, and disagreements with, professional weather forecasters, especially those of the United States Weather Bureau. "It was unfortunately bitter cold," he wrote, "and the wind was so powerful that one always had to hold on to something to keep one's balance. I dressed in all the extra clothing I had and managed to stay out nearly the whole afternoon studying the view with my map...

"The sunset was beyond description...

"The day before, shortly after I told the guide I wanted to stay over night, his apprentice came and said that the meteorologist, who lives the whole year on the summit, declared that in the morning there would be a bad snow storm and he sort of implied that we had better start down that afternoon. But I did not want to miss the sunset and besides if we started down then I would have to walk from Eibsee to Garmisch in dark. To me the weather seemed very promising as there was this strong west wind and the clouds were very high and continually decreasing in size and number and the barometer was particularly high. That evening I spoke myself to the meteorologist and he said that it could not possibly be good weather the next day. As a matter of fact the following day was one of the finest of the whole summer. Not a single cloud all day. Such is the wisdom of weather-prophets."

Many of the friends and associates of Irving Langmuir who came to know him later in life automatically ascribed his great passion for mountain climbing, hiking and skiing to the mere fact that he had attended a German university. "He went to Göttingen," seemed to explain it all.

Göttingen did indeed do a lot for Langmuir. But we should be clear about the things it did not do.

We have already seen that Irving had been a dedicated mountain climber since his thirteenth year, when Arthur and Herbert had initiated him into the gleaming-white magic of the Alpine mysteries, and, with Papa's blessing, he had become a lone celebrant of the lofty rites.

As for skiing, it was Langmuir who introduced skiing to Göttingen, where the sport had been unknown, just as he was later to introduce it to Hoboken, New Jersey and Schenectady, New York. Langmuir was one of the first American ski enthusiasts.

On November 1, 1903 — after telling Mama he had just bought Voigt's 1410-page *Theoretical Physics,* so dense with difficult mathematics that it took him a full hour to read a page — he told her that he had just sent to Munich for a pair of "Norwegian snow-shoes" (skis) and would try to learn how to use them that winter. "From what I heard this summer it is one of the most glorious sports imaginable — traveling over deep snow about 6–7 miles per hour on the level and 10–20 miles per hour down hill. But it is very difficult to learn. It has become a very popular sport in Germany within the last few years. They say the Hartz is full of Schneeschuläufer every winter. Tufts and Hutchinson [another American] are also going to get skis so we can continue our Sunday walks or slides."

By the end of the month his Norwegian snowshoes had arrived and he was describing to Mama his erratic beginnings as a skier:

"Thanksgiving day we had about two inches of snow. Friday and Saturday were rather warm, but I decided to risk a trip to the Meissner with my snowshoes. The weather was horrible: cold, damp & at intervals flurries of snow. I took the train & arrived at Albingen at 11:00 with almost no hope of finding any snow. All the mountains visible had no snow at least below the cloud line. After six miles walking over very muddy roads, I at last reached snow at 400 meters above sea level. By 500 m there was 2″ of good snow with a crust & I was able to put on the skis. At 625 m there was 4″ snow. Here there was a good hotel & I ordered lunch & while waiting went to the top, 710 m. where I found 8–10″ of fine snow.

"Altogether the trip was a great success. It was easy going on the level or up a slight grade, but I simply couldn't go up a steeper slope than the carriage road. Perhaps this slope [here he drew a steep-angled line]. If I tried too steep a pace I would slip backwards & immediately fall frontwards notwithstanding the stick I was using.

"But the greatest fun was going down hill. I found myself utterly powerless to stop up, even on the gentle slope of the road. I would go faster & faster & finally the skis would become crossed or spread apart or something would happen & I would go over in a heap in the snow in every conceivable position. Each time I almost expected to find the ski straps broken or something of the sort but nothing ever went wrong. I couldn't help laughing at myself. Often I wouldn't go more than twenty feet without a fall. If I tried to use the stick as a brake I would begin going sideways & of course would fall over immediately. One thing is lucky, that is if it is ever necessary to stop quickly all you have to do is to fall & the skis get stuck in the snow instantly. It will take all this winter, I guess, to be able to be steady on my feet."

But Irving got his ski legs faster than expected. Soon he was teaching the sport to a few of the German students. By the ensuing winter he had become expert enough to go skiing to the Harz and the Tyrol. During summers, meanwhile, he climbed some of Switzerland's most challenging peaks — the Wetterhorn, the Breithorn, the Jungfrau, the Monte Rosa.

Arthur later recalled that, in the Dolomites, Irving and a friend made some twenty ascents, among them the Fünffingerspitze and the Langkofel — definitely no chores for novices. "These climbs," said Arthur, "were made without a guide, but using a guidebook listing the various handholds on the cliffs and in the chimneys.

Near the top of one of these chimneys, while holding on by his finger tips, it was necessary to swing out into space with a drop of 500 feet in order to locate a foothold for a further advance."

As for anyone becoming a devotee of hiking at Göttingen — well, it is true that the traditional means of transportation in tiny Göttingen was the human foot. Hardly a vehicle was to be seen in use, except by tradesmen with burdens too heavy to carry. Even the bicycle did not make its appearance in this academic sanctuary until after World War I. But the pace in Göttingen was leisurely, with frequent stops for the waving of hands to punctuate emphatic points, and for the settling of philosophic arguments on street corners. It was axiomatic in Göttingen that the most significant ideas were come upon, not in the cloistered halls of the Georgia Augusta University but — as in the Peripatetic School of Aristotle and Theophrastus — while strolling down, say, the Nikolausburger Weg or across the Wilhelmsplatz on the way to the library.

An integral part of the Göttingen landscape was the sight of the slowly perambulating scholar, hands behind back, head — as often as not — down in rapt meditation, pondering an abstraction. A favorite Göttingen story is the one about the student, shuffling along in this semi-cataleptic state, his intellect contemplating a Great Idea while his glassy eyes contemplated nothing. Thus self-hypnotized, he tripped and fell flat on his face. When someone ran to help him, he remained stiffly horizontal, face to the ground, shouting, "Let me alone! Can't you see I'm busy?"

All well and good, but the stroll was not Irving Langmuir's natural gait. He walked with a quick step even when he was in no hurry. "There seems to be no one at Göttingen who can walk even at a moderate rate for any distance except Tufts and Hutchinson," he complained in a letter to Dean, "and their ambition is not sufficient to make them get up Sunday mornings until about 11:00 o'clock except when the weather is fine, and that it never is here. So the walks for this time of year [December] are usually limited to about one or two hours . . . The Germans are all slow walkers, I think . . ."

Langmuir's most prodigious walking feat while in Germany — and probably for the rest of his life — was described in a letter to Herbert dated June 18, 1905 (in which he mentioned in passing that he had not yet received an answer to a fifty-page letter he had written to Arthur — no mean feat of endurance in itself).

"A couple of weeks ago we were talking about mountain climbing and walking," he told Herbert, "and Dr. Jahn challenged me to a walk from Göttingen to the Brocken which we thought was about 50 miles. So we agreed to take it this last week.

"Thursday, we took our Brocken walk. I went to bed Wednesday at 5.30 p.m., slept about 6 hours, got up at 1 a.m., cooked breakfast and started at 2.20. We walked 27 miles without stopping in 7½ hours then stopped 2 hours and ½ for dinner. Here we both had had blisters and our feet were very sore. We started out again and Jahn could not go fast averaging only 2½ miles per hour. After about two hours in which he was getting more and more tired we agreed to separate. I went on to the Brocken. My blisters by that time had entirely dried up and disappeared and my feet were barely perceptibly sore and I was feeling fresh, much more so in fact than at Sieber where we ate dinner. So from the Brocken I returned as far as St. Andreasburg 10 miles further.

"When we came to measure the distance accurately we found it was less than we thought. In all Jahn went 38 miles and I went 52 miles at an average speed of 3.4 miles per hour with ascent of 4940 feet and descent 3400 feet.

"The next day we both felt fine, our feet were not sore and our legs not the least stiff. I went back to Oderbruch to meet Jahn and we came back to Göttingen together walking about 14 miles."

But if Göttingen had very little to do with Langmuir's prowess as hiker, climber and skier, it did have a great deal to do with the furthering of his intellectual powers, his scientific understanding, and even his social development. Before his first year in Göttingen was over, a Fräulein Martha Kuhfuss was trying to teach him to dance, but without much success. Irving went to a large party at the Kuhfuss home on Christmas Day — which was also the day after Martha's birthday. Two of his American friends were there, as well as two American girls, a pair of sisters named Becker. After much boisterous singing "the gentlemen of the party invited the ladies to the theater where we heard 'Charley's Aunt'."

A few evenings later, the newly social Irving went to a dance at Geismar, a village five miles from Göttingen. Their party consisted of six men and five girls. "Of the six men," Irving wrote Mama, "three could dance and two of these were occupied nearly all the time playing while the other was dancing. But all agreed that the evening was one of the pleasantest ever held by the American Colony within the memory of those present . . ." Thus, while Irving was making German friendships that lasted a lifetime, he was also — there in Germany — tasting for the first time the joys of American companionship.

"I tried two dances," he wrote Mama in that same letter, "but made such complete failures that I gave it up. There is no use of my trying to learn without going to dancing school and that is out of the question." Rhythmic walker and climber though he was, Langmuir seemed to lack the peculiar flow of muscled cadences required of the dance, and he never did get to feel really at home in the ballroom. He had no singing voice either, yet he could whistle beautifully and memorize entire operatic scores. And though no less an authority than Leopold Stokowski — who had occasion to consult the adult Langmuir on the technical problems of symphonic broadcasting — once expressed amazement at Langmuir's uncommonly sharp ear for music, Langmuir never did learn to play an instrument with any facility.

In Göttingen, for a while, he did continue the piano-plunking he had begun in Leipzig that summer. When Dean sent him Wagner's *Lohengrin* for Christmas, Irving wrote Mama: "He must think that I have become a great musician all of a sudden. I did succeed in playing a whole page after *a fashion* with about three hours work. I think that Clement will like to play parts of it, however . . ." (In that same letter he told Mama that his own

Christmas gift list would require an outlay of twenty dollars—which, he confessed, "terrified" him.)

All this, naturally, was peripheral to Langmuir's main purpose in life at Göttingen, which continued to be his scientific studies. Almost from the day of its founding in 1734 by the Elector George Augustus, later to become King George II of England, the Georgia Augusta University at Göttingen had enjoyed an illustrious reputation. And even before the era of Gauss it had attracted some of Germany's finest scientific minds, and had been the seat of the Göttinger Dichterbund, a group of German Romantic poets. Moreover, Göttingen could boast a long tradition of academic freedom.

In 1837 the famous "Göttingen Seven," a group of professors including the physicist Wilhelm Edward Weber, loudly protested when King Ernest Augustus of Hanover revoked the liberal constitution of 1833—and were promptly dismissed by royal order. After that Göttingen went into a period of decline.

But even during its decline, Göttingen's scientific luster was maintained, even enhanced, by the presence there of the great organic chemist Friedrich Wöhler, the man who synthesized urea, and who was the first to isolate the elements aluminum, beryllium, and yttrium. Wöhler was not only an outstanding researcher; he was also an unusually gifted teacher whose spreading renown attracted students from all over Europe. A number of American students of an earlier generation than Langmuir were equally indebted to Göttingen—and specifically to Wöhler—among them Frank F. Jewett and Edgar F. Smith, who later became professors of chemistry at Oberlin College and the University of Pennsylvania. Since Wöhler arrived at Göttingen the year before The Seven departed, and was still there when Gauss arrived, it cannot really be said that Göttingen's scientific development was ever interrupted all.

In addition to the calibre of its faculty and the prestige of its tradition, Göttingen's wealth of institutes offered for the delight of the senses the sheer physical presence of science in all its aspects. At hand was everything from the astronomical observatory to the botanical gardens, and all manner of displays, from the dazzling mineral exhibits to Blumenbach's famous collection of skulls at the anatomical institute — over which one can picture Langmuir lingering long and lovingly.

During his first year at Göttingen, Langmuir was delighted with nearly all his professors. His one disappointment was the great Hermann Minkowski whose course in mechanics and theoretical physics he had looked forward to with understandable anticipation. Irving started criticizing Minkowski's "poor delivery" immediately in his letters home. He complained to Mama that Minkowski "starts on one proof and leaves off and takes up something else that he forgot. He never says what he is trying to prove. But there is no doubt but what he knows his subject. I am sorry I took the course, however."

Klein, on the other hand, he found "wonderfully good. He presents his points in altogether new lights and gives practical and sensible ways of looking at different methods in calculus which usually give trouble. Everyone here says he is the greatest mathematician in Germany. But still he does not treat the subject in the abstract way that most abstract mathematicians would do. He never makes a mistake. Every figure he draws almost geometrically perfect and shows just what he wants to prove."

It was Felix Klein, in fact, who had created the kind of atmosphere at Göttingen that was ideal for a future industrial research chemist. When Klein first arrived at Göttingen, it was a typical German university — that is, the theoretical was almost entirely divorced from the practical. The Ivory Tower was the fashion in intellectual architecture. The prevailing attitude was perhaps best typified by that ultimate mathematical purist, David Hilbert, who referred to applied scientists as "technicians." An oft-told Göttingen tale has Hilbert about to address a gathering of engineers. The program committee, knowing Hilbert's strong views on the subject, pleaded with him in advance to say a few words refuting the notion that the gap between scientists and engineers was unbridgeable. Hilbert, always an accommodating fellow, agreed:

"One hears," he told the assemblage in his gruff Prussian accents, "a lot of talk about the hostility between scientists and engineers. I don't believe in any such thing. In fact I am quite certain it is untrue." A pause. "There cannot possibly be anything in it because neither side has anything to do with the other."

Hilbert freely expressed his views, of course, but it was Klein who set the tone of the place. Klein, a tall, husky man whose genial temperament kept his regal bearing from intimidating people, had always been aware of the pure scientist's contribution to technological progress. A visit to the United States in 1893 impressed it upon him even more sharply.

Klein spearheaded the modernization of Göttingen's scientific and technical institutes, and founded some new ones. And around them grew up Göttingen's thriving precision-instrument industries. It was Klein's influence, too, that opened the way for Göttingen's famous automotive and aircraft experiment station only two years after Langmuir left. Langmuir learned much more than mathematics from Felix Klein. He learned, not by direct instruction but simply by living in the aura Klein created, that there is — or can be — a continual exchange between science and technology that is useful to both.

As P. M. S. Blackett pointed out in 1935, "the Second Law of Thermodynamics arose from the attempt to make steam-engines more efficient... Today this Second Law of Thermodynamics appears one of the most far-reaching of all physical laws... So the most abstract and general of laws arose from the study of that most concrete of objects, the steam engine." Blackett further pointed out that "the work of Appleton and others on the highly conducting upper layers of the atmosphere has given us absolutely new knowledge about our planet and opened up a fascinating field of pure research."

Langmuir ultimately attained a thorough understanding of this vital feedback principle. He knew, better than any other American scientist of his day, that, just as technology is dependent upon the theorists for the bold new concepts which permit its own quantum-jumps of progres so technology helps spur the theorists. How? First, by providing new instruments. Technical aids from the telescope to the transistor, from the cyclotron to the rocket engine, all have opened up vast new research frontiers for the basic scientist. Another way in which technology helps is by merely providing problems that stimulate the theorists to strike out into wholly novel fields for the answers.

This understanding was perhaps Göttingen's most important legacy to Langmuir.

Chapter 7

"What a matter for thankfulness I felt it that the German university does not keep the student so completely in leading strings in his studies, nor so much on the strain by constant examination as is the case in other countries, but offers him opportunities for independent scientific work."

ALBERT SCHWEITZER
Out of My Life and Thought

AT GÖTTINGEN in the year 1904, it was Walther Nernst who became Irving Langmuir's major professor and the director of his work toward a doctoral dissertation. The association was in some respects unfortunate, since neither of these two future Nobel laureates seemed to think highly of the other. Nernst, like Langmuir's Columbia professors, failed to discern in this industrious young American any sign which promised future greatness. And Langmuir, though initially quite enthusiastic about Nernst, soon began to feel that Nernst was a poor instructor, always too absorbed in his own private pursuits to spare any time or attention for mere students.

There was probably some justice in Langmuir's complaint. The mere fact that Nernst saw nothing special in Langmuir at that stage of his development constitutes *prima facie* evidence of inattention. But if Nernst neglected his academic duties somewhat, it was not so he could sing drunken Lieder while sloshing the foam from his overflowing stein at the nearest beer garden. For this was the period when Irving's professor was not only hard at work on a new Nernst lamp, but was at the same time preparing to enunciate the celebrated statement that was to become known as the "third law of thermodynamics." With Nobel Prize calibre work his preoccupation, it seems uncharitable, at the least, to issue a harsh condemnation of this momentarily absent-minded professor.

After all disclaimers have been entered, it must still be said that Nernst was good for Langmuir. For one thing, he was as much a physicist as a chemist; he has, in fact, been called the father of modern physical chemistry. He could hardly have failed, then, to impart to Langmuir — even if only by osmosis — some understanding of the important relationships between the two disciplines — an understanding which was to prove so fruitful in the younger man's career. And in the Klein tradition, Nernst too was a rare combination of the theoretical and the applied scientist — and some of *that* must have rubbed off on Langmuir.

Nernst had already done outstanding work on osmotic pressure and ionization, and in 1906, Langmuir's last year at Göttingen, Nernst was expressing the classic profound insights into the behavior of matter at temperatures approaching absolute zero, that firmly established him as one of the founders of modern cryogenics. Nernst was not only a theorist and experimenter who later made important contributions to sciences as varied as electro-acoustics and astrophysics; he was also an inventor of some note. Particularly important for the future of Irving Langmuir and the General Electric Company was Nernst's abiding interest in electric lamps — an interest that was commercial as well as scientific.

Langmuir obviously had much to learn from this genius — a man who could achieve such brilliant results on the blackboard and in the laboratory — and who was yet a sufficiently adroit verbal fencer to deliver a perfect, conversation-stopping squelch to the likes of Thomas Alva Edison.

Edison, who liked to think of himself as the sharpest of Yankee traders, though he was in fact a rather poor businessman, loved to bait academic types. And one of the lectures he most enjoyed delivering to those who professed to be pure scientists was to the effect that no concept or invention should be developed unless there is an immediate, sure-fire market for it. The Edison thesis, dogmatically stated, seldom failed to evoke the desired reaction — a violent counterspeech, defending the pursuit of science for its own sake.

When Edison met Herr Professor Walther Nernst of Göttingen — whose electric lamp had enjoyed only a brief popularity — it was hardly to be expected that Edison would resist the temptation to launch into his favorite theme. Nernst listened, deadpan, permitting Edison to expatiate at some length before interrupting to ask quietly, "And how much did you make on your electric lamp?"

"Why — not a dime," Edison admitted.

"I made $250,000 on mine," said Nernst.

Though Nernst was more than a match for Edison, he was no sparring partner for Professor Klein. One day when the two met, Klein remarked, "I'm beginning to slow down, Nernst. My mental powers are not what they used to be."

Nernst, who was fifteen years younger, replied, "Mine, on the contrary, are steadily improving."

"In that case," said Klein dryly, "sooner or later our two curves will intersect."

The problem assigned to Langmuir by Nernst in 1904 was a relatively routine bit of research having to do with interaction of gases in the vicinity of a glowing electric-light filament. It is to Langmuir's credit — and, no doubt, also to Nernst's — that he derived a great deal of knowledge and satisfaction from a chore some other student might have considered pure drudgery.

The nature of Langmuir's thesis work under Nernst is best described by Percy W. Bridgman: "His thesis dealt with the dissociation in various gases produced by hot platinum wires or the Nernst glower. He found two reactions, the dissociation of water vapor and carbon dioxide which, on the surface of hot platinum, proceeded to practically equilibrium conditions. It was further found that the equilibrium condition was carried away, practically without change of composition, by the gas as it diffused rapidly away from the hot surface, thus permitting an analysis of the gas under conventional conditions at lower temperatures. In the first gaseous reaction which Langmuir studied, the dissociation of nitric oxide, this simple state of affairs was not attained and study of this reaction was temporarily abandoned.

"In justifying the simplified picture of the phenomena for H_2O and CO_2," Bridgman went on to point out, "Langmuir had to study and evaluate the transfer of heat from hot surfaces by convection and conduction in the surrounding gas, factors which were to be the subject of much more searching analysis in his later work. He also had to make an elaborate study of the accuracy with which the temperature of the platinum wire could be deduced from its resistance. Although the general topic of the thesis would conventionally be classified as chemistry (dissociation in gases), and although some use was made of the chemical formulas for mass action, nevertheless nearly all the manipulations and the details of the analysis would be classified as physics."

This work was to become the springboard for some of Langmuir's greatest research. It led directly, as Kenneth H. Kingdon has pointed out, "to an understanding of the unexpectedly much greater importance of thermal conduction, as compared with convection, in determining the heat loss from a filament" in its immediate neighborhood. It also sparked Langmuir's later research in the field of heat transfer — even during his brief, difficult period at Stevens Tech.

In the face of the young graduate student, lit up as much by curiosity as by the glow of the incandescent lamp, we see mirrored the symbol of the later Langmuir as well. He was fascinated by the sheer simplicity of the experimental setup — a simplicity for which he was to maintain a lifelong predilection. Here, within the tight confines of a transparent glass lamp containing a filament, the experimenter could manipulate the temperature of the wire at will and see what happened either in a vacuum or to a gas — a controlled quantity of any gas, or any combination of gases. It was a perfect little world for studying the behavior of electrons, atoms, and molecules. No one was to take greater advantage of this austerely economical apparatus than Irving Langmuir. He wrung from it, over the years, a motley assortment of unlikely treasures, from a revolutionary new welding torch to a revolutionary new atomic theory.

What had been arbitrarily assigned him as a routine problem for a doctoral dissertation thus became one of the themes running through his life, like a leitmotif running through one of his beloved Wagner operas. He happened to work on an electric lamp because his professor happened to be interested in electric lamps. Now he was destined to make radical and lasting improvements in electric lamps. And one of the improvements would be achieved by the use of argon—the same inert gas discovered by Rayleigh and Ramsay which Arthur had told Irving about that night in Brooklyn when he had told him about his engagement to Alice Dean — that same non-reacting gas which, despite its laziness, Langmuir was to harness for man's use. As it happened, Rayleigh and Ramsay were jointly awarded the Nobel Prize for that same discovery that same year — 1904.

There, in Göttingen in 1904, the pattern of Irving Langmuir's future seemed to be taking shape. But meanwhile a great deal of debate about that future had been taking place back home among Mama and Irving's brothers — a debate largely provoked by the uncertainties expressed in Irving's own letters home. The question was: Should he prepare himself to become a commercial chemist, like Arthur, and perhaps make a lot of money, like Arthur — or should he devote himself to pure research, in which case he would probably remain poor but might make some great contribution to science. Irving obviously leaned toward the latter choice, but he was far from certain that he had the capacity to follow Rayleigh and Ramsay — or, for that matter, Nernst — and it would be quite a blow, later in life, to discover that one was not only a pauper but a mediocrity as well. Langmuir knew this was a gamble, and he was willing to take it. But he needed encouragement from someone he respected. The encouragement was not forthcoming from either Mama or Arthur. But at an opportune moment, a long letter arrived from his brother Herbert.

The letter, dated December 13, 1904, accompanied a prospectus of the Carnegie Institute, particulars about positions at the University of Colorado, and a copy of Hugo Münsterberg's *American Traits*. The pertinent portion of Herbert's letter follows:

"The other matter in connection with you that has occupied me somewhat is your own future. I have therefore studied into the matter in various directions and thought about it a great deal and give you the results in this letter.

"The whole matter revolves itself into the question whether you have, or have not exceptional ability in pure science research. If you simply have a well-grounded knowledge and a thorough efficiency, you should certainly go right into the business of chemistry where you will be of most use to yourself and everyone else. But if you are the exceptional man, it is, in my opinion, your duty to be one of the pioneer scholars in America. Münsterberg says there is no scholarship in America. But if there is none, there shall be, and it is time for the young men of brains to be pioneers in the cause. He says there are traps and pitfalls along the entire path of the would-be scholar; which only bears out my statement that you will have before you a continuous fight to keep your spirit pure and your aim high.

"The pressure of the mercenary spirit here is almost overpowering. A man's success is almost entirely judged by the money he makes and that general opinion weighs heavily upon anyone who tries to resist it. And yet you know and I know that money is not the great source of happiness but much more a sense of efficiency, an interesting occupation and the leisure to be human. All of these surely go with a scholar's life, provided of course he obtains enough money to eat and dress and amuse himself a little. About the latter there will be no question, I think, at least after a year or two, so that the only real obstacle, the absolute necessity of a decent livelihood, is non-existent.

"The time has come when this country must have her distinctive scholars. If they do not get great honor now, they surely will by the time you have done anything particularly worthy. Meanwhile you will have the incalculable advantage of a great aim with all that it contributes to happiness and the full life. I often wish that I were in a position to give full scope to my aspirations and my enthusiasms and were free from the necessity for the petty compromises and small selfish aims of a business life. There is a great deal that is noble and inspiring in business, and business can always be conducted in the better way, but it is a lower thing for some men than research and scholarship.

"Most of us are suited to nothing else but business, not being finely enough organized mentally to spend our careers in other than active work. But you perhaps are one of the few with creative brains. If you are (and don't decide so unless you have good authority) you will betray your true self if you devote your life selfishly to private enterprises and personal acquisition.

"And the minute you allow yourself to deviate from the path of pure science, you will lose something in character, and more still in the power to aspire and the possibility to be truly happy."

Herbert obviously felt that Irving was one of the exceptional minds, and he was certain what Irving's choice would be. He deemed this letter so important that he copied it into his diary and marked it "for future reference." Herbert had always felt that he had been untrue to himself by choosing a business career instead of continuing his education and going into some field that would have provided broader intellectual and cultural satisfactions. He did not want Irving — whom he had always believed the brightest of the family — to make the same mistake.

"I thank you exceedingly for all the trouble you have taken to look out for good opportunities for me," Irving wrote back. "Certainly I feel at present as though I would be more fitted for and would enjoy more thoroughly research work rather than industrial work. The Carnegie Research Assistantships please me more than anything else and I feel sure that I would not have great difficulty in getting one... Your letter contains a vast amount of good advice and is well worth keeping and reading several times."

In December of 1932, at the family reunion in Englewood, New Jersey, assembled in honor of Irving's departure to receive the Nobel Prize, Herbert could not resist bringing out his diary of 1903, and reading to a surprised audience of Langmuirs the letter he had written to Irving in 1904. It brought a moving response of tears and well-deserved applause.

Among the possibilities that opened up for Irving before he received his Ph.D. degree from Göttingen in 1906 and published his thesis — "Über partielle Wiedervereinigung dissociierter Gase im Verlauf einer Abkühlung" — was an offer to join the faculty at the Stevens Institute of Technology.[1] The offer came in June of 1905 in the form of a letter from Dr. Thomas B. Stillman, who had acted on the recommendation of a Professor Miller at Columbia.

Stevens Tech, located in Hoboken, New Jersey, was only ten years older than Irving Langmuir. A nonsectarian college, mainly for men, it had been founded by Edwin August Stevens, the son of John Stevens and brother of Robert L. Stevens — all three Stevenses being well-known engineers. It was the first American institution to grant the degree of Mechanical Engineer.

Dr. Stillman, who had offered Langmuir the job, was head of a two-man chemistry department. Irving, if he accepted the offer to become an instructor, would be the third man in a growing department of what appeared to be a dynamic young institution. We do not know the considerations that impelled Langmuir to take the position, but early in 1906 he arrived in Hoboken in time for the opening of the spring semester. As it turned out, in

[1] "Really," wrote Mama to Dean in 1905, "it seems to me he had better go to night school to study grammer and English so he can write a good letter before he takes *any* position in college . . . Did you ever know a man of 24 of any intellect to write such baby letters?" She went on to complain about Irving's "unformed, childish sentences and misspelled words." Though Mama was most intolerant of any criticism of her sons by others, she remained, to the end, their severest critic.

choosing Stevens Tech as the high road to scholarly research, Langmuir had been badly misguided.

To many of Langmuir's later friends it seemed curious that such a superb and natural-born teacher should not have been happy in a teaching position. What they overlooked was the fact that Langmuir was a superb teacher only of those who wanted to be taught. He had neither the patience nor the desire to cram facts down the recalcitrant gullets of bored youngsters taking a course because they were forced to in order to get the required number of credits, young men who considered learning a punishment and who would rather be almost anywhere in preference to a classroom or a laboratory. Besides, Langmuir carried a backbreaking work load at Stevens, and the possibility of finding either the time, the energy, or the facilities for research seemed quite remote.

A letter to Dean toward the end of that first semester pretty well sums up the situation. After first apologizing to Dean for letting so much time elapse without writing, he explained: "The work at Stevens has been pretty hard. During about two months and a half there was certainly enough work to keep several men busy and only by neglecting nearly half of it was I able to get along at all. You see the entire year's work was crowded into three months and there was no extra help. Not only that, but the building was hardly ready for use and there was no system or order and no one had any time to get things straightened out. It was very discouraging work for all along I could see that the men were really getting very little out of the course and all because I couldn't get any time to explain things to them and keep track of the work the individual men were doing."

Thus, in addition to having to teach students who were basically uninterested, he had too many students to handle and was bothered by the fact that even those who might have some genuine interest in their studies were perforce being neglected. Moreover, the other professors in the department did not seem terribly interested in their work, and let conscientious young Langmuir bear the major burdens.

"Prof. Stillman," he wrote Dean, "is the professor in charge of the course in quantitative analysis and five afternoons a week I was to assist him with the juniors. Three mornings a week I had to assist Prof. Pond in the qualitative analysis laboratory work with sophomores. Now the work while the classes were there was the smallest part of it. For the juniors I had to make up and measure out accurately solutions for them to analyze and to enter up all their reports in a book etc." This was the young scientist who had opted in favor of helping relieve America's shortage of scholars by going into research instead of industry.

"Prof. Stillman," he continued, "is a rather old man and he never did one bit of work except to walk around the laboratory two or three hours every afternoon and talk to the students (spending much of the time telling them funny stories). The students had no lectures on their work and understood nothing they did; they simply followed the directions in the text book and as a result got rotten results. About three weeks before the end of the term the work was a little easier so I decided to spend two hours a week lecturing the men describing the analyses. There was no provision for the lectures on the schedule and the students at least many of them thought it was a scheme to make them work harder. The laboratory work had been very easy for them so far because they didn't even need to think about what they did.

"So the first time I tried to lecture to them they paid almost no attention, but talked to one another and threw hats etc. around the room. I kept right on, paying as little attention as I could to the matter. The next time the other section of the class appeared and they having heard about the fun the other class had had came prepared to have a still better time so they brought in a couple of old broken bats and a baseball etc. I had my lecture carefully prepared and for a while they listened fairly well as long as I talked about the course in general and what I intended to do, but as soon as I got started on the real subject matter they cut up again. So after giving them due warning I dismissed the whole class not only from the lecture but also from the laboratory work, telling them they could return the next day and try again.

"The next day they came back and were vastly more orderly but still there was a great deal of disorder, for instance I could not turn around to write on the board without having them do such things as pull off each other's shoes etc. so I dismissed them again. That afternoon a committee of the class went to see the president to ask him if they could hold a class meeting the next morning at the end of one of the lectures and whether he would not address them at the beginning of the class meeting. The next day they voted to behave themselves and during the rest of the term there was splendid order.

"It was a very interesting experience but a very hard one. It is the hardest work I ever tackled to stand up in front of 42 men who are trying to make fun of you and to try to make them listen to what you say. I was not at all rattled and felt perfectly calm, but it completely used me up for the day, so that I felt completely exhausted."

Before the semester was over, Langmuir asked for a raise and for an assistant. And before the end of June he was reporting to Mama: "I have seldom been more pleasantly surprised than I was today when I got a letter from Pres. Humphreys notifying me that from Sept 1st my salary would be $1200 a year. After seeing the letter of his which I showed you I never once thought there would be a possibility of getting $1200 but thought it much more probable that I would get $1000 instead of even $1100, especially as I did nothing further about the matter. Dr. Stillman had advised me to see the president again, but I did not, not liking to talk about it until I knew what was going to be done about it.

"As for the other request, that of getting an assistant, the president says that after a careful study of the roster for next year he feels sure I can get along without one, and at any rate I ought to try it. If it does prove too much he says he will be able to get some of the seniors to help enough to relieve me of most of the more routine work.

"So I am feeling very rich and am wondering what I can possibly do with so much money; it amounts to nearly a dollar a day more than I am getting now.

"Today in the laboratory there was an awful mess. Last night I went away and forgot to turn the water off from a condensor which I had been using all afternoon. In some mysterious way the water began leaking during the night so that in the morning the janitor found about $1\frac{1}{2}$ inches of water on the floor of the laboratory and this had overflowed into the next room and well out into the hall. 26 pails of water were sponged up from that floor. But what was worse the water had filled about 15 drawers and made the wood swell so that they could not possibly be opened. Several books and cases of apparatus were ruined and two drawers had to be broken to pieces to get their contents out. Altogether about \$10–\$15 damage which I will have to bear I suppose."

In 1907 the pay raise made him a little happier at Stevens, but not much.

A note to his sister-in-law, Edith (Herbert's wife) in April of that year indicates that Irving did have a little spare time to think about young ladies, but had not yet gained much confidence in his knowledge of what constituted proper comportment in the presence of the stronger sex.

"Last week, Dean and I called on . . . Miss Cushman," he wrote. "We both enjoyed our call . . . greatly, so much so in fact that I am afraid we made a bad blunder in staying so late — almost eleven o'clock. It seemed almost impossible to go any sooner altho I knew I ought to and was waiting for some sort of a chance for a long time. I suppose with practice such things become easier, but to me it seems as if one had to be very rude to get up and go in the midst of an interesting conversation. Is it an unpardonable offense to stay until 11 p.m. when calling for the first time on a young lady? Didn't Herbert say his first call on you lasted till 12 or 12.30 or so? If that is so I feel somewhat relieved."

We have no record of whether or not Irving ever made a second call on the young lady. But we do know that he was still working too hard and finding the lack of free time increasingly frustrating. And Arthur was writing to Herbert: "Irving is making money and laying some aside but I should like to see him get started on that research."

By 1908 Irving had managed to put together some simple equipment and get a modest research program going. As described by Sir Hugh Taylor, "he analyzed mathematically the velocity of reactions in gases moving through heated vessels, dealing with the effects of convection and diffusion. These were shown to act in a way equivalent to a decrease in the velocity of reaction." A respectable enough piece of research, and it provided him with his second published paper. "In this paper," says Percy W. Bridgman, "he revealed the instincts of the engineer as well as of the physicist and chemist, in that he was careful to throw his results into such numerical shape that they would easily yield quantitative results when applied by other experimenters under easily reproducible experimental conditions."

This bit of research only whetted Langmuir's appetite for more, and he increasingly resented the fact that he had to scheme continually to squeeze in odds-and-ends of time for research — and then had only the tag ends of his energies left to devote to it.

By 1909 he was thoroughly fed up with the academic life as exemplified by Stevens Tech. That year, Mama, now sixty, vacationing in Damariscotta, Maine, wrote a long letter to Herbert. Toward the end of the letter she began to write about Irving. "I suppose you know Irving's situation at Stevens. Dr. Stillman is going to resign and Dr. Pond will take his place and he intends to keep Irving just where he is, as instructor with no raise of salary and Irving has told him that he will resign this fall.

"He has worked fearfully hard for three years or more and has done all of Dr. Stillman's work and should legitimately get Dr. Pond's position with a two thousand dollar salary. He asked for eighteen hundred and the title of Assistant Professor and he has been refused both. The President Dr. Humphreys knows nothing whatever about the Chemical department and has let Dr. Stillman, Irving and Dr. Pond run it entirely. Now that Dr. Stillman retires, he puts everything into Dr. Pond's hands and

Dr. Pond is jealous of Irving I think and feels that he has had too much say and he is going to keep him down and thank goodness Irving can resign and get away from a college that cannot appreciate such a man as Irving.

"Why Herbert he has written textbooks and prepared original matter for his classes that has kept him up all night time and time again and he knows as much in his little finger as Dr. Pond knows in his whole body. He is narrow and unprogressive and does not keep up to the time at all. However he has gone to Göttingen this summer to learn something — otherwise he could not manage Irving's department. You know Dr. Stillman has done absolutely nothing and Irving has lectured every day and done superhuman work. It makes me boil to think it has been so unappreciated. I think however it is going to be to his advantage to leave Stevens and get into a larger college later on. He had no time to apply as Dr. Stillman did not return until college closed and then it was too late to look up college positions. I send you his letter which will help you to understand things better perhaps.

"I have no doubt ordinary professors have salaries of fourteen hundred dollars for seven years just as Dr. Pond did but Irving is not an ordinary man. He is way above the ordinary professor of chemistry and you will see him get way ahead in a few years."

Dean, who preserved a copy of the letter just quoted, noted soberly on the bottom of it: "The discussion of Irving's status is typical of her attitude towards all her children. Her fierce loyalty toward their interests is shown by her impatience with anyone who opposed, for whose point of view she had nothing but scorn and intolerance. Her contempt of the low salary offered Irving reflects the extremely high standard of success which she always set for her children."

Even allowing for the exaggeration and distortion of Irving's situation attributable to maternal loyalty, Mama's letter makes it clear that Irving was in a spot. And now that Mama's letter has been exhumed, it becomes necessary to exhume one of the most cherished myths about Irving Langmuir, and to re-examine it in the light of Mama's letter. The myth has been retold in many places — perhaps nowhere more beautifully than in an article entitled "A Summer Vacation," by George W. Gray, which appeared in the *Atlantic Monthly* soon after Langmuir had won the Nobel Prize. (This article, by the way, is probably the best ever written about Langmuir.) In oversimplified form, the myth — which Langmuir himself helped perpetuate, in later years — runs something like this:

Langmuir, when he visited the General Electric research laboratory in Schenectady, New York, in the summer of 1909, discovered Paradise. In Paradise he began research from which he was most reluctant to tear himself away. "September arrived. The classroom in Hoboken was waiting," wrote Gray, "and here was its chemistry instructor in the midst of an engrossing experiment." Who would willingly flee The Garden of Eden? Certainly not Langmuir. He stayed on to pursue The Holy Grail.

The myth is not altogether mythical, of course. The GE lab was for Langmuir the closest thing to a scientific paradise he could hope to find, and he did indeed pursue his research with the intensity ascribed to the Knights of the Round Table in their quest for the sacred vessel.

But it cannot now be overlooked that Langmuir, when he went up to Schenectady that summer, was already out of a job. Or worse — having threatened to resign, but finding it too late to apply for another academic post that year, he might be faced with the possibility of going back, in humiliation, to work for Pond on Pond's own terms — an unthinkable alternative for a young man with the Langmuir pride.

That summer of 1909 Irving had planned to spend his vacation climbing mountains, as he had done the previous two summers. But, at a scientific meeting in Schenectady during the fall of 1908, he had renewed acquaintance with an old Columbia classmate, Colin G. Fink, who was now on the staff of the General Electric research laboratory. Fink, who was working on a method for making molybdenum ductile, seemed quite happy in his work, in marked contrast to Langmuir's disgruntlement with his own situation. During the meeting Fink had taken Langmuir on a brief tour of the place. Langmuir was impressed with the scholarly atmosphere at GE and must have compared it, to the latter's disfavor, with the endless hurly-burly of his harried existence at Stevens. And Langmuir in his turn impressed the laboratory's director, Willis R. Whitney, with the talk he was called upon to give at the meeting.

We have no way of knowing for sure whether Langmuir mentioned to Fink how unhappy he was at Stevens, but it seems likely he must have dropped some hint of it, and Fink may or may not have passed the hint along to Whitney. And Whitney may or may not have had Langmuir in mind as a likely recruit for the laboratory. We do know that a summer job was one of his favorite methods for trying out prospective researchers — a method he used later with Saul Dushman, for example, and William C. White. A summer's employment was an ideal way to see what a man could do in the laboratory, a means of sizing him up at close range. It was also a good way to let the man experience what the laboratory had to offer him before he made any irrevocable commitments.

In any case, when summer came, Langmuir was invited to spend his vacation in Schenectady, working in the GE laboratory. It was not difficult for Langmuir to decide to forego his mountain climbing. He could climb mountains any summer. He would have been unforgivably obtuse not to recognize in GE's invitation the hope of a graceful egress from his impasse at Stevens. When the invitation came, he accepted it with alacrity.

Chapter 8

"Your theory is getting you. You think you know so much that you won't be able to see and report the news."

Editor S. S. McClure in
LINCOLN STEFFENS' *Autobiography*

IN 1892 the two largest electric combines in the United States, the Edison General Electric Company and the Thomson-Houston Company merged to form the giant General Electric Company. But the ink on the merger papers was scarcely dry when the Panic of 1893 hit the nation. The same set of economically depressed circumstances that permitted Arthur and Irving Langmuir to live so cheaply over in Brooklyn almost did GE in. The company did manage to survive the depression, however, and by the time the century's end approached GE was not only back on its feet but expanding again.

One of the things that began worrying GE's technical director E. W. Rice, Jr., and Albert G. Davis, head of the company's patent department, was the dearth of radical new ideas from which new products might be developed to help meet increasing competition. Most engineers whom Rice consulted seemed to doubt that any radical new developments were possible in electricity. Copper was obviously the best conductor. And how could iron be improved upon as a magnetic material? As for lamp filaments and brushes for motors and generators, who could conceive of anything replacing carbon? Rice found these objections tiresome, and unwarrantedly pessimistic.

The company was not altogether barren of research and development efforts, of course. Elihu Thomson — the Philadelphia high school teacher around whose inventions the Thomson-Houston Company had first been formed — still maintained his laboratory at Lynn, Massachusetts. And the redoubtable Charles Proteus Steinmetz was going full blast in the laboratory he had set up in the barn behind his Schenectady house. But this wasn't enough, not nearly enough, Rice felt. And Thomson and Steinmetz agreed.

Thomson, says Kendall Birr in *Pioneering in Industrial Research*, "envisioned a research laboratory which would search out scientific principles and act as a source of technical information for the company. Both Thomson and Steinmetz favored a laboratory free from production worries and able to pursue fundamental experimental investigations."

Once the idea was agreed upon, Rice had to decide on a director. It was of the utmost importance to get the right man. Steinmetz, for example, would never do. For all his brilliance and imagination, he was the ruggedest of individualists, and definitely not the man to head a team. Thomson was not interested. He protested that he was too old, and, besides, had never cared much for administrative chores. But he knew a young chemistry professor at the Massachusetts Institute of Technology who might fill the bill if Rice could induce him to take the job. His name was Willis R. Whitney.

Rice looked Whitney up, interviewed him in October of 1900, and was so taken with him that he offered him, on the spot, the directorship of the new GE laboratory. Whitney was dubious. He was happy at M.I.T. "Working with Professor A. A. Noyes," wrote Laurence A. Hawkins in *Adventure into the Unknown*, "he had contributed to the development of the modern theory of solutions and devised a process for recovering and separating the alcohol and ether which were going to waste at the plant of the American Aristotype Company, later purchased by Eastman

Kodak. That was his first direct contribution to industry. His most important work at that time was on colloids, on which he threw new light that attracted the attention and respect of chemists everywhere." At M.I.T. Whitney had also done pioneer work in electrochemistry. He proved, for example, that corrosion is an electrochemical phenomenon — and on the concepts he derived from this knowledge are based the means for controlling corrosion that are still in use today.

Whitney appreciated the opportunities for research that an institution like M.I.T. offered, and was not at all sure an industrial laboratory would provide problems of sufficient interest and variety. Having enough problems — and not dull problems — was vital for Whitney. Arthur D. Little, the famous consulting chemist of Boston, remembered that once, after having dinner with Whitney in Syracuse, New York, "when the conversation reached the eternal verities," Whitney told him "he didn't want to go to Heaven unless there were problems there."

Whitney was not only a dedicated researcher; he was also an enthusiastic teacher. Between teaching and research, he was supremely content on the campus. He had already turned down one chance to go into industrial research when Arthur D. Little himself had invited him to join his consulting firm. "I would rather teach than be president," he told Little.

But Rice of GE did not give up so easily. He was impressed with the unique combination of qualities Whitney seemed to possess — genuine brilliance of intellect, laboratory knowhow, modesty, affability, an enthusiasm for scientific research, a knack for explaining science — and for communicating his own enthusiasm. Rice was sure Whitney was the man for the job, and he was determined to get him.

Rice finally hit upon the right formula. He persuaded Whitney to try it on a part-time experimental basis, spending as much time as he could in Schenectady without severing his connection with M.I.T. Rice promised him he could write his own ticket — inelud ing the continuation of his own research while at GE. Always game for an experiment, especially such an attractive one as Rice offered, Whitney finally assented, and, almost at once, began his long-distance commuting between Boston and Schenectady, spending half of each week in each place.

Whitney did not really accept the job on a permanent, full-time basis, or move his family down to Schenectady, until May of 1904; but on the basis of this initial agreement an elated Rice announced to GE stockholders at the end of 1901: "Although our engineers have always been liberally supplied with every facility for the development of new and original designs and improvement of existing standards, it has been deemed wise during the past year to establish a laboratory to be devoted exclusively to original research. It is hoped by this means that many profitable fields may be discovered."

By this pioneering act — setting up a laboratory with fundamental research as its chief objective — General Electric established a radical precedent that heralded a new age of enlightenment for American industry. GE scientists, the chief among them being Irving Langmuir, were soon to prove beyond any reasonable doubt that a corporate investment in brainpower — in abstract thought and in science pursued for no other reason than that some first-rate scientist wanted to pursue it — could pay off in ideas that spelled new products and big profits.

The new day might not yet have dawned, however, had a lesser man than Willis R. Whitney been selected for this trailbreaking task. For one thing, Whitney was sufficiently interested in practical applications to win the confidence of plant managers and engineers. He approached them, in all sincerity, not as a know-it-all telling them what the score was, but as an eager student wanting to be taught. Yet he was determined to staff the lab with men of such scientific calibre that he could turn them loose — free to pursue their own research, free to publish their findings under their own names (not the corporation's), free to attend scientific meetings, free to talk to one another about their work (which was not the practice, for example, in the highly compartmentalized German industrial laboratories, where each researcher's work was secret from the others — even others working in the same laboratory). In brief, Whitney's genius with people was nowhere more evident than when he was dealing with people of genius. Whitney, as E. W. Rice was to write much later, "sacrificed his personal researches and concentrated on the making of men."

When Irving Langmuir arrived at the General Electric research laboratory in July of 1909 he was astonished to find a milieu saturated with the spirit of academic freedom. He must have remembered, perhaps with some amusement, Herbert's letter to him in Göttingen, with its dire intimations that to go into industrial research was tantamount to selling one's soul to the utilitarians. As it turned out, it was at Stevens Tech that he found himself a slave to unrewarding routine; he might as well have taken a frankly clerical job, like Einstein's at the patent office in Berne, and at least had his evenings free to think. Here, ironically, in a laboratory financed by one of those greedy, soulless corporations with purely mercenary intentions, he found basic research so respected that its practice, for its own sake, was actually encouraged!

The paradox of GE did not, of course, prove that Herbert had been wrong. Universities larger and better-heeled than tiny Stevens Tech did, of course, support extensive research facilities. And the GE lab was exceptional — the only one of its kind, in fact. And Herbert could not have known about it at the time he wrote his letter, since the GE laboratory was only in its infancy then. Whitney had, in fact, started out cautiously and modestly by sharing the laboratory in Steinmetz's barn, until it burned down in 1901. So Herbert's advice had been sound. And Irving's pursuit of that advice led him to GE.

Whitney was the perfect man to be Irving Langmuir's boss. As an appreciator of real scientific ability, he was all in favor of allowing it maximum scope for its operations. And he was exactly cut out for Langmuir's own peculiar set of characteristics. Whitney, too, understood the value of research unrestricted by purely utilitarian boundaries, and the unpredictable nature of the feedback between science and technology. He, too, was a physical chemist, trained in Germany. Whitney's university had been

Leipzig, Langmuir's second choice, and his mentor had been Wilhelm Ostwald — who, it will be recalled, was not actively teaching at the time Langmuir visited Leipzig.[1] Whitney was also fascinated with biology — and this, especially as exemplified in natural phenomena in the field — was one of the outdoor hobbies that he, like Langmuir, loved to pursue. Anthropology was another Whitney hobby.

It is difficult to categorize Willis Whitney. The sign on his office door read: "Come in — rain or shine." Owlishly good-humored behind his spectacles, he seemed simple and straightforward; yet, he was a complicated personality. With his homespun wit and cracker-barrel philosophy, he sometimes seemed a corny conglomeration of Will Rogers, Edgar Guest, and the Reverend Norman Vincent Peale. Yet he was saved from naïveté by a leaven of tart sophistication, and his interests were so broad as to call up, for comparison, names like Leonardo and Aristotle.

Whitney was no professional back-slapper. His buoyant optimism and his love of people were as genuine as they were ingrained. He may not quite have believed with the poet that "all's right with the world," but he at least went along with Dr. Coué on the supposition that things were getting better and better every day. He was a true man of the nineteenth century in his faith in the perfectibility of man through science. As Kendall Birr put it, Whitney was "a chronic optimist, constantly contending that people are growing better and more enlightened while their knowledge of and power over nature grows proportionately." Langmuir, too, had a good share of this brand of faith and optimism, and it helped give him his high sense of mission.

---

[1] It is probably just as well that Ostwald had been temporarily out of circulation. Ostwald's presence was, for Langmuir, one of Leipzig's feature attractions. Had he been lecturing, Langmuir might have come under his spell and chosen Leipzig instead of Göttingen. And if he had, he would undoubtedly have heard Ostwald expound on his belief that, since it would always remain impossible to prove the existence of atoms or molecules, chemists should avoid the use of such hypotheses. And if Langmuir had heard him at such an impressionable age, he might have believed him. And if he believed him, he might have failed to do some of his greatest work, which was based on a serene belief in the existence of discrete atoms and molecules.

Whitney believed in the efficacy of just "monkeying around" in science — another penchant shared by Langmuir. And Whitney had no patience with scientists who talked themselves out of research projects — snarling themselves in their own semantic webs — by assuming they knew what would happen without trying it. He used to say, with typical obliquity of expression: "Inactivity and inappreciation in the presence of the infinite, undeveloped truth are the most inexcusable types of error and unfaithfulness."

What he meant by this is best demonstrated by a story told by Laurence Hawkins, who worked for Whitney for many years:

"The State entomologist at Albany wrote to Dr. Whitney asking if insects could live in a vacuum. Whitney showed the letter to one of the physicists and asked if he wished to try the experiment. The answer was that it would be a waste of time, for it was well known that life could not exist without oxygen. Dr. Whitney responded that on his farm the turtles buried themselves in the mud each fall, and the mud became covered with ice and snow, so that for months the turtles were getting little oxygen, but they emerged full of life in the spring. This brought out the remark, 'Oh you mean hibernation?' Dr. Whitney said, 'I don't know what I mean, but I want to know if bugs can live in vacuum.'

He then took the letter to another physicist. Meeting with the same lack of interest there, he used another example: 'I've been told that you can freeze a goldfish solidly in a cake of ice, where he certainly can't get much oxygen, and can keep him there for a month or two, but if you thaw him out carefully he seems none the worse for his experience.' This time the reply was, 'Oh, you mean suspended animation!' Again Whitney disclaimed any meaning other than his desire for the facts as to bugs in vacuum..."

What annoyed Whitney was the disinclination on the part of either scientist to place bugs in a vacuum and *see* what happened. So he decided to perform the simple experiment himself.

"He accordingly procured a fly and a cockroach," Hawkins goes on, "placed them in a bell jar, and exhausted the air, whereupon they apparently died promptly. But after some two hours, when he gradually admitted air, the cockroach first waved its feelers, then staggered to its feet, and was soon trotting around with customary nimbleness, while the fly meanwhile suddenly came to and began buzzing around seeking an exit."

Whitney often used this story to point his moral. And the same message was often driven home by Whitney's assistant director, who succeeded him in 1932. This was William D. Coolidge, another brilliant and generally underrated scientist, who, like Whitney, had gone to M.I.T. and Leipzig and had returned to teach at M.I.T., where he remained until Whitney brought him to GE in 1905. "We rarely know enough to be sure that even a seemingly foolish experiment may not teach us something of value," he was fond of saying. His parable was:

"Early in the history of tungsten contacts for automobile ignition I took some out to Dayton to Mr. Kettering. While I was there he operated them on a bench set-up and I was horrified when he picked up an oil can and approached the contacts with it. I knew that oil would put the contacts out of business, or thought I did — that they must be kept clean. But the experiment proved very illuminating. Oil was bad for *platinum* contacts, but gave only a very temporary setback to the operation of the tungsten contacts. They sputtered at first and then went on as smoothly as before."

Scientists at the GE laboratory, then, were seldom permitted to forget one of the cardinal tenets of its research philosophy, which went something like this: Logic is of course an indispensable tool of the scientist. But it should be used to reveal problems, not to obscure them. Hence, any fresh situation was to be approached with a fresh eye, and any "knowledge" of the situation gleaned purely by analogy with similar situations in the past was to be considered ready to discard without regrets and on short notice. This tenet became one of Langmuir's own.

All Langmuir knew of the laboratory when he reported for his summer job on July 19, 1909, was the fleeting impression he had received during his brief autumn visit. Now that he had the opportunity to walk around, talk to people, and inspect the place at leisure, he was fascinated and incredulous. "Gulliver saw no stranger sights at the storied Academy of Lagado," Bernard Jaffe tells us, "than Langmuir witnessed here. Before him were men peering reverently into the mysteries of science under the guidance of a tall, simple, hearty philosopher [Whitney], master over men and matter."

Langmuir especially lingered over the lamps. The atmosphere which permeated the laboratory, added to the glow of the brightly alive filaments in their glass cages, brought back the feeling of Göttingen, a feeling of a vital quest for deep mysteries locked in the wire and in the glass and in the gas — and even in the emptiness of the vacuum — mysteries that, once unlocked, would provide the key to even deeper mysteries. Langmuir's feeling for the lamp was not unrelated to that which the Oriental mystic experiences when he sees the universe mirrored in a lotus petal — though Langmuir's curiosity was more physical and less metaphysical.

It is not surprising that the same comparison occurred to Whitney as he watched the young acolyte. "There is something in Langmuir's work," he wrote years later, "that suggests, by sharp contrast, an oriental crystal gazer seated idly before a transparent globe and trying to read the future without doing anything about it — a hopeless philosophy. In my picture an equally transparent and more vacuous globe takes the place of the conventional crystal sphere. It is a lamp bulb, a real light source. Langmuir boldly takes it in his hand, not as some apathetic or ascetic Yogi, but more like a healthy boy analyzing a new toy even as Langmuir himself studied and fixed the complex watch of his boyhood days, but seeing visions, too, of many new things. There might have been nothing in that vacuum, but he was driven by insatiable curiosity to investigate and learn for himself."

In lingering over the lamps, Langmuir got particularly interested in a problem that was occupying Coolidge at the moment. Coolidge was trying to produce a tungsten-filament lamp that would be superior to any other on the market — superior because tungsten could withstand higher temperatures than any other known solid. Hence it should logically supersede the earlier carbon and tantalum filaments. But tungsten was an extremely hard and brittle substance, not amenable to being drawn into a fine wire filament. Coolidge had applied himself to the problem and had just succeeded, in 1908, in making tungsten ductile — something never before achieved with any of the intractable elements of tungsten's chemical family.

Coolidge had gone on to produce his tungsten-filament lamp. The trouble was that when the lamps were run on alternating current the tungsten became brittle again after brief use, and the filament would reach a point where it simply crumbled when the current was passed through it. Another baffling circumstance was that, of the hundreds of tungsten samples prepared, three of them gave excellent results, with every sign of first-rate durability, even when operating on alternating current — but nobody had any idea why.

Langmuir found himself thinking about the puzzle. Perhaps tungsten, when heated rapidly, had an unsuspected affinity for some gas which it might be absorbing, he reasoned; and perhaps the resulting impurity was what made it break down. He had been invited by Whitney to spend several days looking around and to take his time deciding what he wanted to work on during the summer. Langmuir was intrigued with the tungsten problem. He was also impressed with the high vacuum they were able to attain at GE — much higher than had been possible at Göttingen or Stevens. He wanted to learn more about these techniques. So he volunteered to tackle the tungsten problem. His plan was simply to heat tungsten wires in a high vacuum so that any gases which came out of the tungsten would be easy to measure. He would trap the impurities in the act of escaping. Whitney approved the project. Langmuir quickly set up his magnificently simple apparatus — his lamp, his vacuum pump, and his McLeod gauge — and went to work.

He did not have long to wait before he began getting measurable quantities of gas. In fact, the amount of gas that began emanating from the tungsten filament was nothing short of ridiculous. "Within a couple of weeks," he said, recalling the experiment many years later on the occasion of receiving the Perkin Medal, "I realized that something was entirely wrong with my apparatus, because from a small filament in a couple of days I obtained a quantity of gas which had, at atmospheric pressure, a volume 7000 times that of the filament from which it appeared to have come; and even then there was no indication that this gas evolution was going to stop." He had read — in a book by J. J. Thomson, for example – that metals in vacuum "give off gases almost indefinitely." But seven thousand times their own volume?

Langmuir checked his equipment and ascertained that it was operating perfectly. The error was not there. Could all that gas really have come from that tiny strand of tungsten, no thicker than a hair? Langmuir could not believe it. Yet, the filament was surrounded by a vacuum. Where else could the gas be coming from?

Excited by this new enigma, Langmuir forgot all about the brittleness of tungsten, his stated reason for undertaking the experiment in the first place. "Frankly," he later admitted to Whitney, "I was not so much interested in trying to improve the lamps as in finding out the scientific principles underlying these peculiar effects." He was still in the midst of trying to track down the source of these preposterous quantities of gas when the summer ended, and he was faced with the abrupt termination of his engrossing work.

Whitney, who recognized a true research temperament when he saw one, urged Langmuir to stay on at the GE laboratory. Langmuir did not accept immediately. It was not that he was playing hard-to-get. His hesitation was due to his fear that more might be expected of him than he would be able to deliver. He expressed his concern openly to Whitney — i.e., that he might be using up General Electric's good money on research whose outcome promised no practical use. "I am merely curious about the mysterious phenomena that occur in these lamps," he confessed. Willis Whitney, wise in the ways of research, told Langmuir not to worry about the practical applications. The inquiring mind diligently at work, Whitney knew, seldom failed to produce knowledge. And knowledge, in his experience, seldom turned out to be useless. "You just go ahead," he told Langmuir, "and follow any line of inquiry you like."

After Langmuir's stultifying stretch at Stevens Tech, he could hardly believe his good fortune. If Whitney meant what he said — and he clearly did — then Irving's dream, the same dream he had once expressed to Professor Woodward at Columbia — "to be situated like Lord Kelvin — free to do research as I wish" — the dream was his for the taking. He would be free to attempt the ascent of any research peak, just as Hilary had Everest, simply because it was there. Langmuir seized the dream, and made it real.

Chapter 9

" 'I sometimes think,' said Olivia, 'from watching, of course, because I am not experienced, I think experience can be a — block.' Again she knew it was clumsy, but she knew what she meant.

" 'And why?' asked Angela, amused.

" 'Because if you think you know, you don't ask questions,' said Olivia slowly, 'or if you ask, you don't listen to the answers.' Olivia had observed this often. 'Everyone, everything, *each* thing is different, so that it isn't safe to know. You — you have to grope.'

" 'That would be a nice efficient way to deal with things,' said Angela. She looked up again from the notes she was making. She's not even listening to me, thought Olivia."

RUMER GODDEN
An Episode of Sparrows

LANGMUIR'S hunch concerning the origin of the vast volumes of gas in the lamp turned out to be correct: most of the gas had been coming not from the tungsten filament but from the inner surface of the bulb itself. "What I really learned during that summer," he told his Perkin Medal award audience, "was that glass surfaces which had not been heated a long time in vacuum slowly gave off water vapor, and this reacts with a tungsten filament to produce hydrogen, and also that vaseline on a ground glass joint in the vacuum system gives off hydrocarbon vapor, which produces hydrogen and carbon monoxide."

The minor mysteries cleared up by this initial bit of detective work only augmented Langmuir's desire to further exploit that wonderful .little research microcosm, the electric lamp, and to take full advantage of two laboratory tools in which GE led the world — tungsten filaments and high vacuum. He had been fascinated, since Göttingen, with the weird behavior of gases at high temperatures around a glowing lamp filament. But even the hottest of the Nernst filaments was platinum, with a melting point of 3200°F and it had been impossible to obtain data for temperatures beyond 2000°F. Now he had at his command tungsten, the most indocile of metals until tamed by Coolidge. Tungsten, with its melting point of 6200°F, gave him a high-temperature research instrument without parallel. And the unprecedentedly high vacuum he could create inside the GE lamps gave him precision control over the kind and quantity of gases he could admit and study. The versatile and imaginative use of his simple apparatus brought under Langmuir's observation phenomena as startlingly unexpected as the waistcoated White Rabbit that Alice saw scurrying by, and his pursuit of the phenomena took him into places fully as strange as any that Alice encountered when she chased the White Rabbit headlong down his hole.

The clerk or factory worker who strays from his designated task to pursue some will-o'-the-wisp might be charged with gross dereliction of duty. Not so the scientist. "How much more logical it would have been," Langmuir often said, recalling those first experiments at GE, "if I had dropped the work as soon as I found out that the method I was using was not going to solve the problem of the tungsten wire's brittleness." To have done so, of course, would have been to turn his back on his own scientific curiosity, a practice designed to guarantee barrenness in scientific research — as in any of the other creative arts. "Look sharply after your thoughts," said Emerson. "They come unlooked for, like a new bird seen on your trees, and, if you turn to your usual task, disappear . . ." Willis Whitney fully appreciated this in 1909. That is why he was so willing to let Langmuir go after his new bird, before it disappeared.

Whitney, you see, had great faith in a thing called serendipity —

and Langmuir became not only a convert but an ardent evangelist for the cause. Serendip was the ancient name for Ceylon. One day in 1754, Horace Walpole wrote his friend Horace Mann about a fairy tale he had just been reading called "The Three Princes of Serendip." "As their highnesses traveled," Walpole told Mann, "they were always making discoveries, by accident or sagacity, of things which they were not in quest of." Walpole, as Langmuir was fond of pointing out, had been a great art collector, "and every collector knows that his best finds are often made while looking for something else or simply while browsing." This happened so frequently and seemed applicable to so many of life's activities that Walpole suggested a new word for the English vocabulary — serendipity. It eventually made its way into the dictionaries, but remained little known and less used until it began to become a favorite word among scientists.[1]

In no other field are the results of serendipity so obvious. The history of science is strewn with famous examples: Galvani noticing the odd twitching of the dead frog's leg, Fleming observing the curious penicillium mold in his bacteria cultures, Becquerel frowning at the strange silhouettes on his photographic plates; Richet discovering allergy and Pasteur immunity by accident; Nobel stumbling upon dynamite, Perkin upon synthetic coal-tar dyes, Backeland upon Bakelite; and so on and on. Just as Saul went forth to seek his father's asses and found a kingdom instead, and just as Columbus, seeking the Indies, discovered a new world, so have many of the greatest scientific discoveries been chanced upon. Scientists are always careful, of course, to emphasize that

---

[1] At a meeting of the American Chemical Society in 1957, a chemical engineer named Bernard E. Schaar did his vocal best to dislodge the word serendipity from what he considered its ill-deserved favor among scientists. Schaar had recently come upon a rare book in a Chicago library which contained a 1722 translation of the tale of the three princes, and he was convinced that busy Mr. Walpole had just skimmed through the tale and misunderstood it completely. "Serendipity," Schaar insisted, "from its erroneous conception by Walpole, to the inspired meanings invented by lexicographers, does not have a leg to stand on as a substitute for the phrase — accidental scientific discovery." But it was as futile as telling a group of American schoolboys that Washington really had *not* chopped down the cherry tree.

mere chance is not enough. As Joseph Henry once said (before Pasteur made his own more often quoted remark in a similar vein), "The seeds of great discoveries are constantly floating around us, but they only take root in minds well-prepared to receive them."

Serendipity has been variously defined. The magazine *Business Week* once explained serendipity as "a four-dollar way of describing what happens when a man winds up with a better mousetrap while he's working on how to keep people away from his door." Langmuir's own simple definition was as good as any: "Serendipity is the art of profiting from the unexpected." And serendipity was often selected as the theme of Langmuir's later lectures. His speeches during the 1940s and 1950s include titles like "Planning Unplanned Research," "Unforeseeable Results of Research," and "Freedom — The Opportunity to Profit from the Unexpected."

Langmuir's message — a message meant for corporations, government agencies, universities, in fact anyone administering scientific research in an age when grants were tending more and more to be earmarked for specific projects, with "progress reports" required to justify the next appropriation — was essentially the same as that enunciated by Josiah Royce. The "noble play" of the scientist, said Royce, "is a mere expression of a curiosity which former centuries might have called idle. But the result of this play recreates an industrial world." At GE, Langmuir was permitted to play nobly, and he recreated an industrial world. Langmuir frequently cited his own research as a prime example of serendipity at work.

When Whitney hired Langmuir, he did not lay down any specific program of research for him. He simply let the new man do what he pleased. Langmuir was given first one assistant, then others as he needed them. Any equipment he expressed a desire for was placed promptly at his disposal. He did not even have to tell anyone what he wanted it for.

Whitney would drop around regularly to kibitz. He never said, as a research director might have felt he had a right to, "Damn it, Langmuir, haven't you figured out a way to improve that lamp yet?" All he ever said was, "Are you having fun?"

After nearly three years at GE, with GE getting no return for the money he was spending having fun, Langmuir began to feel a bit guilty. "I'm having a lot of fun," he told Whitney one day, in response to Whitney's standard question. "But I don't know what good this is to the General Electric Company."

"That's not your worry," said Whitney. "It's mine."

Whitney was supremely unworried. Even looking at it from a strictly utilitarian viewpoint, GE was in the lamp business, after all, and Langmuir represented a long-range capital investment. The more he learned about what went on inside electric lamps, the better it would ultimately be for GE.

And Langmuir was learning a great deal about what went on inside lamps. "For my study of the effect on gases," he wrote later, "I had to devise new types of vacuum apparatus. I needed particularly to be able to make a practically complete quantitative analysis of gas which would occupy about 1 cu. mm. at atmospheric pressure. In this sample of gas we could determine the percentage of oxygen, hydrogen, nitrogen, carbon dioxide, carbon monoxide, and the inert gases.

"In regard to the fate of the different gases which I introduced into the bulb, I found that no two gases acted alike..."

The knowledge Langmuir had already picked up in his intensive study of lamps served him well when his first important lead came along. "From my work on lamps I knew approximately the relation between the resistance of a tungsten wire and its temperature, and could thus use a tungsten wire as a kind of resistance thermometer. By connecting a voltmeter and ammeter to the tungsten filament... I could determine the temperature from the resistance and also find the heat loss from the filament in watts. I wanted to see if anything abnormal happened when the temperature was raised to the extremes which were only possible with tungsten."

Nothing abnormal happened, with the heat loss through each gas following its expected curve quite closely. But when Langmuir got to hydrogen, the highly abnormal began happening. "The results greatly interested me," he wrote later, with his customary understatement, "for they showed that the energy loss through the gas, which increased in proportion to the square of the temperature up to about 1800°K., increased at a much higher rate above that, until at the highest temperatures the energy varied in proportion to about the fifth power of the temperature." In other words, hydrogen, when the temperature of the tungsten filament reached about 3600°F, suddenly began gobbling heat with a much greedier appetite than before, until its voracious tapeworm was consuming five times its normal intake. The average researcher would have been nonplussed. But Langmuir's well-prepared mind, confronted with a situation so unpredictable as to be absurd, began suspecting almost immediately what he had chanced upon.

The hydrogen molecule consists of two hydrogen atoms held together by a strong chemical bond — a bond so strong that no chemist had ever been able to detect hydrogen atoms, if they existed, in the free state. Langmuir now believed it possible that, at the point where the gas began acting in such a radically different manner, the heat had finally been able to rip the molecule apart into separate atoms. If so, he had discovered atomic hydrogen. What's more, he could create it at will.

Now, Langmuir reasoned, the atoms could not remain separated for long. Their little valence tentacles would make them eager to get together again. If the hydrogen molecules were indeed dissociating into atoms, the atoms would migrate rapidly away from the filament, then recombine into molecules the instant they got far enough away from the filament's rending heat. When the current was turned off and the lamp allowed to cool, then all the hydrogen inside should be back in its normal molecular state again.

The trouble was that, instead of recombining into molecules — or, perhaps, in *addition* to doing that — the hydrogen vanished. Just like that. No question about it. The gas pressure, each time, dropped to zero. And the hydrogen couldn't very well be getting out of the lamp through some mysterious leak because once *enough* hydrogen was let in, it finally remained and was just as detectable and measurable as you please. Wherever the missing hydrogen was hiding, the hiding place had room for only so much hydrogen and no more — and it *must* be in its atomic state, or it would not cling so readily and so obstinately to whatever it was clinging to. And the "whatever" had to be either the filament, or the bulb itself. It was easy enough to get the filament hot enough to shake loose any hydrogen the tungsten might be hanging onto. Langmuir quickly satisfied himself that the hydrogen was not concealing itself in the invisible crevices of the tungsten lattices. The only thing left, then, was the glass bulb.

Langmuir put it in an electric furnace and baked it. But he had to come close to melting the glass before anything happened. Under the heat torture the glass finally yielded up its prisoners — or, perhaps more accurately, it was freed of the leeches infesting its surface. Thus smoked out, the hydrogen atoms swarmed forth like bees from their hives. Hydrogen atoms? Well, Langmuir could not imagine what else they might be. And from theory one would expect hydrogen atoms to act in exactly that manner. And yet — Langmuir needed one more test to convince himself.

If it was indeed atomic hydrogen he was dealing with, it should have a stronger affinity for oxygen than for the glass surface; its chemical preference should therefore be to dissociate itself from the atoms on the surface and combine with the oxygen atoms to form water. Now, to join two atoms of hydrogen with one of oxygen in the making of H_2O is a formidable feat, achieved only recently by means of the fuel cell, and requires an extraordinary amount of force. Every marriage of hydrogen and oxygen is a shotgun wedding. Throw them together under any normal courting circumstances — i.e., in their molecular form — and they will remain forever shy of one another. It takes some outside act of violence to knock their heads together — an electric spark, say, or some energetic quantum of high-frequency radiation. Throw oxygen together with *atomic* hydrogen, however, and there should be lightning courtships and spontaneous mass marriages, without benefit of nudging from matchmaking chaperons.

So Langmuir repeated the experiment. Only this time instead of baking the bulb, he left the lamp at room temperature and slowly admitted small quantities of oxygen — which instantly disappeared. When a certain saturation point had been reached, the oxygen seemed to lose interest in the further repetition of its disappearing act, and elected to remain onstage. And the amount of oxygen which had vanished was exactly the amount that would combine with the amount of hydrogen that had gone into the bulb's surface and was now pulling the oxygen in after it.

The mysterious goings-on in the lamp had now ceased being mysterious:

Just as it takes the impact of a neutron to cause uranium fission (unknown, of course, in those days), so it took the impact of the intense tungsten heat to break apart the hydrogen atoms. And just as the breakup of uranium atoms drains from their nuclei the fantastic quantities of energy released in an atomic-bomb explosion, so the breakup of hydrogen molecules into separate atoms drained enormous quantities of energy from the tungsten filament. Hence the great heat loss above the critical temperatures.

The hydrogen atoms, moving away from the filament too energetically to recombine, satisfied their cravings for chemical union by latching onto the first atoms they came in contact with — the atoms of the glass lamp. Hence their disappearance.

Once the oxygen was introduced, the hydrogen atoms acted like a band of promiscuous cave men who — having picked up the only females available in the cave — hastily jilted them and dragged in their own preferred mates as soon as they hove into sight and got within grabbing distance. (Each bigamous oxygen atom, of course, needed two willing hydrogen atoms before it was happily dragged in.)

Hence the disappearance of the oxygen — with the lonely leftovers shut out of the cave, floating aimlessly in the limbo of the lamp's empty spaces.

Only when he could explain all the phenomena in the lamp, and convince himself that the phenomena were exactly what one would expect from hydrogen atoms and from nothing else, was

Langmuir satisfied that he had made chemical history by discovering atomic hydrogen.

"I was naturally much interested in getting other information in regard to the properties of these hydrogen atoms," Langmuir wrote. "A large number of experiments, extending over several years, were thus made in the study of atomic hydrogen. Nearly all those experiments would have seemed quite useless, or even foolish, to a man who was making a direct and logical attack on the problem of improving tungsten lamps."

These foolish experiments led down unfamiliar, twisting byways which broadened unexpectedly in places, then narrowed almost to disappearance, then zigzagged erratically without warning. Langmuir followed each road patiently. Many led to dead ends. But many brought him to happy, unsought destinations.

Where did these useless experiments lead him, for example?

To deep insights into the nature of the electron, the atom, and the molecule — and thus into the structure of matter in all its forms — and a fruitful new atomic theory.

To a profound understanding of the behavior of gases in incandescent lamps, and consequently to better lamps; and to a fascination with the dynamics of gases at high temperatures and low pressures which gave him the first vague understanding of plasmas — now belatedly the subject of such intensive research by those interested in plasma-jet engines and controlled hydrogen fusion — and thus established himself as at least the great-grandfather of the still-infant science of magnetohydrodynamics.

To new methods of evacuating lamps, and consequently to more efficient vacuum pumps, and to the discovery of space charge and the proof of pure thermionic emission, which in turn led to new electronic devices, improved X-ray tubes, and dozens of patents in the field of radio engineering.

To experiments in atomic-hydrogen flames and thus directly to the atomic-hydrogen welding torch.

To a new theory of adsorption, an understanding of catalysis, and the discovery of monatomic films, which opened up the whole field of surface chemistry that won Langmuir the Nobel Prize.

To breakthroughs in old fields and the creation of new ones which opened vast new research vistas for other scientists.

To enormous and well-merited prestige and profits for the General Electric Company, whose success encouraged other companies — in the United States and abroad — to establish basic research laboratories of their own,[1] thus accelerating the pace of scientific and technological progress everywhere.

And to other wonderful things, numerous and varied.

Later in life, Langmuir promulgated a theory in which he divided all occurrences in the universe into two types, one of which he called "divergent phenomena." A divergent phenomenon is what happens when a small, unpredictable happening sets in motion a chain of other events, thus exerting on the future a cumulative influence out of all proportion to its own size. There was never a better example of a divergent phenomenon than that of the influence on the future of science exerted by Langmuir's early observations of infinitesimal particles of gas in a tiny lamp bulb.

While Langmuir was carrying out his experiments with hydrogen, he was concurrently conducting experiments with other gases. "I wanted to introduce each different kind of gas that I could lay my hands on into a lamp with a tungsten filament and find out definitely what happened to that gas," he said. He did as he wanted, often with eyebrow-raising results.

"It was the universal opinion among the lamp engineers with whom I came in contact," said Langmuir, "that if only a much better vacuum could be produced in a lamp a better lamp would result. Dr. Whitney, particularly, believed that every effort should be made to improve the vacuum, for all laboratory experience seemed to indicate that this was the hopeful line of attack on the problem of better lamps."

Whitney himself later said: "Before Dr. Langmuir joined our research staff everyone, from Edison down, had sought to improve

[1] Langmuir often went out of his way, however, to emphasize his firm belief that industry should feel an obligation to support basic scientific research, regardless of any payoff in profits, because of the debt which all industry owed to science for its very existence.

the vacuum of the incandescent lamp. Will it stay better if initially made better, or does glass leak, even a little? Is the glass some sort of sponge which slowly gives off absorbed gases? Is it perhaps like some hydrated mineral, such as mica or basalt, slowly yielding water of composition to the vacuum? To what extent does the... filament carry within itself gases which later cause deterioration?"

Langmuir too asked himself questions like these. But he was, at that point, barren of any good ideas on how he might make that emptiest of voids any emptier. So he decided to turn the study upside-down. Instead of trying to improve the vacuum, he would give his attention to "the bad effects of gases by putting gas in the lamp." This, as Zay Jeffries has pointed out, seemed somewhat like treating a case of arsenic poisoning by administering massive doses of arsenic. But Langmuir's approach actually made excellent sense. "I hoped in this way I could become so familiar with these effects of gas," he explained, "that I could extrapolate to zero gas pressure and thus predict, without really trying it, how good the lamp would be if we could produce a perfect vacuum."

He found in what ensued a moral to be pointed out as a principle of research that others might follow. "When it is suspected that some useful result is to be obtained by avoiding certain undesired factors, but it is found that these factors are very difficult to avoid, then," he advised, "it is a good plan to increase deliberately each of these factors in turn so as to exaggerate their bad effects, and thus become so familiar with them that one can determine whether it is really worth while avoiding them. For example, if you have in lamps a vacuum as good as you know how to produce, but suspect that the lamps would be better if you had a vacuum, say, 100 times as good, it may be the best policy, instead of attempting to devise methods of improving this vacuum, to spoil the vacuum deliberately in known ways, and you may then find that no improvement in vacuum is needed or, just how much better the vacuum needs to be." Thus Langmuir adapted to science Blake's maxim: "The road of excess leads to the palace of wisdom."

As Langmuir continued his studies, his mind kept returning to the question, "How good would a lamp be if it had a perfect vacuum?" And he was beginning to get some inklings of an answer from observing what happened when the vacuum was purposely ruined by admitting various gases into the lamp. He also began to understand another worrisome phenomenon: The surfaces of all vacuum lamp bulbs began to blacken after a certain period of use, and the blackening itself cut down the useful lifetime of the lamps. This was another problem which nearly everyone believed could be solved if only a better vacuum could be produced. Of all the gases Langmuir introduced into his lamps, only one caused blackening — water vapor. How did it cause it? And if water vapor *was* the principal cause, how did it get into the lamp? Did the lamp's normal operation somehow produce a minute but damaging quantity of it?

Langmuir got absorbed in the problem and determined that he was going to track down the source of the bulbs' blackening. (Langmuir firmly believed that it does no violence to the scientific spirit to let one's curiosity be challenged by a problem that already exists — even a practical one.) When Detective Langmuir went after the vandal that was blackening the bulbs, he pursued the culprit with the ingenuity of a Sherlock Holmes and the tenacity of a Javert. Here is his own sleuthing report on the Case of the Blackened Bulbs:

"The serious blackening that occurred with only small amounts of water vapor depended upon a cyclic reaction in which atomic hydrogen played an essential part. The water-vapor molecules coming in contact with the hot filament produce a volatile oxide of tungsten, and the hydrogen is liberated in atomic form. The volatile oxide deposits on the bulb where it is reduced to the metallic state by the atomic hydrogen, while the water vapor produced returns to the filament and causes the action to be repeated indefinitely." The water vapor could keep going back for another load of tungsten! "Thus, a minute quantity of water vapor may cause a relatively enormous amount of tungsten to be carried to the bulb.

"The question then arose whether the traces of water vapor, which might still exist in the well-exhausted lamp, were responsible for the blackening which limited the life or the efficiency of many of these lamps. We made some tests in which well-made lamps were kept constantly immersed in liquid air during their life, so that there could be no possibility of water vapor coming in contact with the filament. The rate of blackening, however, was exactly the same as if no liquid air had been used.

"Having thus proved that the blackening of a well-made lamp was due solely to evaporation [of the tungsten], I could conclude with certainty that the life of the lamp would not be appreciably improved even if we could produce a perfect vacuum."

Meanwhile Langmuir's other gas studies were yielding results which hinted that there were more ways than one to improve a lamp. Among the gases whose behavior he studied intensively were nitrogen and mercury vapor. He had been eager to see if the nitrogen and mercury molecules would, like the hydrogen molecules, be torn asunder into separate atoms under the assault of the fierce tungsten temperatures. But they were not. They withstood the thermal blast and remained stable. In observing the gases, Langmuir did not forget to observe the filament, and he noticed that, in the presence of these gases, the tungsten filament could be kept heated close to the melting point for far longer than was possible in a vacuum. "Thus the rate of evaporation was greatly decreased by the gas," he observed, "many of the evaporating tungsten atoms being brought back to the filament after striking the gas molecules.

"By this time I was familiar with all the harmful effects which gas can produce in contact with filaments and knew under what conditions these bad effects could be avoided. In particular, I realized the importance of avoiding even almost infinitesimal traces of water vapor.

"Thus, when I found a marked effect of mercury vapor and nitrogen in reducing the rate of evaporation, it occurred to me that it might be possible to operate a tungsten filament in gas at atmospheric pressure and obtain a long useful life."

When Langmuir told Whitney about his new idea — a gas-filled lamp — Whitney said, "You're dreaming!"

But, having great respect for Langmuir-type dreams, Whitney let him go ahead and make the dream come true. It was not easy. But once Langmuir was convinced his idea was valid, he could pick off the problems, one at a time, patiently and painstakingly perform the necessary experiments, and come up eventually with an ingenious answer for each of them. Langmuir's application for a patent on the gas-filled lamp — applied for on April 19, 1913 and granted three years later as Patent No. 1,180,159 — is a classic of its kind. "To anyone sufficiently interested," says Zay Jeffries, "it will not only provide a clear picture of the invention but also it will show the complex relationships of solid and gaseous materials, geometry, temperature and electrical characteristics. Only one who had made profound scientific studies was capable of combining these variables to produce a practical gas-filled lamp."

The best gas for Langmuir's lamp, by the way, turned out to be his lazy old friend, argon.

"The advent of the gas-filled lamp resulted in a second revolution in incandescent lamps [Jeffries wrote], ... This lamp made a mockery of a statement made by Mr. Alexander Siemens about 1905. He said that it was 'very doubtful whether it will be possible to construct a much more economical glow lamp [than the vacuum tungsten], so that the consumer will have to look for further economy to the improvement and cheapening of the electrical supply.' "

The gas-filled lamp, which was much more efficient than comparable vacuum lamps and gave a whiter, brighter light, was soon winning a large share of the lamp market. "Without minimizing the importance of the fluorescent lamp," says Jeffries, "the gas-filled lamp is, at the beginning of the sixth decade of the twentieth century, well nigh indispensable. These lamps are made throughout the world by the hundreds of millions per year. The numbers of types, wattages and voltages run into the hundreds. They best serve the lighting needs for so many uses and in so many places that it would be futile to try to enumerate them. These lamps embody the gas tight light transmitting bulb of Edison, the tungsten filament of Just and Hanaman and Coolidge and the construction and gas filling of Langmuir.

"Langmuir's contribution is so basic that it has survived herculean attempts to obsolete it and the time cannot now be foreseen when it may be displaced."

This research has been described at some length not because the gas-filled lamp revolutionized the lamp industry, nor even because Langmuir's invention is still saving the American public more than a million dollars a night on its electric light bills every night of the year, but because there is no better way to understand a master scientist than to see him at work.

Chapter 10

"To live is to love; all reason is against it, and all healthy instinct for it."

SAMUEL BUTLER

VERY early in his career at General Electric, Langmuir began to acquire a reputation as a marathon thinker. He could focus his remarkable powers of concentration on a problem and think about it hard and effectively for hours at a time, patiently turning it over and over, inspecting it and dissecting it until he knew his way to the heart of it and back. Yet his mind was so agile that, when necessary, he could broaden his focus to take in a number of related problems and—like a chess master playing several opponents simultaneously—keep track of every detail. He had the intellectual energy to direct a number of concurrent research projects and at the same time to keep up with, and think critically about, goings-on elsewhere in physics and chemistry.

With it all, he always seemed to have energy left over to remain interested in everybody else's work, offering a steady outpouring of ideas and suggestions. In short, his colleagues soon began to notice what Mama had noticed when Irving was still in knee pants – that "his brain is working like an engine all the time"—and they were understandably awestruck by the phenomenon.

As one might expect, Langmuir's diaries of the period are full of notes about work at the laboratory. Here are some sample excerpts from early 1910:

"Arranged to have Winne take charge of work on Pacz paste under my direction."

"Askt[1] Whitney to let Adams work for me."

"Developt[1] further my bombardment theory of gas production in lamp; also theory of spattering. Discust[1] these at length with Whitney, Fink & Adams."

"Coolidge made wire which remained ductil[1] after heating to ca 2500° in H_2. Robinson made finished lamp ductil."

"Fink obtained first piece of ductil W without mechanical working — i.e. by pure heat treatment."

Other 1910 entries remind us how easy it is, in the retelling, to forget that the course of true research seldom runs smooth. For example:

"Frodsham blew up H_2 generator."

"Van Brunt burned his eyes with fusd KCN. I took him to the hospital & then to Dr. Reed."

"Robinson broke the lamp that Sweetser & I had exhausted 2½ months."

"Sabin & Green cut up by explosion of H_2."

"Set fire to Frodshams rubber tubs supplying O_2."

And it is not only equipment that occasionally acts up or breaks down under the stress of an intensive research program:

"In evening Frodsham, Sabin & Fink came in my room one after the other. Fink in good mood, had lost all jealousy & hard feelings."

"Frodsham got into row with Fink over things Fink had said about Sabin. Frodsham wants to fight, wants me to be his second. Frodsham has been working too hard over H_2."

"Frodsham has spoken to Fink & straightened matters out some.

---

[1] Langmuir at this stage was an ardent advocate of phonetic spelling, and he practiced it, though inconsistently, in his diaries. Thus "called" became "cald", "watched" became "wacht," "missed" became "mist," and words like "mobile" and "ductile" lost their final e's.

Fink tells Coolidge of occurrence. Coolidge asks me details. Later Coolidge tells Frodsham to ease up."

Langmuir's role was not always that of referee. There were times when, sufficiently provoked, he could call up the temper he had been so famous for as a boy. "Found that Palmer had not started work on new vacuum oven," he noted one day, "altho he had told me 3 weeks before that it was being made & had almost daily told of its progress. I had a good row with him, cald him a liar etc. He was angry at first & later apologized & said he would have it done as soon as possible."

These were of course isolated incidents. On the whole, Langmuir was supremely happy to have plunged, at last, into the kind of research he had been longing to do. In so doing, did he now dedicate himself so wholeheartedly to his work that, forgetful of all else, he began leading a monastic existence? Did he, absorbed in his equations and his instruments, work obsessively through holidays and weekends, and far into each bleary-eyed night? Nothing of the sort. His diaries of the period are so full of outside activities that one wonders that he got any research done at all.

It appears that, for a while at least, with the unaccustomed privilege of giving his research his undivided attention while in the laboratory, the very ability to stretch himself to the limit during working hours left him freer than ever to relax on off-days and after hours. The social flowering that had begun in Göttingen and all but withered in Hoboken burst into full bloom in Schenectady. Irving Langmuir had had the opportunity to do a good many things that most other men of his age had not. But in his twenty-ninth year, he knew that there were areas of experience where he was rather a late starter.

He was still somewhat stiff and diffident in his personal relationships, even with other men, until he got to know them fairly well. With young women he was downright awkward. Langmuir's trouble was not true shyness. It was just that somehow the Langmuir boys had never learned what most people, including even members of primitive tribes, seem to absorb effortlessly as part of the atmosphere they grow up in — the thing that anthropologists call phatic communion and that ordinary folks call smalltalk, the art of speaking words which are merely social noises without even a pretense at communicating any information.

Langmuir was now trying hard to break down the barrier of his own reserve, partly because, as he confessed in his diary, "I seem to be much more interested in people than usual." And people seemed to sense it, and they responded. Though he remained a total loss at smalltalk, he was eager to talk *about* almost anything — and to *do* almost anything. His appetite for all kinds of experience was almost indiscriminate. He wanted to do all the things he had never done before without giving up any of the old things he liked.

During the year 1910 he still hiked and climbed and did a lot of canoeing and camping-out at places with names like Fat Man's Misery, Indian Ladder, and Lake Desolation. He also skied, and he taught others to ski. He continued to skate, and he added the speedy sport of skate-sailing to his athletic repertory. He badgered friends into teaching him to play tennis. He learned to bowl, took horseback-riding and dancing lessons, joined the Golf Club, went sleighing in the moonlight, swam, hunted, fished, and became a scoutmaster. He traveled to scientific meetings and delivered papers on the results of his first researches. He drove a horse-and-buggy and began to get interested in that new gadget — barely out of its experimental stage — the motor car. He took pictures everywhere and spent a lot of his spare time in the darkroom.

As a good-looking eligible bachelor with an assured future, Langmuir was considered an eminently good catch by Schenectady mothers with daughters of marriageable age, and he never wanted for invitations. He went to dances, masquerade balls, and bridge parties. He started reading novels, short stories and plays, went to play-reading sessions and meetings of the Literary Society, joined the Dramatic Club and even made the cast of a few productions. He attended concerts and lectures, went to picnics, teas and outings with an impressive variety of young women —

not one of whom he referred to familiarly, by her first name, even in the privacy of his diary.

Despite the constant round of activities, Langmuir's life managed not to be utterly frantic. Under the impact of such a quantity of experience, he did not neglect to savor its quality. A few more excerpts from his 1910 diaries are indicative:

After sleeping on the porch of a hunting lodge: "Wake up at 3:30 am & watch Venus & the moon close to it. Listen to wonderful songs of birds, thrushes & a bird with a melancholy clear sweet song of one note (preceded by a note one-third lower). Heard this bird on Killington Peak. Then go down by trail to Richardsons Lodge. Take short cut over beautiful fields gaily colored with great variety of grasses and ferns. Fine skiing country. Finally back to East Dorset & train."

"In afternoon wacht ice go out of river. Great sight. Water 17.8 only 2' below bridge. Rabbit on moving ice."

In the Adirondacks: "Thaw, rain, low clouds. Loafd until 10 am, then chased deer, catching one sick one."

"Met Mr. Mondragon who walks 42 miles, eats 1 meal daily."

On a camping trip: "Rain. Cookt good breakfast before large fire. Climb Killington & build fire on top. No view, only fog. Very markt difference between development of leaves on top & below. Only small buds on trees near top. Fine balsam. On way back stop by Waterfalls & watch boy fish. Walkt down the brook. Try to get boy enthusiastic over skiing with some success."

"Rowed to other end of lake where found guide (John Guyre) with whom I put up for the night. Interesting character. Told me of skiing in that country. Bee hunting. Fire warden on Pharoah Mtn. says bee stings are good for rheumatism."

Langmuir's first friends in Schenectady were, of course, the men he worked with at the lab. He liked Whitney at once, and soon grew very fond of Coolidge. But the men he went with during social evenings and on weekend excursions were his old friend from Columbia, Fink, and other young researchers like Frodsham, Sabin, and Van Brunt. He was, as might be expected, interested in their work; but he was also interested in them as people. He rejoiced in their achievements and was dejected at their failures. He was troubled when they squabbled, and he followed with sympathy the fickle fluctuations of their romances. It was Langmuir to whom Van Brunt confided the news of his engagement, and Langmuir whom Frodsham asked to be best man at his wedding.

Outside the laboratory Langmuir's earliest friends were the Gibsons, who lived across the street from his bachelor quarters in the boarding house at No. 4 Union Street. Langdon Gibson, already a well-known naturalist and explorer, and the young GE scientist were first drawn together by their mutual interest in the outdoors. With Gibson and his two sons, De Wolf and Burdette, Langmuir often went on hiking, canoeing and arrowhead-hunting expeditions. They went on boat trips, too. On one of them, in the Gibson sloop *The Virginian,* Langmuir met, in Maine, Gibson's brother, Charles Dana Gibson, creator of the celebrated Gibson Girl.

It was Langdon Gibson who taught Langmuir the art of skate-sailing. By carrying a carefully-cut canvas sail with him while on ice skates and tacking with the wind, Langmuir learned he could turn himself into an iceboat. On a frozen lake or river he could make speeds up to an exhilarating forty miles per hour. Skate-sailing, like skiing, remained a lifelong passion, and in later years he taught the sport to a good many winter visitors to his place at Lake George.

It was Gibson, too, who got Langmuir started in what was to become another enduring interest—the Boy Scout movement. The organization had been founded in Great Britain only two years earlier by Sir Robert Baden-Powell. Now, in the year 1910, it was just getting its start in the United States. It was to be built around a nucleus of earlier organizations like Daniel Carter Beard's Sons of Daniel Boone and Ernest Thompson Seton's Woodcraft Indians. Dan Beard, a good friend of Gibson's, enlisted his support, and Gibson helped recruit Irving Langmuir as one of the first scoutmasters in the Boy Scouts of America. Langmuir protested that he was not cut out for the task, but Gibson knew a "natural" when he saw one. He had observed the way his own two boys were drawn irresistibly, like moths to the lamp-light, to the ever-exuberant young scientist who was so full of fascinating information and so eager to share it with others.

The boys often went across the street to visit Langmuir in his quarters, and he spent enough time at the Gibson home to become an unofficial member of the family. He was a regular guest at Sunday dinner, where Mrs. Gibson always provided a few uncomfortable moments for Langmuir by scolding him for not going to church. Langmuir taught the boys how to print and develop their own pictures, and how to play chess. He taught them the rudiments of the physical sciences and showed them how to make their own slide rules. He was always appearing at the Gibsons' with apparatus he had designed to demonstrate Brownian motion, or chemical powders that would blaze with brilliant colors when sprinkled on the fire, or a miniature model illustrating how a volcano works, or a microscope with infusoria on slides to look at.

One evening De Wolf, then about twelve years old, came running excitedly up to Langmuir's room with an idea for a perpetual motion machine — a Rube Goldberg contraption whose main element was a glass reservoir where the flow of mercury turned a paddlewheel which in turn ran a motor. Langmuir had De Wolf draw up careful plans, on school paper, for the device. The next day he brought De Wolf down to the laboratory, took him to the glass-blowing department and had them blow a glass reservoir to his specifications. Step by step Langmuir, with De Wolf at his side, had the whole machine built. Then he explained to De Wolf why it didn't work. "He could have told me the same thing without going to all that trouble," De Wolf Gibson remembered years later, in his vice-presidential office at Air Reduction Sales Company, "but then I wouldn't have learned anything."

The Gibson boys were delighted to discover that there were things Langmuir, their inexhaustible teacher, wanted to learn from them. Tennis, for example. But tennis was a sport which maintained only a very brief hold on his interest. Langmuir loved to feel his muscles in free motion on a hike, or to move against the challenge of gravity up a mountainside, or to manipulate the wind's force to propel himself across the ice. But he had never had any desire to participate in team sports like baseball or football. Now he learned that he did not like any kind of competitive sports, even when only individuals were pitted against one another. He also learned that he cared little for fishing or hunting. The taking of game or fish to appease one's hunger was understandable. But the wanton killing of wildlife was not, in Langmuir's book, to be rated as a sport. One entry in his 1910 diary reads: "I go hunting with Mr. Gibson & the boys. By auto to Charlton. Get no partridges or wood-cocks, but see both. Burdette shoots chipmunk & meadow lark ($25 Fine) with his fathers consent. Disgusts me with hunting." Langmuir's children remember that their father never carried a gun or allowed any firearms in the house.

Another outdoorsman Langmuir met in 1910 was a GE engineer named John Apperson. "Appie" was a tall, rugged bachelor who possessed legendary stamina and an Indian's knowledge of woodlore. Throughout his long life he disdained to take any bride but the wilderness.

Apperson later became Langmuir's neighbor in an adjacent campsite at Lake George, and they were partners-in-conservation who worked and lobbied hard to protect the Adirondacks against the encroachments of civilization.

With all this activity, Langmuir was getting quite interested in politics, and would occasionally sit up late arguing about women's suffrage or the single tax. It is startling to learn from the 1910 diaries that Irving Langmuir, that rock-ribbed anti-New Deal Republican who was once singled out by the short-lived liberal New York newspaper *PM* as the archetype of the archconservative, was in those days socialistically inclined. His entry for June 25: "Take Miss Mason to hear Debs at Mohawk Theater. Wonderfully fine speaker & not too extreme. Great enthusiasm." On July 24: "Fred is becoming quite a socialist, I think largely through my influence." On November 7: "Straw vote in lab gives

Socialists 22, Democrats 15, Republicans 14, Prohibitionists 6." And on November 8: "Election Day. Vote Socialist ticket."

The 1910 diaries are also notable, as already mentioned, for the sheer quantity of young females encountered. He only occasionally made comments about them — e.g.: "Walkt home with Miss Brown whom I like very much. Miss Yates very attractive but not so strikingly sensible as Miss Brown." Langmuir saw no one of the young ladies with great frequency or consistency, and if his relations with any of them were more than conversational and casual, his diaries do not reveal it.

On June 29 he made a routine entry: "After dinner went to Garden Party (St. George's Church) at Brandywine Park. Mr. Haygood introduced me to Miss Meserole & Miss Tildsdale. Danced with Miss Meserole twice." Marion Mersereau, whose name Langmuir had misspelled, was visiting her sister in Schenectady at the time, and had to go back to New York City the next day. But she would be coming back to Schenectady for more visits. And she was to become Mrs. Irving Langmuir.

And what, meanwhile, was happening to the other Langmuirs?

Arthur was prospering as usual and, with Alice, traveling quite a bit. He stopped in Schenectady in May, on his way back from Montreal to New York. Irving took him canoeing up the Mohawk, showed him around GE, introduced him to some of his friends, and sent him away quite impressed.

Herbert came visiting too. He was now out in California running the Western division of the New York Life Insurance Company, and had come East to be initiated into New York Life's "$200,000 Club." He got Irving to invest modestly in some California real estate, and Irving reported that he was looking "fine & prosperous & important."

Dean — with whom Irving still skied and climbed mountains occasionally — got engaged, got out of Williams College, and went to work for Western Electric.

Aunt Fannie came visiting from Brooklyn and brought news that Cousin Ducie had become engaged to a Dan Collins.

Mama fell ill in Venice, lost 35 pounds, and, frightened, came back to New York for treatment and recuperation. After a visit with Dean in Williamstown, Massachusetts, she came to Schenectady in July. Irving's succinct diary entries tell the story:

July 9: "Got horse & rig & spent 3 hrs looking up rooms for mother. Engaged rooms at 14 Front Street."

July 10: "Finisht writing to mother in morning."

July 14: "Mother and Mrs. Centameri came on 7 pm train to Scotia. Drove to 14 Front Street. Rooms not suitable. Mother can't go out of house for meals. Should not climb stairs. No other place to go so took them to Edison Hotel. Later found that there are 2 good rooms at 4 Union Street." This was Irving's own boarding house.

July 15: "Lunch with mother at hotel. She did not sleep but feels well. Took them around to 4 Union. Very much pleased with rooms."

July 16: "Mother not so well... Took mother out to see sunset..."

July 17: "After dinner 4 pm took mother canoeing. She was very enthusiastic."

July 18: "Mother receives calls from Mrs. Mason & Miss Curtis. Is invited to tea Wednesday, given for her."

July 19: "Mother is enjoying Schen immensely. Feeling much better than in Williamstown."

July 20: "Mother goes to tea given for her by Mrs. Mason. She meets many pleasant ladies, who welcome her cordially."

July 21: "Mother receives 2 or 3 calls & calls on 2 or 3 ladies."

When it became obvious that Mama was going to stay, Irving augmented the meager furnishings of her rooms with some furniture of his own. It had been in storage since he had moved to Schenectady from Montclair, New Jersey, where he had briefly owned a home while teaching at Stevens Tech. Enjoying Irving's attention, and blossoming in the hospitable climate of Schenectady, Mama soon was leading a full life of her own, and Irving was free to live his. By the time her sixty-first birthday came around, on October 5, she seemed to have fully regained her strength.

There was hardly a facet of living that Langmuir neglected during that busy year of 1910. He heard the Weber Quartet at the YMCA and went to the Williams–Yale basketball game. He played the part of Othello in *Mrs. Jarley's Wax Works,* painted-up and turbanned and wearing an outfit Mama had brought back from Algiers. He helped his Boy Scout troop, the Ravens, build a log cabin in the woods. As best man at Frodsham's wedding, he almost forgot to pay the minister his twenty-dollar fee, and had to get out of his carriage and run back to the church in the rain. He was nearly upset in the rapids on a canoe trip. At Barnum & Bailey's Circus, the tent burned down just as the performance was to begin. "Great sight," Langmuir reported. "Great excitement but no panic. Many women & children had to be held. That no fire extinguishers were available was disgraceful." He was disappointed with Halley's Comet, finding it less impressive than Comet 1910A. He went calling on Charles Proteus Steinmetz and noted only that he was "very positive in his assertions." He helped the Gibsons decorate their Christmas tree and remarked that "Mr. Gibson hangs up his trousers insted of his stockings."

Having a "very jolly time" at a gay New Year's Eve party, Irving Langmuir completed his first full calendar year in Schenectady. He was beginning to make a life for himself — and beginning, in the zestful process, to make scientific history.

Chapter 11

"I think, on the whole that scientists make slightly better husbands and fathers than most of us, and I admire them for it."

C. P. SNOW

JUDGING from the casual reference to her in his diary entry of June 29, 1910, the "Miss Meserole" that Irving Langmuir met that evening at the church social made no special impression on him. She was apparently just another name in his catalogue of young ladies. The impression Langmuir made on Marion Mersereau, however, was immediate, powerful, and — as it turned out — lasting. Marion's girl friends had advised her earlier to be on the lookout for a handsome chap named Gorton Fonda, and to prepare herself to be devastated by the sight. Fonda, who also worked at the GE lab, did appear. He came, in fact, with his friend and colleague, Irving Langmuir. Though he was as handsome as advertised, Marion could later not even remember what he looked like. But the image of Irving Langmuir came through sharp and clear. She preferred his rugged, scholarly good looks to Fonda's more dashing flamboyance. She liked the way he talked, the way he laughed, and even the awkward — though eager — way he danced.

Marion herself was normally rather shy with young men. But with Langmuir she found herself talking freely, even volubly; and it seemed to her they found much in common to talk about. When she left St. George's Church that evening, it was with the definite hope that she might somewhere again run across this earnest, good-humored, thoroughly pleasant and attractive man.

Might it have been Langmuir's reputation as a brilliant and fast-rising General Electric scientist that impressed her, as it did so many of the Schenectady girls? Well, Marion had indeed been told that Langmuir was a successful chemist. But she thought a chemist was someone who filled prescriptions in a drugstore. Hence she could hardly have been influenced by the same considerations that led so many Schenectady mothers to eye him hopefully as a potential son-in-law. There is no way of knowing, at this late date, whether Marion's mother was among those who viewed Langmuir in this calculating light. But if she did, it seems likely that Mrs. Mersereau had him in mind — not for Marion, who, after all, lived way off in New York City with her aunt — but for her other daughter, Dorothy, who lived with her there in Schenectady.

Irving met Dorothy on October 27 of that year, about four months after his meeting with Marion. Here again — though he spelled the name correctly this time — his diary entry is laconic and unrevealing: "Went with mother to dinner at the Kelloggs. Met Miss Dorothy Mersereau & Mrs. Mersereau." No other comment. But Langmuir's friends recall that he seemed charmed by Dorothy, a bright, vivacious girl who was generally considered to be more strikingly pretty than her sister Marion. Langmuir saw Dorothy now and then, as he did many other young women of his acquaintance.

In 1911, when Marion moved to Schenectady, he often saw both sisters together. It was hard to tell which of them he preferred — or even if he thought of either one of them romantically. There are a good many references to the Mersereau girls in his 1911 diaries. Most of them merely report: "Cald on Mersereaus," or "Dinner at Mersereaus." On May 28 he noted an all-day canoe party which included "Mrs. & Miss Mersereau"; but the only incident he deemed worthy of special mention was the loss of his thermometer. On July 11: "Misses Mersereau come down & hear Pianola and see microscope in evening." On July 13: "River tea. Mersereaus . . ."

By July 18 Langmuir seemed to be drifting in Dorothy's direction: "Party. Storey, Fonda, White, Coffin & I invite Mersereaus & Miss Kellogg to illuminated 'regatta' on river followed by dance. I spend evening on river with Dorothy M. & study the stars, etc. Later on get to clubhouse in time for some dances."

But subsequent entries again become quite impartial. Langmuir picnicked with both of them, danced with both of them, and never expressed preference for either of them — or curtailed his activities with any of his other lady friends. By October, however, he seemed finally to be leaning toward Marion. On outings, she accompanied him where Dorothy preferred not to, climbing the steeper mountainsides with him, and exploring the wetter and dirtier caves without worrying about whether her clothes might be soiled. She seemed commendably adventurous, in sympathetic rapport with his own enthusiasms and, quite simply, willing to go wherever he wanted to go and do whatever he wanted to do.

Legend has it that Langmuir, absorbed in his work and completely uninterested in girls, finally married because his mother insisted on it. One evening at supper, the story goes, Mama said firmly, "Irving, I really think it is about time you got married."

And Irving said, "All right, Mama."

And that night on the Scotia Bridge, walking home with a Miss Osborne, whom he had just met for the first time, he proposed. When the astonished young lady protested that they hardly knew one another, Langmuir shrugged his shoulders and went on to another, less embarrassing topic. The story is no doubt apocryphal, like so many told about Langmuir.

There did seem to be a conspiracy of Schenectady mothers to get Langmuir married off — and the situation was rendered more acute when his mother joined the conspiracy. But Irving, having just discovered in his late twenties that females can be as much fun as science, was not yet ready to restrict his theater of operations. Besides, he was no Mama's boy. The truth of the matter is that Irving was more annoyed than not with his mother's continuing attempts to manipulate his life and career, and he was stubbornly resistant to most of her blandishments. It was not, in fact, until after Mama had moved from Schenectady back to New York City, in October of 1911, and had departed on another round-the-world cruise, that Irving finally proposed to Marion.

He first proposed to her on November 5 (though he does not mention it in his diary) on an outing at Beaver Camp, where Langmuir and his Boy Scout troop had built a log cabin. Surprised, and not quite convinced he meant it, Marion put him off. But when he proposed again on November 25, on a trip to Manchester, Vermont, she said Yes. The next day's entry reads: "All go up at Equinox. Marion a wonderful climber. Better than ail the others." The following evening, November 27, Irving and Marion told Mrs. Mersereau about their engagement and discussed possible wedding dates. On November 30, Irving cabled Mama, who answered two days later from Calcutta. Then he wrote to Arthur, Herbert and Dean, and announced the engagement to all his friends and colleagues at the laboratory.

In February Irving and Marion rented the apartment on the upper floor of 26 Wendell Avenue, Schenectady. There was some discussion, in view of Irving's avowed lack of religious faith, about whether or not they should marry in church. Though Marion herself was not an assiduous churchgoer and had no serious objection to Irving's agnostic views, her grandfather had been an Episcopalian clergyman. "I really would feel more married, somehow, with a church wedding," she told Irving. So the wedding took place — at 4:30 p.m. on April 27, 1912 — on the site of their first meeting, St. George's Episcopal Church, Schenectady. Irving was thirty years old and Marion twenty-eight. Marion's sister, Dorothy, served as maid of honor. Dean — whose wedding Irving had attended in December — was best man, and Gorton Fonda was one of the ushers. After the reception, Irving and Marion left for Albany by automobile (Irving had recently purchased an Overland), and had dinner in their room at the Ten Eyck Hotel. Their honeymoon trip took them through New England, to New Jersey seashore resorts, and up to the Catskills. They got back to Schenectady on May 17. "Arrived 2 AM," Langmuir's diary reads, "& opened lock on front door with toothpaste." It was the beginning of forty-five of the happiest married years on record.

In the beginning Mama was a little troublesome. She got back from the Far East before the wedding, and took an apartment next door to Irving and Marion. Nothing could ever persuade Mama, to the end of her days, that it was not her prerogative, even her duty, to keep a forceful guiding hand in the lives of her sons, and of her sons' sons. The easygoing Marion was usually submissive enough. But when Mama went too far, Marion knew how to assert herself with sufficient vigor to earn the strong-willed old lady's respect. By the time Mama moved away from Schenectady again, a tacit understanding had grown up between mother and daughter-in-law to the effect that advice in certain areas would be welcome — or at least tolerated — but in other areas the No Trespassing sign would be strictly enforced. Thus, through the years, they enjoyed a most amicable relationship, with a minimum of friction.

During their early married years the Langmuirs lived a relatively quiet life. Though they occasionally had company for dinner or visited friends in the evening, they were neither party-givers nor party-goers. After they moved, in 1914, to a house at 16 Rugby Road, they did a fair amount of gardening, and Langmuir enjoyed doing odd jobs around the house. They enjoyed the outdoors together even more than they had in their courting days as Marion added skiing and skate-sailing to her accomplishments. She often accompanied him on trips as he traveled with increasing frequency to scientific meetings and symposia around the country. On one extended Western vacation in 1915, they zigzagged across the United States, stopping to climb mountains and to go on horseback into Indian country.

In the few years between his marriage and America's entry

into World War I, Langmuir's scientific productivity accelerated and, at the same time, broadened in scope to take in most of the lines of research that were to bring him international fame and a lifetime supply of honors. He continued to pursue, without letup, his experiments in high-temperature, low-pressure chemistry. He had begun his studies of thermal effects in various gases. Soon he was absorbed in studies as diverse as thermionic emission, surface chemistry, and the structure of the atom.

Though Langmuir kept unusually complete laboratory notebooks, mention of his work often spilled over into his personal diaries — e.g.:

"Read paper on Recent Advances in our Knowledge of Laws of Radiation & Application to High Temp. Meas. before local section ACS."

"Thorium Nitrate wire interesting at lab for the last couple of weeks. It goes bad after 24 hrs in lamp."

"I read my paper on Heat Conduction & Convection in Gases at Extremely High Temperatures."

"Colloquium. I talk on Dissociation of Hydrogen into Atoms."

"I send off my patent application for N_2 lamps."

"Meet Tone and Allen at Saranac Lake & negotiate license to manufacture monox."

"Go up to Institute Bldg. & spend day getting lamps ready with Winne. In evening read paper on W lamps of High efficiency."

"Cleveland: Hyde's laboratory. I give talk on gas reactions & clean-up in vacuum."

"Get thermionic currents 2000 times those found some months ago."

"Colloquium on Optical Glass. Work on Low Pressure Reactions paper in afternoon."

"Work on paper & theory of adsorption."

"Took 8:10 train to Boston where I read paper on theory of Heterogeneous Reactions . . ."

"See Stanley at Great Barrington about making vacuum pump."

"Start to write abstract on Mercury Vapor Lamp."

"Workt on space charge equations with plus & minus ions."

"Work on Electrochemical theories: Become convinced that electrolytic potentials are due to contact E.M.F. between Metals. Am amused by Ostwald's Electrochemics."

"Meeting of Amer. Phys. Soc. Read two papers & discuss Wilson's paper on new Hydrogen pump. Am relieved to find Wilson got idea of using wide slit from us."

"Workt all evening & until 3 am on extension of Nernst's theory of electrolysis (kinetics)."

"I gave Colloquium at laboratory on a new viewpoint in regard to electrochemical action."

"Read paper on Vapor Pressures."

"Symposium on Surface Phenomena. I read paper on Contact Potentials."

"Getting very interesting results & ideas in connection with surface tension & adsorption."

"During the past month have spent most of spare time writing my long paper on Constitution of Solids & Liquids, 1st Part."

Et cetera.

By 1916 Langmuir's reputation was growing to the point where he was increasingly in demand as a lecturer. The talks were usually on some aspect of his own research, but some began to branch out into his philosophy of science, and to topics like "Industrial vs. Pure Research." He usually prepared his lectures with some care and, as he gained in scientific stature and in confidence, he spoke well and, as one of his colleagues puts it, "he put on a good show." He had already received his first major award, too — the Nichols Medal of the American Chemical Society, which he was to receive a second time only five years later. He was meeting and earning the respect of scientists like Compton and Millikan, Pauli and Rutherford.

It was during this period, too, that Langmuir — watching the work of GE colleagues like Albert W. Hull, Saul Dushman, William C. White (Langmuir's first cousin), and E. F. W. Alexanderson, and often collaborating with them — began to see the commercial payoff of some of his earlier studies of space charge and electron emission in vacua. GE began to produce a series of vacuum and radio tubes with names like pliotron, thyratron, magnetron, kenotron, dynatron, and pliodynatron. Langmuir had coined the first of these Greek-derived names after a conference in November, 1913, with Professor John Ira Bennett, who taught Greek at Union College. The list grew into dozens, then hundreds, as the tubes put out by GE — and later by its competitors — quietly revolutionized the communications industry. Lee De Forest, that prolific pioneer of American invention, later referred to this terminology as "Graeco-Schenectady." Schenectady had indeed become a major center for radio research.

On the evening of August 4, 1914, a GE researcher was running tests on a new recording device in the radio room at Union College. He quit work around midnight, stuffing some of the message tape in his pocket before going home. When he scanned the tape the next day he found the same short message repeated over and over. It had been transmitted by a German-owned and operated station at Sayville, Long Island, and it read: "To commanders of all German ships on the high seas — proceed at once to the nearest neutral port."

World War I had begun.

Just about that time, Langmuir, sailing with the Gibsons on their sloop, *The Virginian,* off the coast of Maine, encountered a big black shape feeling its way through a thick fog off Northeast Harbor. As the vessel drew alongside, Langmuir had a shouted conversation in German with one of the sailors on board. He learned that the ship was the *Crown Princess Cecile,* that it had been bound for Germany with its cargo of gold, but was now seeking asylum in Bar Harbor. (After the United States declared war, the *Crown Princess Cecile* was seized as a prize of war, converted into an American troopship, and rechristened the *Mount Vernon.*)

Someone who had known Langmuir over the years, but only casually, might have wondered where his sympathies would lie in this war between the Allies and the Central Powers. He had after all, often spoken harshly of the French educational system, having been harshly exposed to it at an early age; and he was sometimes critical of other aspects of French culture. On the other hand, did he not seem to favor everything German? He loved the German language and landscape. He appreciated Germany's scientific and cultural achievements. Göttingen was his alma mater of fond memories. And Wagner was still his favorite composer. He and Marion had, in fact, been attending a performance of *Parsifal* at the Metropolitan Opera House in New York on the day war was declared.

But Langmuir never let his enjoyment of German Gemütlichkeit blind him to the less admirable aspects of the German national character — particularly its predilection for absolutism based upon obscure and mystical philosophies.[1] Nor did he let his annoyance with things French keep him from recognizing all that France had contributed to Western culture and its democratic tradition. In any war between France and Germany Langmuir would be unhesitatingly on the side of France. Add to France's side England, a nation Langmuir admired extravagantly, and the Kaiser's Germany would have no chance at all with Langmuir. Add to this Langmuir's own sense of America's growing involvement, and his indignation at Germany's ever-boldening U-boat depredations, and you have a man ready to go all-out for the Allies.

Langmuir not only believed in the Allied cause; he also had great confidence in their ability to win. There were many heated discussions with Dean and with Arthur. Dean would shake his head sadly and say he did not see how the Allies could hope to win. Arthur maintained that the best they could hope for was a stalemate. But Irving, long before America got into the war, stoutly insisted that Germany would be beaten. As early as June

---

[1] In an article he wrote in 1946 Langmuir said: "I lived in Germany as a student from 1903 to 1906 and made many subsequent visits to that country. I was always disturbed by the aggressive, militaristic spirit of the Germans, by their ideas of racial superiority, and especially by their belief that moral scruples should have no place in international relationships. One prominent German told me in 1921 that he considered the United States government criminally negligent in not fortifying the Canadian border."

of 1916 he and Marion had marched in a Preparedness Parade in Schenectady.

Early in 1917, when the Kaiser's government officially adopted a policy of unrestricted submarine warfare, the United States promptly broke off diplomatic relations and started arming its merchant ships. On Good Friday, April 6, with World War I nearly three years old, Woodrow Wilson finally declared war on Germany.

On the day war was declared, E. W. Rice, who had by then become president of General Electric, wired Woodrow Wilson offering the government all of GE's research facilities. But the government did not yet understand — as it later did in World War II — the uses that could be made of science. In those days it took a great deal of persuasion to interest any agency of the government, including the armed forces, in scientific research. There was at least one happy exception to this general attitude — Josephus Daniels, who was Secretary of the Navy.

Daniels had already, on his own initiative, organized a scientific Naval Consulting Board headed by Thomas A. Edison and including GE's Willis R. Whitney; and GE was already engaged in some research for the Navy in communications and submarine detection. Earlier in 1917 the Board had already authorized the Submarine Signal Company of Boston to begin constructing at Nahant, Massachusetts, an experiment station for anti-submarine research. With Whitney personally interested, it was inevitable that Langmuir would be drawn into the program. His diary of February 11 reads: "Sunday: Went out Dr. Whitneys with Hawkins & Coolidge. W told us of the problems put up to Naval Consulting Board by Navy Dept. & asked our help. I see Frank Leavitt about Oxygen for torpedoes."
24: "Several of us go to Newport to see torpedoes made. See

On February 23, he reported: "With Naval Consulting Board went out on a 'tug' to Boston Light Ship to hear demonstration of submarine signalling by Sub Signalling Co . . ." On February
lems Naval Consulting Board. Discuss submarines & torpedoes,
three fired." And on March 3: "Meeting Committee special prob-

detection & defense." Thus Langmuir was already actively engaged in the war effort before the United States was officially at war. Thanks to the foresight of Josephus Daniels and his consulting board, the Nahant station was completed only a day after Wilson's war declaration. To save bureaucratic snarls that would have held up research for unconscionable periods of time, GE undertook its research program at its own expense.

Nahant soon became Langmuir's headquarters. He did a lot of traveling back and forth by train between Boston and Schenectady. Marion usually came long. At first they stayed at the Rockledge Hotel; later they rented a house. Since Irving was out at sea for frequent tests, the Langmuirs sometimes brought along Marion's mother or her sister Dorothy to keep her company.

Working with Langmuir's own research group at Nahant was a GE engineering group under Charles E. Evelith. And only a month after their work began, they were joined by a research team from Western Electric. Langmuir was soon able, too, to draw on the brains of people like Coolidge, who had set up a second experiment station on the Mohawk River, and Hull, who remained in Schenectady. He worked on submarine detectors, underwater signaling devices, and methods for increasing the accuracy of torpedoes.

Throughout most of 1917 and 1918, his diaries attest to his absorption in the antisubmarine work. On May 2, for example, after some encouraging tests with a detection device called the C-tube, he wrote: "Tell Whitney of good results. In afternoon suddenly I develop idea of controlled sound directed torpedo for submarine destroyer."

His September 16 entry reads: "Out on *Margaret*. First test 30 miles out. Splendid results, which prove importance of making device of floats directional. I get compensator idea in the evening & tell Evelith." Two days later: "I ask Hull & Coolidge to try to get directional effects with microphone & compensator immediately. They both succeeded within 2–3 hrs . . ."

As might be expected, Langmuir, in the course of his war work, got interested in a number of things not directly connected with any of his projects. Some of these interests are best described in an unpublished memorandum written by E. W. Kellogg of the RCA Victor Laboratory many years later after a visit made by Langmuir in the company of Leopold Stokowski. "Dr. Langmuir's study of binaural listening and related questions dates largely from his work on submarine detection during the war," Kellogg wrote. "The listening devices employed provided two microphones and two ear-phones with separate channels to each ear and means for altering the time of arrival of the sounds at the two ears. The simplest way to control the time of arrival is to move the microphones. When they are equally distant from the source of sound, the listener gets the impression that the sound is coming from directly in front of him, while if the sound reaches one ear first, the sounds seem to come from the other side. From the precision of settings which it was found possible to make, Dr. Langmuir calculated that the ears can tell a time difference of the order of 10 microseconds...

"Dr. Langmuir has described some tests which he made during the war in which a blind man who had attracted attention by the facility with which he found his way about the streets of Boston, with no guide except street noise, was taken to the Nahant experiment station and asked to describe his surroundings. With noises to guide him such as the echo of footsteps and occasional spoken words, and the noise of the sea, the blind man stopped and pointed to one side or the orther saying: "There is a low building.' 'There is a fence there.' At one point he said, 'There is something peculiar there, something soft.' A load of sea weed was piled against the foundation of one of the shacks. Upon entering one of the buildings, the blind man immediately gave the approximate size of the room. A number of tests were made to find whether he could be confused by echoes. In one test, a person spoke from behind a baffle, the location of the speaker and the baffle being designed to result in the blind man's receiving most of the sound from one of the walls of the room. The blind man pointed directly to the person talking behind the baffle and said 'he is over there but he has something in front of him.' The wall echo, if it gave any impression, simply confirmed his idea of the size of the room or his distance from the wall.

"Dr. Langmuir interprets these and other tests as indicating that the sense of direction is obtained largely from transients and peaks of sound pressure which do not recur rapidly and regularly, but preserve their identity as they are heard directly by the two ears and later as reflections. The first time such a transient reaches the ears, an impression of direction is obtained, and no subsequent arrivals of the same sound can destroy this impression but merely serve to convey additional information. When a person listens to someone talking from across the room at a distance of say ten or fifteen feet and the room is not extremely absorbent, calculations indicate that the sound received directly is only a small fraction of the total sound energy reaching the listener's ears, perhaps 10 to 30%. Nevertheless, so distinct is the impression of the direction from which the sound comes that one normally thinks that nearly all of the sound is coming to him direct. On the other hand, if the directive faculties are absent, one is readily convinced of the correctness of the calculations."

Edward Hennelly, one of Langmuir's research associates at the time, recalls that the pursuit of the principles of binaural sound led Langmuir into some amusing experiences. One evening, riding back to Schenectady on the train, Hennelly was having dinner on the diner with the Langmuirs. Explaining binaural sound to Marion, Langmuir was enthusiastically waving his arms, almost knocking a bowl of soup from the waiter's hand. Then he got up and, to demonstrate a point, whirled around in the aisle like a dervish to disorient himself. "Now," he said, "I don't know which direction is which, and I will pick out certain sounds —"

With everyone in the diner staring, and waiters desperately trying to get around her husband, who was blocking the aisle, Marion, embarrassed, said to Hennelly, "Whatever shall we do with him?"

Hennelly, who had seen a similar demonstration the evening before during dinner at the Parker House in Boston, smiled and said, "Let's just pretend he's with some other party."

Marion smiled too and, tugging gently at Irving's coatsleeve, said, "Sit down, Dear, and let the waiters by." Which he did.

Langmuir worked out some equations dealing with the propagation of sound in water and in air. He grew interested in echo location for the blind. He made some rough notes for designing a doctor's stethoscope based on the binaural principle. But there was a strict limit to what he could do in 1917 and 1918, with the war on. This time Langmuir could not follow his curiosity where it led him. His work at Nahant had to pursue a definite goal, and serendipity had to be shelved for the duration. His World War I work did turn out to be useful in later years, though, when he helped Stokowski and RCA Victor improve the quality of music reproduction and consulted with the Bell Telephone Laboratories in the development of stereophonic sound. He even applied his knowledge to designing a better geophone to record and detect sound waves passing through the earth. Thus he tracked sound, to good purpose, through all three states of matter — gas, liquid, and solid.

During the war years Langmuir did not permit his antisubmarine work to shut out his other scientific pursuits altogether. Nor did he throw himself into it to the exclusion of all other activities. His diary entry of February 26, 1918, is fairly typical: "Stormy. Go out on *Margaret* but come back before lunch. Work on paper on Adsorption. Marion & I go to Prof Elihew [sic] Thompson's & see Jupiter, Saturn, Mars etc. & hear organ."

In November of 1917, a research team from Nahant headed by Evelith sailed for England on the U.S.S. *Delaware* to demonstrate some of the newly-developed detectors to the British. The Admiralty was so impressed that by January of 1918 it had organized history's first sub-hunting expedition. When divers brought back proof that at least one U-boat had been sunk in the English Channel, quantity production was ordered on the devices in both England and the United States. Meanwhile Langmuir and his colleagues were dreaming up and testing new and improved gadgets. In the course of the testing Langmuir more than once had occasion to be grateful for his sea legs. On October 24, 1917, for example, during deep-sea tests on the *Malay,* he wrote: "Start out early but East gale drives us back. Forward hatch carried away. Wind 52 mph at noon, 63 mph at 6 pm. Anchor in harbor & can't land all day."

On February 28, 1918: "Go out on *Margaret* with Varley. In adjusting trim in brackish water we unexpectedly submerge 2 ft over hatch, leaving Varley to climb up periscope. Test MB-tube & 3-K-Units... Collide with some object which strikes side of sub & heels her over. Evening hold meetings to plan deep sea test."

On March 2, at sea: "Expect to go to 1400 fathom line 100 miles S of Block Island but our engines break down & SC 178 is out of gasoline so we stop at 300 fathom line. Heavy E swell & moderate W breeze, brilliant day. Everyone sea sick (except me). Sleep in forecastle with crew. Listen for 5 hrs. Evening go up to Crows Nest while we return." The next day: "Westerly gale during the night. Engine breaks down again. Takes 18 hrs to go 80 miles. Roll about 40°. Mason thrown from bunk & table breaks loose. Whole crew very sick. No meals served. We reach New London at 11 am."

All this new effort bore fruit in new devices. But they came too late to be used. Even so, the ones already in use did their job well. The submarine menace was brought effectively under control by war's end, and much of the credit for the success of the antisubmarine campaign belongs to Irving Langmuir.

Before the war ended, Langmuir was pulled out of Nahant by Whitney, who had drafted him for another wartime project. Whitney, who had been appointed to the Nitrate Supply Committee, was made responsible for all research on nitrate production at Muscle Shoals on the Tennessee River. He asked Langmuir to concentrate on the chemical problems of nitrogen fixation. Langmuir agreed, and decided he could do the job in Schenectady as well as anywhere. He was just as pleased with this turn of events, since Marion had undergone serious surgery earlier in the year, and though she had fully recovered, he was glad of a situation that would enable him to spend more time at home with her while still contributing his bit to the war effort. The Langmuirs returned to Schenectady in September of 1918, moving in temporarily with Marion's mother. Though the war was not yet over, and one of Langmuir's first acts on his return to Schenectady was to register for the draft, he and Marion — who had been wanting to be parents for a long time — decided they would soon adopt a boy.

Late in 1915, with a polio scare in New York City, Dean had brought his three-year-old son, Robert, to Schenectady to live with Irving and Marion. Robert stayed for nearly a year, and Langmuir's 1916 diaries were full of little references to Robert.

"Taught Robert FEE-FI-FO-FUM."

"Build snowman for Robert."

"Took Robert to B & B circus. He was too much impressed to talk."

"Playing with Robert & Jack & Bobby Beale."

"Robert announces at 1:30 pm that he is going to the Laboratory too. He disappears & we spend 2½ hrs looking for him & notify the police. He is found by some ladies down on Dock Street still on his way to Lab. He has had a fine time. I spank him."

In 1918 again Robert had spent seven weeks with his Uncle Irving and Aunt Marion. They enjoyed having a bright, active youngster around the house. They were fond of the neighbors' children, too, and Irving often romped with them and taught them tricks. On their Western trip they had made the acquaintance of Herbert's four boys, and Irving had spent a lot of time with them. He was entertained by Arthur's children, too, and he and Marion were both eager for children of their own. When none had come, in the seventh year of their marriage, they decided to adopt one or two. Langmuir noted the decision in his diary entry of October 1, 1918. By October 12, he was writing of his newly-acquired two-year-old son. "We buy clothes for Kenneth & take the 1 pm train for Schenectady... He good all the time. Rather serious. Buy more things and take carriage to 6 Ardsley Rd [Mrs. Mersereau's home]." By December they had moved into a new house on Stratford Road.

During the busy year 1918, Langmuir was made a member of the National Academy of Sciences and was awarded the Hughes Medal of the Royal Society of London. But, more important, he and Marion had acquired a son and a home of their own. And the war ended, as Irving had been certain it would. He had never been too lost in his research to take a keen interest in following the war's progress in detail. On September 30, 1918, he wrote in his diary: "Hawkins announces Bulgarias surrender. Very little interest taken by most people. I don't think the importance is realized. I think it probable that Turkey will do the same within a week; Austria will follow suit within 4 to 6 weeks and there is a reasonably good chance that Germany will surrender before Christmas."

Langmuir's estimate, as we all now know, was very close. After the armistice on November 11 Langmuir discontinued his work on nitrogen fixation, and the nitrate plant at Muscle Shoals remained unused until 1933, when the area was taken over by the Tennessee Valley Authority.

Chapter 12

"Through all the years of my formal schooling, no scientific concept seemed to me more elegantly beautiful than the Langmuir–Lewis atom."

COLONEL JOHN PAUL STAPP

ALMOST as soon as he was settled back in Schenectady, Langmuir permitted himself the luxury of working on a new theory of atomic structure. The idea had begun to germinate before America's entry into the war. As early as 1916 and 1917, he had written two remarkable papers on the constitution and fundamental properties of solids while he was, in Bridgman's words, "under the spell of two of the lectures in this country by W. H. Bragg describing the recent epoch-making work of father and son on the X-ray structure of crystals." The Bragg lectures — which had a great deal of influence on Langmuir's theories of adsorption — also influenced his ideas on atomic structure. The work of the Braggs was, of course, only one of the many sources exploited by Langmuir's eclectic intellect in building up the theory which, he hoped, would help create "a new chemistry, a deductive chemistry, one in which we can reason out chemical relationships without falling back on chemical intuitions."

Throughout his antisubmarine researches at Nahant and at sea, these ideas had hovered tantalizingly in the background of his thoughts, but he was able to focus his attention on them only sporadically. Once the war was over and it was no longer his bounden patriotic duty to give detection tubes and nitrogen fixation his highest-priority attention, he went back to his old custom of working on what interested him most. The result was a theory which — though the sensation it created was brief — many still regard as one of the major achievements of Langmuir's career.

Certainly his basic conception of the atom as a nucleus surrounded by concentric electron shells made much more sense to chemists than, say, Niels Bohr's planetary model of the atom, which shed no light whatever on how chemical reactions take place. Langmuir's atom turned out to be inadequate for the purposes of nuclear physicists, who soon moved in other directions in a still-unrequited quest for an explanation of the atom's inner workings. But Langmuir did succeed in bringing satisfactory order for the first time to a chaos of seemingly unrelated data, and there has yet to be put forward a better explanation for the chemical behavior of the atom.

Langmuir's theory could only have come from a man with an abiding interest and a superb competence in physics combined with a vast, detailed knowledge of specific chemical reactions. And Langmuir would naturally be the man to fuse physics and chemistry — or, rather, to harness physics to the uses of chemistry — in this fashion. He was, after all, as much a physicist as a chemist. He routinely attended just about as many meetings of the American Physical Society as of the American Chemical Society. He delivered as many papers of interest to physicists as to chemists, and he received just as many job offers from the physics departments of universities as from their chemistry departments.

Not that it was a brand new notion for a chemist to be interested in atoms. But the interest was usually confined to the atom's interactions with other atoms. In brief, chemists were concerned with purely chemical reactions which, in their view, had nothing to do with the internal structure of the atom. Indeed, it was with great surprise that they received the news — in 1897, when J. J. Thomson unveiled the electron — that the atom *had* an internal structure. The atom had been considered to be the solid, ultimate and indivisible particle of matter. In Langmuir's day, for all practical purposes, chemists still looked upon the atom in that light, for what went on inside an atom — if anything — was irrelevant to its behavior in the company of other atoms. But as Langmuir thought more and more about the atom, he began to suspect that its internal structure had as much influence on its chemical behavior as an individual man's character has on his social behavior. Langmuir was especially intrigued by the role of the electron, that tiny unit of electricity which he had been studying so intensively over the years in his electric lamps and electron discharge tubes. In the previous century the Swedish genius, Baron Berzelius, had expressed the belief that chemical reactions must have something to do with the electrical polarity of atoms. But a good many advances remained to be made, including the discovery of the electron itself, before a notion like Berzelius's could be anything more than a vague hunch.

Langmuir had eagerly followed every advance in atomic theory. And whenever he encountered some physicist he admired, like Arthur Holly Compton or Robert Andrews Millikan,[1] he would engage him in a discussion on the nature of the atom. When he met Wolfgang Pauli on a train ride to Chicago, or when Sir Ernest Rutherford came visiting the GE lab, or when Gilbert Newton Lewis sat across the luncheon table at a scientific meeting, Langmuir would inevitably want to talk about their atomic theories and experiments, and the implications to be drawn from them.

Langmuir had often puzzled over the mystery of valence — a rather fuzzy term designating the peculiar affinity which atoms had for other atoms (but only for certain other atoms, and only

[1] Millikan was one of Langmuir's scientific idols, but he emerged a somewhat tarnished one after a day in court in March, 1917. Langmuir himself was frequently called upon to testify in patent suits. He usually took great pains in preparing his testimony so he could offer an airtight scientific presentation, thoroughly documented. At one such hearing, Millikan testified on behalf of the Western Electric Company, and Langmuir noted in his diary: "I am surprised & disappointed at character of Millikans testimony . . . He is careless & unscientific in his statements & very much influenced by prejudice."

under certain conditions, and only in certain fixed proportions). Chemists had been baffled by the valence concept ever since Sir Edward Frankland first introduced the idea back in 1852 — and, much earlier than that, had been baffled by the varied phenomena which the concept encompassed. Why would hydrogen atoms unite with oxygen atoms but not with neon atoms? What was the nature of the bond that held the two atoms in a hydrogen molecule so tightly that, inside the incandescent lamp, fantastic forces were necessary to pull them apart? And why were elements like hydrogen, fluorine and lithium so highly reactive while others like nitrogen and argon would not react at all? Langmuir felt that somehow those inert gases that had intrigued him so since childhood could prove a key to the mystery. Meanwhile, no one had the answer. No one had even made a really satisfactory guess.

Langmuir was arriving at a guess of his own in the year 1919, when two important papers appeared — one by Heidelberg's Albrecht Kossel in *Annalen der Physik,* the other by California's Gilbert Newton Lewis in the *Journal of the American Chemical Society.* Each independently proposed similar ideas — based upon the earlier but much vaguer suggestions of Abegg — but, of the two, Lewis's presentation was much more complete and comprehensive. Levis, that great and grossly underpublicized scientist, suggested a new static model of the atom as a possible replacement for Bohr's restless, orbit-hopping planetary model — which, in any case, applied only to the hydrogen atom. Lewis envisioned a stationary nucleus surrounded by cubical electron shells. The cube nearest the nucleus was the smallest, and the cube farthest away the largest. This octet theory (octet for the eight electrons which the outer shell required for stability, one electron at each of the cube's eight corners) of atomic structure was no half-baked notion; it was based upon an impressive quantity of experimental data and treated — as it of course would be by Lewis — with great mathematical sophistication.

Lewis's theory, especially his conception of the paired electron bond, was not popular in the scientific community, especially among the physicists. For one thing, the idea of stationary electrons was altogether unacceptable to the nuclear-physical scheme of things. For another, the cubical atom was in direct conflict with Bohr's model. Both could not be correct. But Langmuir stated firmly that "the theory of valence recently advanced by G. N. Lewis seems to offer by far the most satisfactory picture of the mechanism of chemical combination that has yet been suggested."

Lewis's paper appeared in December, 1916. Shortly after its publication, Langmuir — whose thoughts had been running in a similar vein — had an ideal opportunity to discuss the theory of the cubical atom with its author. On December 27 they both attended a symposium on the structure of matter at Columbia University, where Langmuir gave a paper on "The Structure of Solids and Liquids, and the Nature of Interatomic Forces." On the 28th they went to a meeting of the American Physical Society at the City College of New York. They had lunch together that day, but there was still so much left over to talk about that they arranged to meet again the following day at the Harvard Club to continue the discussion.

Though Langmuir was critical of some aspects of the Lewis theory, he finally used Lewis's idea as the basis for his own theory, and the Langmuir model became known as the Lewis–Langmuir atom. In referring to this designation later, Lewis took pains to make it clear that, though the hyphenation might imply "some sort of collaboration," there had been none. "As a matter of fact," he wrote, "Dr. Langmuir's work has been entirely independent, and such additions as he has made to what was stated or implied in my paper should be credited to him alone." The word around the scientific community, after Langmuir's work on atomic structure had gained such renown, was that Lewis was angry because Langmuir had "stolen" his ideas, and that he never quite forgave Langmuir for the theft. It would seem out of character for Lewis, however, to maintain such an attitude. Langmuir freely acknowledged his debt to Lewis, and referred frequently to Lewis's work as the starting point for his own. In a letter to *Nature,* for example, on April 29, 1920, Langmuir — replying to a critical letter which had appeared in an earlier issue — said in the first paragraph, before answering the specific criticism, that "it is scarcely fair to Lewis to refer to the theory as 'Langmuir's theory'." He continued to emphasize Lewis's contribution even though, as David Harker has pointed out, "Irving Langmuir seems to have been engrossed with the problem of chemical binding at about the time that G. N. Lewis' paper appeared, and quite probably had been thinking along the same general lines."

Lewis himself, in his own book on the subject in 1923, wrote that the task of getting across his theory "was performed, with far greater success than I could have achieved, by Dr. Irving Langmuir in a brilliant series of twelve articles and in a large number of lectures given in this country and abroad. It is largely through these papers and addresses that the theory has received the wide attention of scientists."

More often than not, scientific ideas arise from other scientific ideas. This free cross-fertilization has been one of the great catalytic factors in the acceleration of scientific progress. A scientist does not hesitate to elaborate on some other scientist's ideas any more than — say — Liszt hesitated to compose variations on a theme of Paganini's, or Shakespeare to borrow a plot from Holinshed and use it as raw material for a great poetic drama. Langmuir had a particular facility for adapting other people's insights to his own uses — and on the other hand freely gave of his own insights for other people's uses. A scientist who works and travels in stimulating scientific company, who talks with scientists and reads scientific publications, who regularly attends many meetings and symposia, can never be quite sure where the germ of an idea may have come from. And ideas may occur spontaneously and independently, as was apparently the case with Lewis and Kossel. (Born and Landé, by the way, without knowing anything about the work of Lewis, also arrived at the theory of the cubical atom.) Newton and Leibnitz each invented the calculus independently. Darwin and Wallace each arrived at a similar theory of evolution. Adams and Leverrier each predicted the presence of the planet Neptune. The history of science is full of such instances.

Almost invariably there ensues a violent controversy among the partisans of the respective scientists involved, on the mistaken assumption that one must have stolen the idea from the other. At the very least there is a squabble about who made the discovery first. Langmuir was occasionally involved in such priority controversies — one with Professor R. W. Wood of Johns Hopkins, for example, over the atomic hydrogen welding torch. But they always ended amicably. If Langmuir found out that the other party had indeed been first, he would not hesitate to acknowledge it. But if he felt he had been first — especially if the priority meant patent rights for GE — he would go to a great deal of trouble to convince the opposing claimant. The controversies seldom left any rancor in their wake, though Langmuir's blunt pointing-out of scientific error now and then left the proponent of the picked-apart idea smarting and somewhat resentful.

In the case of the Lewis theory, there was never any open controversy. There was not even any question of priority. From his very first paper on the subject, Langmuir made it clear he was building on the ideas of Lewis. What, then, were the Lewis partisans so perturbed about? In their view, the theory they regarded as Lewis's was taken over by Langmuir — who, because he was already famous and because he made a lot of noise about it, wound up getting all the credit. Some made it sound like an intentional fraud perpetrated on the public by Langmuir. Kinder souls preferred to think the public had simply misunderstood.

Writing about Langmuir in his biography of Lewis, for example, Arthur Lachman says: "Lewis's views appealed to him so strongly that he devoted himself to spreading that gospel, not only in publications and lectures in America, but abroad. Huxley performed a similar labor of love for Darwin...

"There is a curious result of Langmuir's crusade," Lachman continues. "The word 'octet' is attributed to him. Many not-so-alert chemists confused the two names, and the new theory became widely known as the Lewis–Langmuir theory, sometimes as the Langmuir–Lewis, and occasionally as the 'Langmuir theory'." The clear implication here is that Langmuir merely promoted Lewis's ideas and added virtually nothing of his own. Actually, the final, viable theory is so much more Langmuir than Lewis that it would require no confusion of names at all to call it simply the Langmuir theory. Perhaps the greatest value of the Lewis theory — as Joel Hildebrand has pointed out — was its influence on the development of Irving Langmuir's thinking. Well — no matter. Each scientist acknowledged his debt to the other. Call it the Lewis–Langmuir theory.

In any case, Langmuir, instead of arranging his electron shells in cubical patterns, arranged them in concentric shells around the nucleus. He agreed that chemical affinity was due, as Berzelius had guessed, to the atom's electrical charge — and that only the outer shell of electrons was involved in a chemical reaction. He was enough of a physicist to feel uneasy about purely stationary electrons and made provisions for their motion: "the electrons in atoms are either stationary or rotate, revolve, or oscillate about definite positions in the atom." He later emphasized that "the positions of the electrons shown in the diagrams may be regarded as the centres of their orbits." In any case, if the outer shell were filled with its proper quota of electrons, then the element would be stable. If the outer shell had too few electrons to fill it, the shell would have room to accept the electrons from the incomplete outer shell of some other atom; thus it would react chemically — and the number of electrons in the outer shell would precisely determine and limit its possible interactions with other atoms. Using this as a working hypothesis, Langmuir, equipped with an intellectual tool which had only recently come into the world, set about to construct a model of the atom that would satisfy the requirements of the physicists and at the same time explain every known variety of chemical reaction.

The new intellectual tool at Langmuir's disposal was a table of atomic numbers given to science by a brilliant twenty-three-year-old Britisher named Henry Moseley. Moseley had been born the same year as the poet Rupert Brooke, and was destined to die the same year, from the same cause — World War I. While Brooke died of blood poisoning on an Aegean island, Moseley fell with a Turkish bullet through his head at Gallipoli. The premature cutting-off of Moseley's life at the peak of his creative powers was the same kind of loss to science as Brooke's death was to poetry. It was in 1912, the year Langmuir married Marion Mersereau, that Moseley made public the result of his studies in the X-ray spectra of the elements. He had succeeded in putting the periodic table of elements in good working order for the first time since Mendeleyev conceived it. Langmuir used Moseley's table as his starting point. In the table, each element had been assigned an atomic number based on its electrical charge, and the elements were arranged in families according to their chemical characteristics. Moseley's arrangement was particularly pleasing to Langmuir. It seemed to confirm what he had long believed — that the inert elements held the key to the riddle of how atomic structure was related to chemical behavior.

Helium and neon, for example, were in the same family because neither one reacted chemically at all. This would mean that their outer electron shells were filled. Helium is No. 2 (two electrons) and neon No. 10 (ten electrons) on Moseley's table. Langmuir surmised from this that helium had a single shell of two electrons. Element No. 3, with a third electron, would have to start a second shell with it, and the second shell would not be complete until it contained eight electrons — or a total of ten for the atom (i.e., non-reactive neon).

Now, Lewis had accounted for atoms up to scandium (No. 21), but Langmuir went on to the heavier elements to theorize that the stable shells of electrons, going out from the nucleus, contained two, eight, eight, eighteen, eighteen, etc., electrons. Atoms with the full complement of electrons in their outer shells were stable; those in between were active. Thus hydrogen, with only one electron, would have room for another, hence would be eager to combine with other hydrogen atoms — or with elements like chlorine and fluorine, which also had extra electrons to share. An element like carbon, No. 6, would have four electrons in its outer shell. With room for four more, carbon could combine with a variety of elements into a fantastic number of compounds; and, as any student of organic chemistry knows, it does indeed. Langmuir's theory left room for the correctness of Bohr's, emphasized the strong points of Lewis's and at the same time accounted for the complex and multitudinous activity of the chemical world. Even Langmuir's first paper, says David Harker, "modifies and extends the Lewis theory of atomic and molecular structure to such an extent that it comes close to unifying the whole of chemistry under one theoretical framework. Furthermore, the way in which Langmuir treats the arrangement of the electrons in atoms seems to foreshadow the concepts of quantum mechanics."

"When we remember," Harker says again, "that quantum theory had just been born when Langmuir made his postulates, that neither quantum mechanics with its indeterminacy principle, nor the Pauli exclusion principle had yet been formulated, we can only marvel at the intelligent insight and practical grasp which pervades his concept of atomic structure."

In June of 1918, with the war still on, Sir Ernest Rutherford visited Schenectady, and Langmuir served as his host. At that point, Langmuir was still turning over in his mind his incompletely formed ideas on atomic structure. Never a man for keeping his ideas to himself, Langmuir had already expounded them at great length to his colleagues at GE, inviting their criticism and argument which they were not slow to provide. Now he expounded his ideas enthusiastically to Rutherford, who, much impressed, urged Langmuir to work them into publishable form at the earliest possible moment.

The earliest possible moment came as soon as the war was over. Langmuir's diary of March 1, 1919 reads: "Have been working all month on 'Arrangements of Electrons in Atoms & Molecules.' Most interesting paper to write that I have attempted. New York: Amer Phys Soc meeting. I read 10 min paper on Atomic Structure. Am asked at end of meeting to show slides etc. Talk for 1/2 hr..."

On April 9: "I read paper 1 1/4 hrs (section Inorg & Phys Chem) on Electrons in Atoms & Molecules. It arouses very great interest (more than among physicists)." On April 10: "I am asked to repeat the reading of my paper. E. C. Franklin asks me to take Phys Dept at Stanford Univ. but I am not interested. GE Lab is too good." On April 11: "After night on train, back to Schen. L. W. Jones & Clowes & others called my attention to agreement of my theory with organic comps. I will examine them more fully." On April 12: "Sat: Tel call from Washington to give my paper there. Spend morning in library & afternoon at home studying organic N, S & O compounds. Find wonderful agreement with octet theory."

A heavily technical paper lasting for an hour and fifteen minutes is long even for a scientific meeting. The deliverer of such a paper does extremely well to hold his audience. To be asked to deliver it over again the next day for the benefit of those scientists who, attending other meetings, had been unfortunate enough to miss it, as well as for those who wanted to hear it again, is about as high a compliment as a scientist can be paid. Throughout 1919 Langmuir was giving lectures on atomic structure—in one instance, at the University of Illinois in October, a series of seven lectures. And when he was awarded the Nichols Medal of the American Chemical Society again in 1920, it was for his work in the structure of atoms and molecules.

A cautionary note should be added to keep from overrating the long-term value of Langmuir's atomic theories, and P. W. Bridgman's comment is as good as any for this purpose. "It seems to me," says Bridgman, "that in his octet theory of valence, Langmuir pushed to its legitimate limit, and perhaps even exceeded that limit, his extraordinarily vivid way of looking at things in terms of completely articulated mechanistic detail. Now inside the atom, where the uncertainty principle rules and the electron has lost its individuality, this concrete picture must ultimately fail. Mathematical insight, with its probability amplitudes, takes over, and chemical valence becomes the sort of thing that it is in Pauling's treatment of valence as a resonance phenomenon. It would appear that Langmuir recognized that he was getting into continuously less congenial territory, because after the first burst of papers . . . and after the unpublished foray into the quantum theory in 1920 . . . he discontinued work on the structure of the atom . . ."

Still, many facets of the Langmuir theory remain valid, and

many phases of chemical activity still remain to be better explained than Langmuir's theory explained them. The Lewis–Langmuir atom was an elegant feat of the creative scientific imagination and a landmark in the history of science, and Bernard Jaffe still considers it "the crowning triumph of Langmuir's career."

He had already achieved international fame for his inventions and for his experimental forays into hitherto unexplored regions of science. Now he had proved himself to be a monumental theorist as well. And ahead of him was still most of the work which he, late in life, was to rate as his most important — the surface chemistry studies that brought him the Nobel Prize, and the controversial research in weather control whose mention can still start heated arguments wherever meteorologists gather.

Chapter 13

"The man who has reverence . . . feels in all that lives, but especially in human beings, and most of all in children, something sacred, indefinable, unlimited, something individual and strangely precious, the growing principle of life, an embodied fragment of the dumb striving of the world."

BERTRAND RUSSELL

"TAKE ride in Hupmobile at 5:30 between Troy & Albany," wrote Langmuir in his diary of March 20, 1919. "Get stuck in deep mud & have to dig out with spade. Takes an hours hard work. Kenneth much impressed & rather terrified by seeing wheels spin in mud. He says, 'Poor automobile — lost her feet.' "

The regular appearance in Langmuir's diaries of notes on Kenneth's sayings and doings indicated how much fun he was having being a father. When Kenneth was four the Langmuirs decided it was time to adopt a little sister to keep him company. Her name was Barbara. Soon thereafter Barbara too began being quoted in her father's brief daily entries. He took delight in her amusing "Barbaraisms," as he called them, and, throughout her childhood, recorded them in his diary — e.g.:

"Barbara asks who recess is. Marion tells her that recess is not a person. Barbara insists 'Recess' is a little girl that Kenneth plays with every day at school."

"Barbara shelling peas with Marion puts certain pea pods aside in a pile & when Marion asks why the pile? Barbara: 'I'm going to give them back to Charlie & make him give us new ones. He didn't put any peas in these pods.' "

"Barbara admires someones toilet water but informs person that hers doesn't smell as good. Mrs. X asks B where she gets hers & B says, 'From the toilet, of course.' "

Though Langmuir was already world-famous when Barbara joined the household and was never without a paper to work on at home, he did not disdain to change his daughter's diapers, bathe her, and put her to bed. Langmuir was an interested and a gentle father, always ready to interrupt his work to give the children his attention. He liked taking them on trips, and teaching them skills like skiing, swimming and skating. Though a patient — even an indulgent — father, his patience was not inexhaustible, and he could be a firm disciplinarian. Once, on the way back from Lake George, the children were fighting noisily in the back seat of the car. After repeated admonitions, all ignored, Langmuir finally snapped, "Now stop it at once, or I'll stop the car and spank you both." But the squabble continued with no diminution in the volume of sound. Langmuir pulled over to the side of the road, took out first a protesting Barbara, then Kenneth, spanked them soundly, and redeposited them in the back seat, from which no murmur issued all the rest of the way home.

"Father didn't spank us often," Barbara recalls, "but on the rare occasions when he did, we remembered it." One memorable spanking took place when Barbara, age ten, got into the medicine cabinet and liberally sampled the dog medicine. Afterward, she stood up (the more comfortable position) and wrote "I will not get into the medicine cabinet" a hundred times — misspelling medicine all hundred times. For severe offenses the children would be sent to their rooms alone, a punishment they considered much worse than spanking.

In their early teens, both Kenneth and Barbara were ardent movie fans, and each kept a scrapbook of favorite movie-star cut-outs. One disputatious afternoon when they refused to stop battling for possession of a particularly choice photograph of Greta

Garbo, their father ended the argument by forcibly confiscating the picture and ripping it in half.

Kenneth and Barbara fought only rarely, however, and they were, on the whole, sufficiently well-behaved to make rigorous discipline unnecessary. Most of the time Langmuir could simply enjoy them. His enjoyment of Kenneth was somewhat limited — and vice versa — by Langmuir's insistent attempts to teach science to a boy who had no interest in science. But Barbara was a girl, and since it was not terribly necessary for girls to learn science, she and her father were much freer to enjoy one another.

Barbara had an excellent singing voice, and Langmuir was delighted at her appreciation of the music he himself liked best. He played, for her edification, classical music rolls on the old Pianola he had purchased while still a bachelor. He also played her his operatic and symphonic records by the hour. (Here again Kenneth — though fond of music — was not overenthusiastic about long doses of Wagner and Beethoven.) He told her the stories of all the great operas, especially Wagner's Ring Cycle — "being careful of course to gloss over the immoral parts".

Holidays were always festive occasions in the Langmuir household — Christmas most of all. In the typical American family, the presents are all in a heap under the tree on Christmas morning, and the children indulge in a mammoth gift-unwrapping orgy before breakfast. The Langmuirs preferred to spread the fun of anticipation and discovery over the entire day. Irving and Marion would spend a good part of the day before Christmas thinking up likely hiding places for surprises. Irving would stay up quite late — sometimes until 4 a.m. — taking meticulous pains with the elaborate tree decorations.

On Christmas morning the children were kept happy with small gifts and toys in their stockings. At the breakfast table there would be little surprises — gifts in the napkins, perhaps, and coins (sometimes gold pieces) under the plates. Then more of the same at lunch, as well as a big, homemade snowball full of German Christmas cookies. By late afternoon the children would have found — with the help of parental hints — just about all their presents from

Mother and Father. Then there would be a fancy supper, usually attended by enough guests to make it a real party (Langmuir was always an energetic and high-spirited host). Only then would the presents from their friends and relatives begin to appear. Thus, for Kenneth and Barbara, Christmas would last from the moment they got up in the morning until the final tucking into bed at night.

Though Langmuir was the most considerate and attentive of fathers, he was a man with legendary powers of concentration. As might be expected, he occasionally became so preoccupied with what he was doing that he would be oblivious to all distractions, including the children. He would simply forget they were there. Forgetting they were there was not a serious matter at home. But forgetting them in other places cost Marion many a gray hair. There was a time at Lake George, for example, when Irving, with six-year-old Barbara in tow, got immersed with Apperson in plans for an Adirondack conservation bill they intended to push in the next session of the New York state legislature. The conversation started in the boatyard at Bolton's Landing. Barbara, bored with the talk, wandered around happily inspecting the boats.

A long time passed before she realized that her father and Apperson had both gone and she was alone in the boatyard.

Marion was quite upset when Irving returned alone. "Where is Barbara?" she demanded to know.

"Why — why, she must be with Appie." They quickly found Apperson, whose camp adjoined theirs. "Barbara? Why, I thought she was with Irving."

Barbara meanwhile was walking the mile and a half back to their camp, intuitively taking the right road, but crying bitterly all the way. Incidents like this — happily rare — provided the only occasions in their long marriage when Irving Langmuir was scolded by his wife.

The Langmuirs, like Irving's own parents, did a fair amount of traveling, both in the United States and overseas. When they did, Kenneth and Barbara were often left — as Irving and his brothers had been — with relatives (usually the Mersereaus) or at boarding schools. But the trips that Irving and Marion took were much less frequent, and they did take along the children more often than Irving's parents had. And they always maintained the big house at 1176 Stratford Road as an enduring backdrop for the children's home life.

Kenneth and Barbara were both pridefully conscious of the fact that their father was a famous man. "Gee," said one of Barbara's classmates one day, "I didn't know your dad was important enough to be in the textbooks. You never told me. Aren't you proud of him?"

"Of course I am," said Barbara. "But I was taught never to brag."

Being Langmuir children was not an unalloyed blessing, however. Once, at boarding school, a teacher chided Barbara for not grasping some subject fast enough. "Surely the daughter of Irving Langmuir can do better than *that*."

"Oh, but he's not my *real* father," Barbara would explain.

Unlike Kenneth, Barbara was not at all sensitive about being an adopted child, nor did she feel any obligation to be unfailingly brilliant in her studies. But it was harder for Kenneth. He was a boy, and more was expected of him. It was, in fact, clear to him that he was expected to follow in his father's scientific footsteps. Even geniuses have their blind spots, and Irving Langmuir's blind spot obscured from him the true nature of his son, Kenneth — and the resulting blight on their relationship lasted much longer than it should have. Kenneth was an intelligent and sensitive boy, but his interests ran to the arts rather than to the sciences. He enjoyed the outdoors, but could not work up his father's kind of dedication to the vigorous mountaineering life. He was an easy-going, charming, and good-looking boy with a different outlook on life and with different interests. Langmuir finally came to realize this, and to accept and appreciate Kenneth for what he was.

Kenneth's diffidence as a young boy would probably not have bothered Langmuir as much had he not been so accustomed to being a great favorite with children — especially with boys, who were usually enthralled by the fascinating things he taught them.

"He was like a great big magnet in the neighborhood," recalls Harry Summerhayes, Jr., who was to become a GE engineer and marry his neighbor, Barbara Langmuir. "There was a charged atmosphere around him. Anything he wanted to tell you seemed exciting because he was excited about it. It couldn't seem dull if he thought it was important. If he wanted to tell you about it, you wanted to hear it. And he never talked down to you as far as subject matter was concerned. He always described things in simple, down-to-earth terms, and always thought up graphic demonstrations. And he made it all fun.

"He always had iron and magnesium powders around so he could make fancy-colored fires in the fireplace. He always had a fresh way of looking at things, too. For instance, when there was a pretty sunset, he might bend over and look at it between his legs. It would seem silly, but he would urge you to try it, and when you did you would be amazed at how remarkably fresh and different the sunset looked from this new angle."

When the Langmuirs — Irving, Marion, and their new son Kenneth — went out to California to visit Herbert's family in 1919, they got acquainted with Herbert's four growing boys — Charles, David, Peter, and Alex. The boys — encouraged by their father, who, in earlier days, had encouraged his own younger brother Irving — were already interested in radio and electricity. Sitting on the beach, they fired questions at him from all sides, and he instructed them with gusto, drawing diagrams and circuits in the sand. "Those sessions on the beach," David remembers, "were the first of thousands of hours of instruction we were to get over the years from Uncle Irving."

The Langmuirs took two of the boys, Charles and David, back to Schenectady with them on the train. Choosing the Santa Fe route, Uncle Irving provided them with guidebooks, maps, and plenty of pads and pencils for the train ride. He encouraged them to write down their thoughts and impressions of what they saw, just as his parents had encouraged him and his brothers to write things down. They used up reams of paper in transit, while Uncle

Irving taught them scientific games and string tricks, explained how the mountains had been formed, what made the train run, and the nature of the forces that supported the railroad bridges that took them over the rivers.

Langmuir's nephews, and later his grandnephews, often came to Schenectady or Lake George to spend their vacations, and some of them worked briefly at the GE lab just for the experience. When Herbert's son, Alex, expressed an interest in chemistry, Langmuir started sending him chemicals to analyze. When Arthur's grandson, Donald, got interested in geology, Langmuir took him on half a dozen trips through upper New York state to visit mines and quarries. One summer at Lake George, he outlined an entire course of science study for Donald's older brother, Bruce, and made it a point to instruct him every day, in between meteorological experiments. Langmuir instructed interested youngsters to the limit of their capacity — and occasionally his enthusiasm carried him beyond the limit. There exist several versions of the story about Langmuir expounding the principles of electricity and magnetism while driving from Lake George to Schenectady, only to find that the beneficiaries of the lecture, two exhausted young relatives in the back seat of the car, had slept through most of the discourse.

Langmuir could poke fun at his own over-eagerness in this respect. Once, while David was visiting in the summer of 1922, he noted in his diary: "Leave the lake at 6 am for Schenectady with David. I continue instructing David. Mrs. Smillie, who is Kenneth's nurse, remarked that I had instructed him (David) until she 'should have thought the poor boy was nearly dead'."

When a boy was bright, Langmuir often expected him to be equally bright in all subjects. He was rather impatient when Alex — who showed such promise in chemistry — was slow in catching on to calculus. "Nevertheless," says Alex, "Uncle Irving was the best teacher I ever had. He managed to communicate his own sense of joy and wonder in contemplating the intricate and orderly structure of things, and the intellectual beauty of nature's laws."

While Langmuir lavished his pedagogic attention on his relatives, he did not discriminate against non-relatives. When people came visiting — or when the Langmuirs went visiting — the grown-ups were often neglected by Langmuir in favor of the children, whom he collected around him with the ease of a Pied Piper. Their parents would find them in the back yard, as likely as not, where Langmuir could show them all sorts of tricks using whatever was at hand — sticks, stones, pieces of string, buckets, hoses, and whatnot. He might tie a stone on the end of a string and say, "Now, let's talk about the pendulum." Or he might be whirling a pail of water over his head while the children wondered why the water did not come pouring out of the upside-down bucket. Or he might do the poker-and-compass trick, giving the iron poker a good hard knock with a hammer to loosen its crystals, then magnetizing it. (This trick got him in trouble with a sister-in-law one day when he knocked the brass handle off a prized poker.) If the child was too little to talk or listen, Langmuir would simply bounce him up and down on his knee while chanting:

In phase,
Out of phase.
In phase,
Out of phase.

It was not only science that Langmuir taught to so many boys. He taught them music and chess and swimming. He bought them skates and skis and aqualungs, and taught them how to use them. He took them aquaplaning, airplane riding, and mountain climbing, snorting at them if they were sissies about the cold and snow.

On a variety of camping trips and weekend excursions, more than one generation of boys learned from Langmuir such useful bits of knowledge as how to make a sturdy lean-to on a windy mountaintop, how to hang food on string from high tree branches so the bears couldn't get it, how to drive off snoopy porcupines with a stick and flashlight, how to tell edible mushrooms from the poisonous ones. He explained about the formation of clouds and dew, about the pecking order of birds, and about the geological cataclysms responsible for the peculiar rock formations. He was always one for the direct demonstration. Once, with a group of Boy Scouts who got worried about the ants in their sugar, Langmuir assured them that the ants were not only harmless but nourishing, scooped up a spoonful of the creatures and ate them.

He was as generous with his money as he was with his time and energy. At the beginning of the summer of 1929, for example, when David and Alex were preparing to take jobs for the summer, Uncle Irving impulsively offered them a thousand dollars each to take a trip to Europe instead. He quickly calculated that they should be able to do it for eight hundred dollars each and still have two hundred dollars left over — just about what they would have netted from their summer jobs. Once taken with the idea, he mapped out a suggested itinerary for them, gave them detailed instructions for the climbing of dozens of mountains with which he was intimately acquainted in Switzerland and Germany, told them where they could get the best glass of beer in Göttingen, lent them his movie camera with fourteen hundred feet of film, and furnished them with his old Wagner librettos, profusely annotated from Göttingen days, to help them appreciate the Ring Cycle when they saw it at the opera house in Munich.

Aside from his own young relatives and friends, Langmuir made it a point to furnish the means — and often the personal locomotion — to get underprivileged children into the out-of-doors where they, too, could learn to swim, skate, ski, and climb mountains. Indebted to Langmuir are any number of boys' clubs, boys' camps, children's homes, industrial farms, schools, and the Boy Scouts of America, in whose behalf Langmuir freely spent his money and himself. Anything Langmuir took delight in knowing or doing, he was eager to teach to young boys. And their eager response provided his greatest gratification.

It was not surprising, then, that Langmuir could hardly wait for his own son to grow old enough to start instructing in a similar fashion — a son of his own, available full time in his own home, to mold into a great scientist and outdoorsman. The instruction started early. Poor Kenneth, a captive pupil, felt as trapped as little brother Dean had, back in the old days in Paris. Only Kenneth had no one to holler to for help. His only defense was non-response. The Passive-resistance tactics worked, and Langmuir ultimately had to beat a retreat. He was as disappointed as Kenneth was bewildered. The frustration inherent in this unfulfilled father–son relationship was the closest thing to a dark cloud in the otherwise sunny Langmuir household. But the situation was never permitted to reach the tragic point of open enmity. Langmuir finally did learn to accept his son, and enjoy him for all his fine though nonscientific qualities — and only then was Kenneth finally able to really appreciate his father.

The trouble, if it can be called that, between Kenneth and his father would probably have gone all but unnoticed in any other normally troublesome household. The minor conflict was disturbing only because the Langmuirs lived a close to idyllic family life. The loving understanding and devotion felt and practiced by Irving and Marion Langmuir for one another was the kind of thing one sees on a television soap-opera, thinking: "How corny. How implausible. It just doesn't happen." But in the case of the Langmuirs it happened.

Irving had a standing order with a local florist shop to have flowers delivered to his wife every Monday. And every week, through the years, the flowers came, as a reminder of what they had between them. Their quiet compatibility, which grew over the years they shared, is perhaps best illustrated by a simple incident. They were in New York City, staying at the Prince George Hotel, while Langmuir attended a scientific meeting. It was about four in the afternoon, and Marion was just coming back to the hotel after a shopping tour, when a big Copenhagen Blue vase in a shop window across the street caught her eye. She crossed the street to look at it. As she crossed, she noticed that Irving, too, without seeing her, was crossing the same street. He was crossing it to look at the same vase in the same window.

Naturally, they bought it.

Chapter 14

"It may be observed, in general, that when young men arrive early at fame and repute, if they are of a nature but slightly touched with emulation, this early attainment is apt to extinguish their thirst and satiate their small appetite; whereas the first distinctions of more solid and weighty characters do but stimulate and quicken them and take them away, like a wind, in the pursuit of honor; they look upon these marks and testimonies to their virtue not as a recompense received for what they have already done, but as a pledge given by themselves of what they will perform hereafter, ashamed now to forsake or underlive the credit they have won, or, rather, not to exceed and obscure all that is gone before by the lustre of their following actions."

PLUTARCH'S *Lives*

LANGMUIR was one of those rare minds that could take in whole forests of science without missing a tree. His far-ranging intellectual sorties into new territories were watched with admiration by an ever-growing Langmuir fan club whose members included some of the world's foremost scientists. They appreciated his work for its own sake, of course; but they were also grateful for the fact that his flair for wringing practical applications out of his basic research findings had made it easier for scientists everywhere to get money for their work.

Even in Europe, Dennis Gabor recalls, "we all 'lived on Langmuir' in the sense that whoever wanted to do a little research, not just development, invoked the name of St. Irving. His great successes helped to make the hard-headed businessmen understand that research can pay."

In the years following World War I, as Langmuir's interests broadened and his powers reached full maturity, honor followed honor, culminating in the Nobel Prize in 1932. A bare catalogue of Langmuir's principal awards during this period reveals the astonishing scope of his work. The first postwar medal to arrive, early in 1919, was the Royal Society's 1918 Hughes Medal ("in copper, because of the war"). Then, in 1920 — the same year in which Langmuir's old Göttingen professor, Walther Nernst, was awarded the Nobel Prize — Langmuir won the Rumford Medal of the American Association for the Advancement of Science for his work on thermionic emission and the gas-filled electric lamp. In 1920 he was also awarded, for the second time, the Nichols Medal of the American Chemical Society, this time for his researches in molecular physics and his theory of atomic structure. In 1921 Northwestern University and the University of Edinburgh gave him honorary doctorates. In 1925, his alma mater, Columbia, followed suit.

Also in 1925, Rome's Royal National Academy of Lincei gave Langmuir its coveted Stanislao Cannizzaro Award, calling him "one of the most brilliant and original exponents of the most modern atomistic chemistry and physical chemistry." In 1928, the year after Langmuir invented the atomic hydrogen welding torch, he got the Society of Chemical Industry's Perkin Medal for discovering atomic hydrogen and finding ways to apply it to human needs. In 1929 he was elected President of the American Chemical Society and received honorary doctorates from Princeton University and from Berlin's Technische Hochschule; and Columbia gave him its Chandler Award, named after one of Langmuir's former professors, for his work on the "electrochemical interactions of tungsten, thorium, caesium and oxygen." Langmuir's own private Roaring Twenties ended with the award, in 1930, of the American Chemical Society's Willard Gibbs Medal for fundamental work on atomic hydrogen, surface reactions, high vacua, thermochemistry and catalysis. This was the same year he flew with Charles

Lindbergh and consulted on music reproduction with Leopold Stokowski, whose box he shared at the symphony and whose apartment he used while in Philadelphia.

The pages of Langmuir's diaries during this period — and from then on — are studded with famous names. To report his daily life was, perforce, to be a name-dropper. Lunch might be with Orville Wright or Herbert Hoover. Dinner might be with Charles Kettering or Nicholas Murray Butler. His house guest of the moment might be J. J. Thomson or Guglielmo Marconi. His host might be Lord Rutherford or Max Born. On his travels he always stopped to see his friends, an increasing number of whom were celebrities. And whenever they came to Schenectady (and he often invited them), they stopped at the Langmuirs'. Langmuir liked nearly all of them, and thoroughly enjoyed the stimulation their company provided. He was especially impressed by Charles Kettering, whom he considered "a wonder." And if Langmuir had a scientific idol, it was undoubtedly Niels Bohr.

Langmuir first met Bohr in the fall of 1923. They had corresponded briefly about Langmuir's atomic theories in 1921, but their first face-to-face encounter took place in Amherst, Massachusetts. Bohr had come to Amherst to give a talk on the philosophy of atomic theories, and Langmuir had driven up to hear him. Before the formal evening lecture, the two had had a chance to get acquainted at the home of Professor Howard M. Doughty. Their brief chat turned into a two-hour talkfest, and they were so taken with one another that Bohr rode back to Schenectady with the Langmuirs the following day. He stayed with Irving and Marion for a few days, visiting the General Electric facilities, meeting Langmuir's friends and colleagues, and touring the surrounding countryside. "Never before," wrote Langmuir, "have I met anyone who impresses me more and inspires me more — scientifically — than Bohr." A month later he went to Chicago to hear Bohr lecture again. Over the years Langmuir's respect and affection for Bohr grew into something close to hero worship. During his European visits, Langmuir nearly always stopped in Copenhagen and grew almost equally fond of Bohr's wife and children. Whenever he and Bohr met, Langmuir — never a spendthrift with complimentary remarks — always made some comment in his diary like: "He is the most marvelous man I know."

Langmuir's first postwar journey to Europe took place in the summer of 1921. Combining vacation with his scientific business, he and Marion headed first for Switzerland, where Langmuir, after only a few days of casual hiking around nearby mountains and glaciers, suddenly decided it was high time he climbed the Matterhorn. The fact that he was now past forty did not deter him in the least from tackling the highest of all the Swiss Alps with practically no advance conditioning. He begins his account of the ascent in his diary of August 29, 1921: "Yesterday on train to Zermatt a guide, Alois Pollinger, spoke to us. He has climbed all over the Alps and in the Andes . . . Today we started with him and his 18 yr old son Karl to Matterhorn. Marion had no trouble from altitude of 11,000′. Had tea at Schwartzee Hotel. To bed at 8 pm. Temp. 35°. One foot of snow on the ground on shady side of ridge."

August 30: "I was awakened at 1:50 am and we left at 2:40 am. Beautiful night with thin crescent moon. I found it hard climbing so fast in the dark, soon began to be winded easily. At about 5:30 arrived at Solvay refuge and we stayed there about ¾ hr. Suffered greatly from lack of breath and once or twice from faintness and sudden dizziness. Thought at one time that I could not reach the top. Climbing very uniformly steep, using hands 95—99% of time. But no really difficult places except above the shoulder, where we used the numerous ropes provided. Intense and sudden gusts of wind on top, making it necessary to lie down and hold on to each other. Temp probably about 20°F. Very hazy. Arrive on top at 8:20. Leave at 8:30 am. Arrive at hotel 1:20 pm. Leave 2:30 and arrive Zermatt with Marion at 6 pm. I was very tired (in arms) and winded all way down peak and very stiff in thighs from Matterhorn . . . Down by trail above Stoffel Alp. Next Day: extremely stiff, especially towards night. To bed right after dinner but could not sleep because of pain in right leg above knee. Knee swollen and very sore."

But by the time they reached Paris on September 5, his leg was nearly back to normal again. From Paris they went to London, then hurried on to Edinburgh, where Langmuir was scheduled to attend a conference and pick up an honorary degree. Using the home of Professor E. T. Whittaker as their base of operations, the Langmuirs were able to sightsee a bit before the conference began. They especially enjoyed an excursion to Loch Lomond, the antics of the penguins at the Edinburgh Zoo, and a session of the City Council, whose members sat in red gowns and ermine. Irving even had time to do some hasty, superficial research into the Langmuir family background. Before he left Edinburgh, he had delivered a paper on molecular structure to a distinguished and appreciative audience, participated in a discussion on the quantum theory led by C. G. Darwin and J. W. Nicholson, and was the recipient — along with his friend R. G. Wood of Johns Hopkins — of an honorary LL.D. But the high point of his visit was probably the Royal Society dinner — where he sat next to Lord Rayleigh, his boyhood hero and now one of those doing him honor.

One incident in Edinburgh is worth noting because it is so typically Langmuir. "Go with Whittaker to call on H. S. Allen in afternoon," he wrote on September 14. "Discuss Quantum Theory; particularly ring electrons performing function of both circular and elliptical orbits. I point out error in Allens treatment of elliptical orbits. We discuss possible physical reality of 4-dimensional (relativity) tubes of force... I conclude that Quantum Theory is essentially tied up with relativity theory."

Langmuir was always "pointing out errors" in other men's work. And occasionally the erring soul would get angry, and Langmuir would be surprised and puzzled. He liked other people to correct his own errors — which were not rare, since he did not mind sticking his neck out with positive assertions (such as, for example, the conclusion just quoted about quantum theory and relativity). He assumed, therefore, that others would not mind — in fact, would welcome — his criticism of their ideas. Were not scientists, after all, in pursuit of truth? And was there any real point to making scientific assertions other than to have them held up for critical scrutiny by the scientific community? Part of the fun of science, to Langmuir, was throwing out challenging ideas, then being forced to defend them — and whoever won, the critics or the defender, a closer approximation of the truth was arrived at in the process, and science was the richer for it — and so, therefore, were all scientists.[1]

When Langmuir criticized, there was absolutely nothing personal in it. But since he swooped so eagerly for the attack — eager more for the play of ideas than in proving anyone wrong — if the target of his criticism did not know him, he might feel that the attack was meant to be personal. "Having Langmuir 'point out an error'," one of his old colleagues recalls, "was like having a boulder land on you." His diaries are dotted with entries like one dated October 12, 1912: "Meeting of American Phys Soc. at Columbia Univ. Saw G. A. Pfeiffer & had long talk with Richardson. He cannot adequately defend his theory." There is nothing to indicate that any hard feelings resulted from this discussion, or from the incident in Edingburg, but it is a fact that a few sensitive scientists never forgave Langmuir for the bluntness of his criticism.

From Edinburgh, Langmuir went to Glasgow, where he had to confer about a patent appeal on the gas-filled lamp then pending before the House of Lords. Then to London, where he was "taken sick with Ptomaine from mussels eaten at lunch at the Savoy. Go to the Savoy and tell them about it." From London Irving and Marion went to Paris, where Mama awaited them. One evening they all went to the Folies Bergère. "Very spectacular," Langmuir wrote. "Fine dancing, apparently naked women. Some very immoral plays. Also stomach dance side-show." Next

[1] David Langmuir recalls an occasion when Joseph Becker of the Bell Laboratories wrote a paper which disapproved quite emphatically of a Langmuir theory. Langmuir went back over his experimental data, recalculated, found he had erred, and published a new paper admitting that Becker was right and he was wrong. The two became good friends.

day he took Marion to visit his old École Mange classrooms at the Lycée Carnot and found them "not greatly different from time I was there." They saw Ibsen's *Enemy of the People* at the Comédie Française, and *Faust* at the opera, went to see the Louvre, Napoleon's Tomb, and the Cathedral of Notre Dame. (As with nearly all of Europe's great cathedrals, Langmuir admired the architecture but disapproved of the services — which to his jaundiced, irreligious ear never rang with sincerity.)

After Paris they took in Brussels, Amsterdam and Berlin, stopping to inspect industrial laboratories and attend scientific meetings, and making a side trip to Göttingen, where Irving was able to show Marion his old room by virtue of the fact that "present occupant is out fighting his duel." The Langmuirs still had Frankfort, Munich, Vienna, Budapest and Copenhagen on their itinerary, but an urgently cabled SOS from Whitney in Schenectady made them cut short their trip to Berlin.

Of Langmuir's many travels in the twenties, his 1927 European journey was perhaps the most interesting. He and Marion boarded the S.S. *Rotterdam* on August 7 with an ambitious, conference-laden itinerary ahead of them. But a pall was cast over the whole trip by what seemed like a minor accident on the afternoon of August 12. "At 2 pm while taking a brisk walk on deck," Langmuir wrote, "slipped on wet deck (altho sanded) and broke metatarsal in left foot (next to little toe). Walked on it for a little while but it 'clicked' so I examined foot & found it broken. Dr. Kelly confirmed it."

The doctor bandaged his foot and told him he could walk on it. "But I take no chances," Langmuir wrote, "and ask for crutches and get them." The next day: "Get doctor to loosen bandage. Too tight." Irving and Marion had been planning to head first for the Rhine, then Switzerland, but now they decided to go directly to Paris instead. On August 15 he reported: "X-Ray shows that 2nd and 3rd metatarsal are broken. Go to Hotel Maurice." On August 16: "See doctor again. Will have cast put on as soon as swelling goes down." On August 18 (after many walks in the interim): "Doctor put foot in cast and molds foot to right shape. No pain... Can feel the bones grate together. Get new crutches." On August 28 (after more touring, and lots of walking everywhere): "Walk through Chantilly on crutches. Foot very bad. Much pain. Cast too loose. Doctor says to stay off foot for 8–9 days." And on September 1: "Have foot re-set at Amer. Hospital."

Langmuir's original travel plan would have taken him from Switzerland to Poland to attend a conference on pure and applied chemistry. But on September 2 he wrote: "Have of course given up trip to Warsaw... Plan to stay absolutely quiet in room and then on Sept 9th to Como." He actually put off his Italian journey until the 12th, when he caught the Simplon Express to Milan. By then his foot was feeling much better. He had a wonderful time at Como, where he gave a paper on electrical discharges in gases at low pressures, and had a chance to talk with Bohr and Born, Franck and Fermi, Eddington and Rutherford, Debye and Frenkel, Sommerfeld and Heisenberg, Bragg and Levi-Civita.

From Como the scientists went touring around Italy. In Rome on September 20, Langmuir's foot was feeling well enough to discard his crutches in favor of a cane. But when part of the official tour that afternoon included a visit to Mussolini's villa, where the Italian dictator, strutting up and down, personally received each scientist in turn, Langmuir avoided his turn by pleading his broken foot as an excuse.

By September 27, after Naples and Pompeii, Sorrento and Amalfi, Langmuir was on the Isle of Capri. "Cab to Anacapri," he noted, "and then we climb Mt. Solaro (1920′)... Foot feels better after this climb." By the 30th, en route North again, to Venice, he was writing: "Foot seems to improve every day, but ankle swells every night & needs massaging." Next day, in Venice: "Climb Campanile and take boat to Lido. Go for swim. Foot hurts more when I swim. Feels as if it is broken again."

On October 2: "Arrange at Thos Cook & Sons for auto trip to the Dolomites. Foot is bad. Investigation seems to show that bone is not broken but joint near break is cause of trouble. Probably injured cartilage. Ankle more swollen." On October 3: "Foot bad... Foot feels broken. Can't walk at all." They had taken a gondola to the station, a train to Mestre, and from there, in a rented car with chauffeur, they had driven a hundred and seventy kilometers before stopping at Cortina — a stop destined to last for weeks. While looking for some crutches in Cortina, they came across a small medical institute, and went in. "A Dr. Malagodi (woman) admits us. X-Ray pictures show incomplete consolidation but no new fracture."

The next day, resigned to remaining in Cortina, a daily routine was begun: "3 hrs sun bath on private porch in front of room. Visit by Dr. M. and a few days later also by Prof. Sangiorgi." October 5: "Instituto is an orthopedic hospital. Bone diseases and fractures. Room for about 80–100 patients. 1st, 2nd and 3rd class Heliotherapy. Dr. Vacelli is the director (away this month). Dr. Putti of Bologna visits all patients about every 15 days. Is well known in US." October 7: "Every day Angelo Gandini gives my foot a hot-box treatment. Foot wrapped in cotton and kept 45 min in box heated to 140–170°C by alcohol flame. Foot looks boiled afterwards. Then vigorous massage."

In spite of this treatment, Langmuir was well enough to travel again by October 21, when he left to attend the Solvay Congress in Brussels. His impressive diary entry of the 24th consists of a mere list of the participants in the congress: "Members: Mme Curie, A. Einstein, E. Guye, M. Knudsen, D. Langevin, O. W. Richardson, N. Bohr, M. Born, W. L. Bragg, L. Brillouin, L. V. DeBroglie, A. H. Compton, P. Debye, P. A. M. Dirac, P. Ehrenfest, R. H. Fowler, W. Heisenberg, H. A. Kramers, W. S. Pauli, M. Planck, E. Schrodinger, C. T. R. Wilson, R. Verschaffelt (sectr), E. Henriot, Aug Piccard, T. H. De-Donder and myself." Marion, who had been looking forward to meeting Professor Einstein, was shocked and disappointed at what she considered his unforgivable rudeness. Though he sat next to her at dinner, he addressed not a single word to her. He was so wrapped up in conversation with the neighbor on his other side that he kept his back turned to her throughout the meal and never even acknowledged her presence.

After all the scientific meetings were over, Irving and Marion, along with ten other guests, were picked up one day by King Albert's royal carriage and driven to the palace for lunch with the King, Queen, and Crown Prince of Belgium. On the following day they left for Holland, where they spent a lot of time with Ehrenfest and the Lorentzes. Ehrenfest, who was not only a great music lover but also an accomplished musician, helped Langmuir forget his still-ailing foot by providing a couple of evenings full of Bach, Schubert, Brahms and Mozart. Langmuir was also charmed by Ehrenfest's son: "Shows me his workshop and his mechanical drawings and perspective drawings. I explain to him the match game. He grasps idea of numbers on dual system immediately. He is only 12 years old. Very bright and enthusiastic. He has never been to school." From Holland the Langmuirs headed for Berlin, and to Göttingen again, where Langmuir noted, in semi-scandalized amusement: "Marion likes beer better than ice cream soda!"

Then to Copenhagen for a meeting of the Academy of Sciences, and a delightful visit with the Bohrs — part of the delight, for Langmuir, being Bohr's five little boys, aged from three to twelve. Then to Cambridge for a visit with the Rideals, and to Cavendish Laboratory to lecture and to see Thomson, Rutherford, and Wilson. Then back to Paris to visit several laboratories, including Madame Curie's. And finally home, on the *DeGrasse,* on a stormy sea whose violence, for once, caused Langmuir more apprehension than exultation because of his incompletely healed foot. But on the second day of the storm, when the blow turned into a full gale, when the waves, magnificent with spindrift, seemed fifty feet high, when the heavy spray came six feet over the bow deck, when the chairs tumbled over and upset their occupants, and when three thick windows on the promenade deck were bashed in by the rampaging Atlantic, Langmuir finally could contain himself no longer. He grabbed his movie camera and tramped all over the ship excitedly taking pictures of the storm. Happily, his recklessness did not cost him another spill, and his foot gave him no more real trouble.

He got back to Italy again in 1930, and this time, uncrippled, he was able to ski and climb all over the Apennines. That same trip took him to a major international conference in Germany. At the Harnackhaus of the Kaiser Wilhelm Gesellschaft in Berlin-Dahlem, at an evening meeting well covered by the local press, Langmuir spoke in still-flawless German before an audience of five hundred that included the likes of Einstein, Planck, Nernst, Polanyi, Pirani, Lise Meitner, and Debye — who had come from Leipzig just to hear Langmuir's talk. At the same conference Langmuir had the pleasure of hearing the heads of the Siemens and the AEG Laboratories deliver what Gabor likes to call "sermons based on the St. Irving text" — i.e., justification of their basic research programs by pointing to the success of Irving Langmuir at General Electric.

Chapter 15

"The scientist does not study nature because it is useful. He studies it because he delights in it, and he delights in it because it is beautiful."

HENRI POINCARÉ

IN THE twenties, too Langmuir took up in earnest what was to become a lifetime hobby — Lake George. He had already made the acquaintance of Lake George on camping-and-tramping trips into the great Adirondack wilderness prior to joining the staff of the General Electric laboratory. Arthur and Herbert had known Lake George, too — even before Irving; they had spent summers in the Adirondacks long before he was old enough to go. But after Irving moved to Schenectady in 1909, his geographical proximity made it inevitable that he would become a devotee of that mountain-girdled lake with its sparkling, spring-fed water, its gleaming white-sand bottom, and its hundreds of tiny islands — exactly three hundred and sixty-five of them, legend has it, one for each day of the year; and an extra, elusive one that only gets itself counted on leap year.

Though there is no ideal vantage point from which to take in Lake George's awesome thirty-four-mile-long sweep in a single, overwhelming view, the lake presents a spectacular variety of vistas, and has never lacked the capacity for inspiring devotion in the beholder. The early European settlers of New York, like the Indians before them, had called it "The Holy Lake" or "St. Sacrament." Later travelers, though less reverent, waxed equally lyrical on behalf of the lake's purely secular qualities. "This lake (like Como and Windermere) assumes the character of a noble river flanked by highlands," wrote Benjamin Franklin De Costa in 1868. "Winding sweetly on its way among the verdant hills, it gradually unfolds its wealth of beauty, surprising and delighting the tourist at every advance by some new and exquisite scene."

Of the early friends Langmuir made in Schenectady, no one had a more passionate attachment to Lake George and the great Adirondack wilderness than John S. Apperson, that strapping son of the woods who possessed almost incredible powers of endurance, and who, had he lived in the West in an earlier day America would have had Paul Bunyanesque legends spring up around him by the dozen. The first mention of Apperson in Langmuir's diary appears on September 23, 1910." Saw Apperson about taking trip up to 'his country'." Langmuir and a young friend took their trip up to Apperson's country the very next day. Though Irving, a naturally rapid-striding hiker, was in excellent condition, he complained, in his diary, that Apperson went too fast and had to keep coming back for them. A later entry reads: "7 men reached the top of Mt. Washington yesterday. All but Apperson were frostbitten."

Loyalty to Lake George and its environs — a loyalty one of Langmuir's relatives once called "Lake-Georgeitis" — is a highly communicable disease, and Langmuir was soon infected with Apperson's chronic contagion. Through the years, Carriers Langmuir and Apperson — acting as knowing Typhoid Marys of the disease — did their best to spread it around in epidemic proportions. It did not take long for young Langmuir to start sharing Apperson's concern for the protection of the Lake George–Adriondack area against the encroachments of real-estate agents and timbering interests. It would be hard to estimate the number of days, weeks, and months he spent, all added up over a lifetime, helping Appie organize conservation efforts. Open a Langmuir diary for almost any year, and the fight was in progress. A few scattered examples:

1916: "Apperson came in evening. He wants to start agitation to get the Federal Government to make the Adirondacks a National Park."

1923: "Mr. Coffin called me in to talk re: Lake George & Apperson. Mr. WJ Knapp had previously seen Mr. Coffin & had tried to get Mr. Coffin to stop Apperson. I spoke for some time & convinced Mr. Coffin that our cause (Lake George & conservation) was a good thing."

1928 (Langmuir in New York City to receive the Perkin Medal): "Go to see Nathan Strauss & Raymond Ingersoll to seek their support for Apperson's plan to get 3000 acres of Knapps land for Lake George Park."

1941 (Langmuir in Washington attending meetings of the American Association for the Advancement of Science — of which he was President that year — and the National Academy of Sciences): "Appy calls in the evening re the purchase (by the state of NY) of Knapps Land at Lake George. I spend the evening calling Hugh Bennett. I try to get Eleanor Roosevelt and VP Wallace but can't." Next day: "Telephoning again re Knapp Bill. I find that Eleanor R. is on the Pacific Coast. C. R. Wilson calls me and tells me that he has had a long talk with Lehman. I suggest responsibilities of the GOVERNOR and public resentment at the lumbering of the land if it occurs on Black Mtn."

1944: "Meeting of the Executive Committee, Board of Directors of the Lake George Protective Assoc. of which I am the President. Now 100 members. We retain Counsel to prevent legislature or to prepare injunction if bill passes to intervene on the side of state in the suit against the Paper Co."

Langmuir's enjoyment of Lake George's beauty through nearly half a century made suffering all the symptoms of Lake-George-itis worth while. Aside from the lake's scenic glories, it was absolutely perfect for swimming, sailing, and aquaplaning in the summer, for skating, skate-sailing and skiing in the winter — and for mountain climbing, camping, and the pursuit of out-of-doors science all year round.

Langmuir went up to the lake frequently before he ever met

Marion Mersereau. After they were married, the frequency increased, since Marion was, if anything, even more enthusiastic about the lake than he. They usually camped out or stayed at Apperson's place on their visits. But the visits were always too brief to suit them. On May 27, 1922, Langmuir noted in his diary: "Rent the 'Fo'castle' from the Loins family up on North West Bay at Lake George. Marion & Kenneth will spend the summer there." The next day: "We rent boat for summer from Mr. Styles. We all take trip to Dollar Island.."

In 1924 Langmuir permitted friends to talk him into buying two lots at Lake Sacandaga, where he had a road put in and built a small cabin. But even as he built, Langmuir knew this was no substitute for Lake George. He persuaded himself, however, that it was "worth having as an investment anyway." Early in 1925 he secretly put a down payment on a lot and house on Tongue Mountain, a beautifully elevated spot on the west shore of Lake George, overlooking The Narrows. On April 28 (when, by coincidence, their new Franklin automobile also arrived), Irving presented the new house to Marion as a birthday gift. She was ecstatic over it, and promptly dubbed it "The Playhouse" — which it remained, in fact as well as in name, for a good many years. In the winter of that same year Langmuir bought some more land at Bolton, down the western shore from Tongue Mountain, at the widest part of the lake (about four miles across). The December 13, 1925 diary reads: "We explore our new land purchased from Becher, at Bolton. I make measurements for map (3.6 acres). Talk to William Hill about the work to be done. Then go with children to see F. R. Smith & Sons in Bolton & order him to make 20′ boat, Puffy Doodle model with 18–20 HP Red Wing motor."

Still later, in 1930, Langmuir bought the south half of Crown Island. Now he was well staked out at his beloved lake, which remained, throughout his lifetime, his favorite retreat. Irving, Marion, and the children spent a great deal of time there, summer and winter. Marion's sister, Dorothy — who, despite her charm and good looks, chose never to marry — moved into a house at Bolton's Landing. Lake George became a vacation spot for the entire Langmuir clan, as well as a summertime social center for their friends. At the lake Langmuir did most of his own manual labor, including much that was not essential for mere maintenance — such as designing and building a variety of unorthodox boats, aquaplanes, skates, skis, and skate sails.

Writing in 1933 in the *Journal of Chemical Education,* Katharine B. Blodgett, a longtime colleague of Langmuir's, talked of the hospitality at the Langmuir Schenectady home, then went on to describe the Langmuir's lake life: "In summer time the same hospitality reigns at their camps at Lake George. Indeed Dr. Langmuir, who is his own carpenter at Lake George, whenever time permits, had to spend a week-end last summer [the year of the Nobel Prize award] making a new dining-table for the porch, ever so much larger than the old table, so that it would be large enough for all the guests at their week-end parties. In the spring, after the ice has left the lake, the family move from their snug winter camp on the mainland to spend their summer week-ends and vacation in their camp on an island. There on hot Saturday afternoons one can see the Langmuir motor-boat, the 'Penguin', out on the lake while the family and their guests take turns at riding the aquaplane towed behind the boat. In the fall their shouts can be heard on the wooded slopes of the mountain where they are cutting ski-trails for the winter's sports. In winter there is no weather too cold for skate-sailing and ski-trips — and always 'Father' is the moving spirit behind the outdoor adventures."

Despite the social atmosphere that prevailed at Lake George, Langmuir always managed to get off by himself, whenever he felt the need — to play, to work, or to think. A typical diary entry reads: "Trip to Lake George. Skate to Dome Island. I sail alone down to Pearl Point. Sleigh from Bolton to Calswell. Wonderful ice and scenery." When Langmuir was there alone, or with only other males for company, he loved to plunge into the icy water at daybreak — even when he was past sixty — for a brisk swim in the nude. Always a vigorous swimmer, he often stroked long distances in the lake's unmuddied waters. Once, after a conference in 1935, he invited Professor Wayne Nottingham of the Massachusetts Institute of Technology out to the lake. When they arrived at the lake shore and Langmuir's shouts failed to attract any attention from the island, he stripped quickly down to his shorts, leaped into the water, and swam the two hundred yards to the island. When he returned with the boat he was surprised that Nottingham should think there was anything unusual about this feat.

"But what if you got a cramp?" Nottingham asked.

Langmuir shrugged. "You've got to die some time."

Langmuir often went to Lake George with Kenneth, or with one or more of his nephews or grandnephews. When he did, he would put the boys to work, at everything from chopping wood to helping with his experiments. It was one of his favorite instruction grounds, too, for teaching the sports and the sciences. He also liked to test the youngsters' stamina, and their ability to withstand the elements. Herbert's son, David, remembers a Christmas vacation spent at Lake George when he was a high-school boy, hating to admit how cold he felt because he knew Uncle Irving would call him a sissy if he complained. Uncle Irving always chose the windward side of a mountain to set up his tent. And on the way up he would put up the car's windshield and say, "Oh, *Boy,* but it's windy up here. Doesn't it feel *wonderful*?"

After bedding down for the night in the pitch-black and unheated Playhouse on Tongue Mountain one evening, Langmuir knew that David must be cold, uncomfortable, and perhaps even a little frightened. "We're pretty well off up here, you know, David," he said cheerily. "Listen to that wind howling outside. Think of all the snow piled up. Think of all the hungry and unsheltered people all over the world. Now, if we would think hard about all the people we might be besides ourselves, and all the unpleasant things we might be forced to be doing out there in the cold world, I'll bet we'd pretty soon realize what luxury we've got, lying here with full tummies in our snug bedrolls."

David smiled in the dark and started whistling Schubert's Unfinished Symphony. Uncle Irving picked up the tune. From there they went on to other tunes. They whistled and whistled, and finally they whistled themselves to sleep.

The hazards of Lake George, amid the pleasures, amounted to more than occasional discomfort. There was always real danger to life and limb, and even though Langmuir liked to encourage adventurous behavior, he warned against recklessness and constantly emphasized safety rules. For anyone inclined to carelessness, there was always a sufficiency of incidents to serve as reminders of the built-in perils of Lake George living. One Langmuir entry reads: "Go over to Appys place and find him next door at the Ehlers trying to rescue a Mr. J. O. Butler & his 6 yr old son who had just drowned while canoeing 100 ft from shore. Spent until midnight trying to find some friend to the Butlers in NY to come and take care of the bodies." Sometimes the misfortune hit closer to home, as it did, for example, once in 1922: "Skating on North West Bay. Beautiful black ice. Dorothy stumbles on skates and breaks both bones above ankle of left leg. Carry her on toboggan to car and then down to Ellis Hospital in Schen."

Often at Lake George, while others fished, swam, skated, or just loafed, Langmuir was busily at work — or at play, it is hard to say which — with his instruments, contentedly making observations and measurements, and filling notebook after notebook with data. Some of his experiments were extensions of his GE projects — having to do, for example, with his surface chemistry or meteorological studies — for which he simply used the lake's facilities. (A minor crisis was caused on one guest-filled weekend when a simple experiment consumed the camp's entire supply of toilet paper.) But more and more the lake itself became a major experiment. He had always been addicted — an addiction he shared with that pioneer atomic theorist, John Dalton — to taking temperatures and noting them down wherever he went. At Lake George he began doing this systematically. First thing in the morning he would get out his thermometer and notebook, wave the thermometer in the air, take wet and dry bulb temperatures, and write them down. He would record humidity, barometric pressure, water temperatures and depth soundings, and with each passing year he devised or borrowed new and more sophisticated instruments for what grew into a mammoth, marathon study of the "energy budget" of Lake George. In good weather he would go out in his boat. In winter he would take out a sledge and dig holes in the ice. No matter what the weather, he devised ways to continue getting his data.

As Vincent J. Schaefer points out, Langmuir had been interested in hydrodynamics at least since his studies, published in 1922, with Harold Mott-Smith, of the flow patterns in rotating liquids. Langmuir was also known to have been fascinated with wave-patterns in the ocean, which he would stand and watch for hours at a time from the boat deck during his numerous trips to Europe. He was intrigued by the action of wind on waves, and curious about the mechanism of the energy transfer that took place in the process. It was on his 1927 trip, while crossing the Gulf Stream just a few days before he fell and broke that troublesome metatarsal, that he made the following observation: "Dead calm. Sea glassy. Lots of Flying Fish. Long strings of bunches of seaweed in parallel lines in direction of the wind. I conclude the lines mark the places of max. surface currents and are due to meeting of transverse currents. Vertical down meeting under seaweed."

The strange, straight windrows of seaweed bothered Langmuir enough to bring the subject up in Cambridge, near the end of his trip, in a conversation with Sir Hugh Taylor and Horace Lamb. "At 8 pm Audit Feast at Trinity as guest of Sir JJ. Afterwards in Combination Room I talk with Taylor on streaks of seaweed in sea. He (and Lamb) cannot explain my observations."

Langmuir had seen such streaks wherever he had seen the fetch of wind acting upon an open expanse of the Atlantic. The more he thought about it, the more convinced he became that the streaks of seaweed he had seen must have been blown all the way from the Sargasso Sea a thousand miles away — quite a transmission of energy from wind to water. The seaweed must line up, he felt, along the rims created by the vortices of wind currents when they met. He checked this theory back at Lake George. "By simple, but carefully planned experiments, using such apparatus as oriented umbrellas and lampbulb floats," Kenneth Kingdon writes, "Langmuir was able to establish that the windrows were caused by wind-induced circulation of the surface water, the water on the surface flowing towards the windrows, downwards under them and up again at a point halfway between them." He continued for many years to carry out experiments at Lake George on the interrelation of wind and water, and the mechanics of heat and energy transmission, establishing new hydraulic principles that have been very useful to oceanographers. He also believed he could account for a number of strange-looking natural phenomena that probably explained many reported sightings of "sea serpents."

"The helical vortices he studied and described were only a small portion of his interest in the interaction between air and water," writes Schaefer. "His largest unpublished work is concerned with the heat and energy budget of Lake George. Using one of the very first bathythermographs invented and constructed by Dr. Athelstan Spilhaus, Langmuir initiated a series of temperature–depth soundings which eventually consisted of more than two thousand such observations made at various stations on Lake George. Based on his Crown Island camp and using motorboat, ice skates, or skis, depending on the nature of the lake surface, Langmuir would measure the temperature of the air and water, the wind velocity and direction and other pertinent atmospheric and water conditions during all types of weather, and at many stations on the lake. Since many of his stations were at locations where the lake was more than 150 feet deep, he used triangulation with shore line and mountain top reference points to fix positions. After World War II a war surplus lifeboat sextant was a treasured instrument.

"Shortly before his death he assembled all of his notebooks, maps, slides, voluminous graphs and reduced data, apparently with the plan to write a paper on this labor of love. This was not completed. All of the data is now in the collection of scientific papers assembled by the writer [Schaefer] and donated to the Library of Congress by Mrs. Marion Langmuir. It probably represents the finest collection of such field observations in existence."

Langmuir's monumental study of Lake George is unique. And when some energetic young man puts it all together — perhaps as a project for a doctoral thesis — and has it published, scientists will know a great deal more than they now know about the patterns of wind and water, the specific mechanisms of heat and energy transfer, and the life cycles of lakes. Yet Langmuir began it all, and continued it throughout the years, just for the fun of it.

As early as a September afternoon in 1926, his nephew Alex — David's brother — remembers Uncle Irving at the lake building a new thermometer — a piece of glass tubing around which he wrapped nichrome wire, then mounted it inside a copper tube. By the time more wires were added, and a cable, and a drum, and a battery, it was a fairly complicated gadget they took out on the boat with them. "Complete Temp Indicator," Langmuir noted, "& in evening we measure temp of Lake. 46° at 174′ depth between Dome Island & Buck Mtn. 66° at surface." The diaries are full of entries like: "With Marion made up sounding line to measure depth of Lake George through ice." Or: "Stay at Crown Island. Build 2 sounding devices; one with steel wire; one with silk line. Bathythermograph data & soundings. Return to Schen."

DeWolf Gibson, well grown into manhood by then, all unsuspectingly paid his old friend, neighbor and mentor a visit at Lake George one windy day, and got trapped into helping Langmuir with his experiments. He had to cut up long strips of red and white cloth, then toss them out of the speedboat — the red on one side, the white on the other — and take pictures while Langmuir eased back to observe the way the colored strips lined up in the wind-whipped water. On one occasion Marion lost a gaily striped and colored umbrella to this kind of experiment.

In the speech he made before Irving's departure to receive the Nobel Prize, Arthur Langmuir recalled: "Last October I was with Irving in a motor boat at Lake George proceeding from his camp on Crown Island against a moderate sea. I noticed that he was timing the waves with a stop watch and he pointed out to me that a wave large enough to have a white cap is nearly always followed by another wave with a white crest. He said that he thought he had worked out the most accurate and convenient method for the determination of wave lengths and wave heights and had developed a formula which would indicate the height of the wave if you determined the time interval between two successive white caps. By this method one could find the height of waves seen through field glasses a mile away."

Many a tourist must have scratched his head in wonder as Langmuir sat, unmoving, for hours at a time in his boat, observing the gentle driftings of strips of rag — a man sitting way out there like that, without even a fishing rod in his hand. People are known to have gone to his aid, thinking he was stranded out in the middle of the lake with a dead motor and no oars. One freezing morning, after Langmuir had vigorously whirled his thermometer, made his notes, then lay down belly-flat on the ice to study the ice surface with his pocket magnifying lens, he noticed — as he got up to brush off the front of his clothes — that two strangers were watching him. As one spoke to the other, his voice carrying farther in the crisp, icy air than he realized, Langmuir could not help overhearing the remark: "I wonder who *that* idiot is?" Langmuir grinned at them with an idiot grin, then, as they went on their way, he went about his business.

Chapter 16

"My son, who was by this time come up with me, followed the whirlwind till it left the woods and crossed an old tobacco field, where, finding neither dust nor leaves to take it up, it gradually becomes invisible below as it went away over that field. The course of the general wind then blowing was along with us as we travelled, and the progressive motion of the whirlwind was in a direction nearly opposite, though it did not keep a straight line nor was its progressive motion uniform, it making little sallies on either hand as it went, proceeding sometimes faster and sometimes slower, and seeming sometimes for a few seconds almost stationary, then starting forward pretty fast again. When we rejoined the company, they were admiring the vast height of the leaves now brought by the common wind over our heads. These leaves accompanied us as we travelled, some falling now and then about us, and some not reaching the ground till we had gone near three miles from the place where we first saw the whirlwind begin.

"Upon my asking Colonel Tasker if such whirlwinds were common in Maryland, he answered pleasantly: 'No, not at all common; but we got this on purpose to treat Mr. Franklin.'

"The rest of the company stood looking after it, but, my curiosity being stronger, I followed it, riding close by its side."

BENJAMIN FRANKLIN

ANOTHER enduring hobby which Langmuir began in the twenties was flying. Once, back in 1911, when he still felt it was daring to flirt with the idea of buying a motor car, he found himself in the middle of an enthusiastic conversation about the airplane.

The discussion took place at Barney's in Schenectady, the site of an informal weekly luncheon meeting. Lunch at Barney's was almost invariably centered around Whitney, who served as unofficial moderator for the small group of GE scientists — usually including Langmuir — who came along. There was never an agenda. The talk drifted where it would. It might be about science; it might be about politics or philosophy; or it might be a mere trading of stories and shop gossip. Any visiting scientists who happened to be on the premises on lunch-at-Barney's day were of course invited along.

On this occasion, Whitney's old M.I.T. colleague, Professor A. A. Noyes, was in town, and at the luncheon table the talk somehow turned to aviation. Whitney turned out to be the most enthusiastic apostle of the airplane. He not only believed it was here to stay; he was emphatically convinced that it was going to exercise a profound influence on the future of men and nations.

As they talked about flying, the idea captivated Langmuir's imagination. It would be fun to go up there and be able to soar among the clouds — as much fun, perhaps, as zooming down a steep and winding ski slope in winter, or whipping, wind-driven, across the Lake George ice while hanging onto a skatesail. That summer — on August 23, 1911 — he saw his first plane in flight. According to his diary, the pilot was Atwood, on his way from New York to St. Louis. But the craft was too far away — about a mile, Langmuir estimated — to get a good view of it. A few weeks later, he was thrilled to see an airplane at close range — even though it was still in its crate, in the railroad station at Albany.

Though he was eager to fly, airplanes were too rare to be readily available in those days. Taking a plane ride would require a lot of arranging — and Langmuir's myriad other preoccupations kept him from doing anything about his desire to go aloft. The desire was not fulfilled until shortly after World War I. He of course made a note of the experience in his diary. The date was April 28, 1919, and he was in Washington. "Go to meeting at Smithsonian Inst.," he wrote, "then to Naval Air Station & go up for 15 min in Seaplane, down Potomac, max. elevation 350 ft. Very fine feeling. My first airplane ride."

From then on, Langmuir flew whenever the rare opportunity arose. Marion had always been apprehensive about the idea of flying (and remained so, for the most part), but Irving was finally able to persuade her to try the experience one day in 1928. His entry for April 5, 1928, reads: "Major Button invites Marion & me to fly over Schenectady in Fairchild 6 seater plane (monoplane). We have 10 min flight." It was apparently around this time that Langmuir was taken with the idea that he might become a pilot himself, and perhaps even get his own plane. It would provide fun, a quick means of transportation and perhaps even a new tool for expanded scientific studies. His diary for June 15, 1928: "60 min flight with Ricard in 6 passenger Stinson Detroiter." November 9, 1928: "1 hour and 1/2 in Ricards Stinson. Flew it myself for 30–40 min. Part of time by instruments in the clouds. Ricard flew in Vertical Banks. Extraordinary feeling but no sense of rotation. Also zoomed over the airport." The very next day: "On way to lake we stopped at Airport & took the children for their first airplane flight." About two weeks later Langmuir went to the aircraft show in Chicago, carefully looking over planes and making voluminous notes. He obviously had been bitten by the flying bug quite seriously.

He stayed over in Chicago to attend an international aeronautical conference. Then: "Fly from Chicago to Dayton. Capt Breene in 3-motored Fokker. 250 miles in 2 hrs and 20 min. Then reception at Engineers Club by Maj Gen Gilmartin. I was in cockpit with pilot, using map."

Early in January of 1929, one of the visitors to the General Electric laboratory was Colonel Charles A. Lindbergh. Langmuir liked him instantly. "Lindbergh was wonderful," he wrote that evening. "Very sincere, frank and keen; he concentrates on the subject being discussed. He gave us many pointers."[1] Obviously

[1] Lindbergh's visit to Schenectady gave Langmuir another "Barbaraism" to record in his diary: "She told someone recently that I assorted Lindbergh thru the works."

Langmuir asked his advice about airplanes. "He advises not getting a machine with a very low landing speed." In the course of their conversation during the day, Lindbergh succeeded in getting Langmuir interested in a number of technical problems — such as improving airport lighting and devising new navigation aids — which he felt needed prompt and imaginative attention. Whitney soon got wind of this. Though he had early prophesied the importance of aviation and was as eager as anyone to see the airplane fulfill its promise, he did not like the idea of his most valuable scientist — who already had plenty of perilous pastimes — taking up still another. "Whitney tells me," Langmuir wrote, "he doesn't want me to work on aeronautical problems which will require me to fly, because of the danger. We'll see!"

The "We'll see!" of course meant that Langmuir had no intention of curtailing his interest in flying. As it worked out, the year 1929 was full of so many other things that his airborne life was limited to commercial flights to scientific meetings, to a flight or two with his friend, Alex Stevenson, and to a couple of frisky amphibious cavortings over Lake Saragota in a pontoon craft with his brilliant colleague Alexanderson. Most of the early part of 1930 was spent in Europe, and it was nearly summer again before he had the chance to do a little flying with another colleague, Vaughn Ferguson. Though Langmuir's other activities and responsibilities did not diminish in the least, he felt that, at the age of forty-nine, he should not procrastinate any longer. His diary of August 13, 1930, reads (the capitals and the underlining are his): "I DECIDE TO TAKE AIRPLANE LESSONS & take 20 minutes in about 4 straight courses learning to operate stick only (no turns). Seems easy. Waterman pilot."

The next day, August 14: "Rain so no lesson. But I take medical exam with Dr. Greene and Stanton. All OK except vision *without glasses* is not up to requirements. Greene must write to Washington for permission to issue students license in this case."

August 15: "Before driving to Lake George 7:30 pm, I have 2nd lesson (15 min). This time make turns, banking up to 30°. Gradually get the feel of proper banking. Have tendency to bank too much."

August 18: "3rd airplane lesson. 45 min (making 80 min total) with Harold Bowen pilot (fun!). Very thrilling. Climb and Glide — turns with 45° banks. Stalls with or without the engine on. These greatly increase my confidence."

August 19: "45 min flight with Bowen. I take off twice, also taxi once across the field and glide down for landing. Try some figure 8s but my turns are poor today (too little stick). Not as good as yesterday. At night (1 pm) I get up and build 'bank indicator.' Brass chain twisted 4 strands."

By September there was no doubt in Langmuir's mind — or his instructor's — that he was going to become a fullfledged pilot. On September 26, two days after buying the Crown Island camp at Lake George, Langmuir drove Kenneth up to his new boarding school (the Storm King School), and came back and picked up his flight instructor, Harold Bowen. Together they caught the 7:38 train to Dayton. From the Dayton station in the morning they took a taxi out to the Waco factory in Troy, Ohio, bought a Waco F monoplane with a Scarab motor, watched it being flight-tested, decided it needed another propellor, had it changed, then took off. They were in Cleveland by early afternoon, and by evening in Syracuse, where they spent the night. Next morning they flew into Schenectady. Thereafter plane-owner Langmuir flew nearly every day, steadily improving his flying skill. By October 3, he was writing: "Discovered cause of my failure to make 3-point landings — did not look at ground side (wing) & lost view forward as tail came down. Today I watched ground under left wing for last 10 feet & made a couple of 3-point landings."

On October 4: "1:30 pm: ½ hr up with Bowen. 3 good and 2 poor landings. ½ hr inspecting plane and engine. ½ hr more with Bowen — good landings. He says enough for today — to come out early Sunday, but I must go to NY. So again at 5:15 after walking around field. He makes no promises. Then 2 times around with Bowen and then: My SOLO flight. Good Landing."[1]

[1] Writing about this flight in a later article about Langmuir in the *New York Times Magazine,* John Pfeiffer said: "His first solo flight has become a legend. An instructor watched anxiously as his enthusiastic pupil took off, gained alti-

He could hardly stand not going up to fly again the next day, but it was Mama's eighty-second birthday and the clan was gathering at Arthur's home in Hastings-on-Hudson, so he and Marion had to drive down early. But on the 6th they left early for Schenectady, and by afternoon he was out at the airport again.

On October 31 Lindbergh returned to Schenectady, this time bringing Mrs. Lindbergh with him. At lunch at the Mohawk Club, Langmuir proudly told Lindbergh that he was now solo-flying his own Waco F. Lindbergh, quite pleased, asked: "Well, now which do you like better — flying or skiing?"

Bluntly honest as ever, Langmuir promptly answered, "Skiing!" and eyebrows were raised in surprise all around the table.

After the Lindberghs had spent the afternoon touring the laboratory, they joined the Langmuirs for dinner at the Van Curler Hotel, then the two men went out to the airport. "At airport," Langmuir wrote, "Lindbergh takes me up in his Bird Plane (over city) at 9 pm." While they were up, they fell to discussing again the problem of better airport beacons, and Lindbergh suggested that Langmuir carry out a series of experiments on light scattering, which Langmuir later did, using a simple mixture of milk and water as his principal research tool. These experiments, incidentally, laid the foundation for the blinking lights later used at airports everywhere.

"During the period of his active interest in aviation," Vincent Schaefer writes, "Langmuir became quite concerned about improvements needed in producing better light signals to increase

---

tude and performed other routine maneuvers. Then the plane suddenly went into a tailspin. For a long half minute the instructor and other observers on the ground held their breath. Finally, by a seeming miracle, the plane righted itself and made a good landing. The novice pilot soon explained everything — he had gone into the tailspin on purpose, just to see what would happen. On hearing of this stunt, a few months later, Lindbergh was so flabbergasted that he could only mutter: 'I never take unnecessary risks.' " Since it was also Langmuir's stated policy never to take unnecessary risks, and since this is the lesson he constantly preached to his children and nephews, the whole incident seems out of character, and "legend" may indeed be the proper word to apply. However, Langmuir *is* known to have been reckless on occasion, and one recalls his remark to Wayne Nottingham after swimming to Crown Island: "You've got to die some time." So it *could* have happened.

the safety of aerial navigation. With Westendorp, who had recently arrived from Holland to join the Research Laboratory staff, he conducted a series of simple but very pertinent experiments dealing with light signals. Such things as the relative visibility of various colored lights, the comparative value of steady versus blinking lights, light intensity and visual acuity were explored. The results of these studies had a considerable influence on the development of adequate facilities in the then rapidly expanding field of aerial navigation. In these recent years when Doppler navigation, the use of radar, radio beams, and many other electric aids are in commonplace usage, the importance of the pioneering work of Langmuir toward improving flight facilities during the 'kerosene lantern on a fence post' period has all but been forgotten."

Less than a week after his brief flight with Lindbergh, on November 5, 1930, Langmuir noted: "Took written exam! . . . Then flight test . . . PASSED!" and on November 26: "Received Private Pilots License No. 17763." Thereafter, weather permitting, many of the family trips — as well as his shorter-distance business trips — were taken in the plane. The children loved flying. Even Marion did not mind. She never did get over her fear of flying in commercial airliners; but she had such complete confidence that nothing would *dare* go wrong with Irving at the controls that she could relax and enjoy the flights nearly as much as he and the children did.

Langmuir not only enjoyed flying; he enjoyed flyers. In Europe early in 1931, he had a long, detailed, technical talk with Dr. Hugo Eckener, captain of the Graf Zeppelin, and invited him to Schenectady. In July of the same year he went to a Chamber of Commerce luncheon honoring Post and Gatty after their return from their round-the-world flight. "I sat next to Gatty, the navigator of the 8 day 16 hr round the world plane trip," he wrote. "Later I sat in the cockpit of the Winnie Mac & had Gattys instruments explained to me. He used gyroscopic horizon & gyroscopic flight course indicator; set by compass every ½ hr."

Langmuir of course kept in mind the uses of science when he flew. Some of the uses were specific. For example, on August 31, 1932: "With Marion & David saw Total Eclipse of sun from our airplane at 9000′ above Rochester, NH... Carried meteorograph for Chas F. Brooks, Blue Hill Obs. (Director)." But most of the scientific use that came of his flights was simply due to the fact that Langmuir, the scientist-anytime-anywhere, was the man sitting up there watching the play of clouds and sunlight, just as he had watched the play of wind and water below. His observations during those early flying days contributed a great deal to his later experiments in weather control. "One of Langmuir's joys in flying," says Schaefer, "consisted of 'cloud dodging.' On a day with the skies well populated with cumulus or stratus clouds he would go aloft alone or with a friend and make a game of brushing the clouds with the wing or wheels or cockpit of the plane. It was during one such flight he noticed that stratus clouds were often so stable that persistent wheel tracks could be made on their upper surface when lightly touched during precision flying. During such maneuvers he also became familiar with some of the optical effects produced by sunlight falling on clouds. I learned a great deal from him about coronas, glories, halos, sun pillars, sun dogs, under suns and related phenomena. He never tired of telling about these effects, photographing them and getting others to notice them."

Yes, Langmuir was the same enthusiastic instructor-of-all in the air as he was on the ground. He never tired of explaining the mechanics of flight or pointing out the wonders of the skies. He even urged his passengers to try their hands at flying themselves The plane also provided Langmuir with another treat for children. He had always taken them skiing, skating, and mountain climbing. Now he took them up in his airplane. And if a boy was intelligent and responsible — like young Aubrey Coyle — Langmuir would let him fly the plane for a while. Vincent Schaefer clearly remembers his own first experience in Langmuir's Waco. "I had just organized a winter sports club and was in the process of negotiating with several railroad companies toward operating a snow train from Schenectady. Langmuir offered to take me on an exploratory flight to search for suitable ski areas. I met him at his home and went to the airport where with some apprehension I climbed into the two seater open cockpit airplane. In a rather casual way he showed me how to fasten my seat belt, a mechanic spun the propeller and in a short time we were airborne. Reaching about 5000 feet Langmuir showed me the basic maneuvers, the stick and rudder controls and then told me to take over! After flying until I had the feel of the aircraft he then had me stall and recover, bank, turn, climb and dive. We then headed for the Catskills and spent the next several hours exploring that area for suitable ski slopes near railroad facilities. Upon our return to the airport I was so cold I could hardly climb out of the airplane and remained in a numbed condition until thawed out with some hot tea at his home."

In 1934 Langmuir sold his old Waco and bought a new one, which Harold Bowen flew in for him from Ohio. But before the thirties were over, Langmuir had decided to give up private flying. "His reasons were adequate," says Schaefer. "He became convinced that the uncertain flying weather of the northeastern United States made the use of a private plane of questionable value for business trips. Perhaps the more important reason for his decision lay in the increasing number of rules and regulations which more and more restricted the flyer who flew for the fun of it." Langmuir wrote an article of complaint called "Air Traffic Regulations as Applied to Private Aviation" for *The Sportsman Pilot* in 1937. "The crowning blow as I remember it," says Schaefer, "was a ruling that flight log books not only had to be of a certain size but must have a cover of a particular color. This to Langmuir was too much and he went out and sold his plane."

Naturally Langmuir did not give up flying altogether. He did a great deal of flying in commercial, military and private aircraft, and would occasionally take the controls. Once, in 1944, he flew a B-17 most of the way from Minneapolis to Lafayette, Indiana. And he began flyng quite a lot for his cloud-seeding experiments during and after World War II. The armed services, Mrs. Langmuir recalls, set a ceiling of ten thousand feet for Langmuir flights, deciding it was dangerous for a man of his age to go any higher. Langmuir ignored the ceiling, and repeatedly flew much higher. During cloud-seeding projects in Central America he frightened passengers occasionally by flying over the craters of simmering volcanoes to see what went on inside. But one sobering Central American experience finally made him decide to stay closer to the ground. He tells about it in his diary of April 20, 1949: "Still no dry ice. We try water balloon seeding. 15 balloons. Take off at 1:50 pm. Reach 22,000′ and I get oxygen jag. Lose my memory of flight. Don't eat supper and go to bed tired. I don't know where I am all night. I don't recognize room." Next day: "Take all day to get over the oxygen jag. Headache (migraine) and no appetite." Langmuir, at the time, had passed his sixty-eighth birthday.

The same year — 1930 — that Langmuir was getting to know Lindbergh, he was also getting to know Leopold Stokowski, who was then conducting the Philadelphia Orchestra. Where the common bond of interest with Lindbergh was aviation, with Stokowski it was music. (Actually Lindbergh and Stokowski were both men with interests much broader than their own specialized fields, and both had first-rate technical minds.) Since his fascination with binaural sound in World War I days Langmuir had been intending to look into ways to improve sound recording. What brought his interest into sharp focus during the year 1930 was a chance meeting on a boat, the *Minnetonka* (he had had reservations on the S.S. *Paris,* but a strike of the engine-room force and kitchen employees held up the sailing). The deck chairs next to the Langmuirs' were occupied by a Mrs. R. P. Crum and her fourteen-year-old son, Bobby. "Bobby is a musical genius," Langmuir wrote, "and serene disposition. Takes any given theme and improvises beautifully on piano. He has recently in Paris produced (recorded) on Columbia records: Walkyre, Manon, Carmen, Schuberts Trio and some of the Beethoven Symphonies." The next day, March 18, Langmuir noted: "I give Bobby 3 themes (written) for him to compose piece without going to piano." The Langmuirs and Crums grew very friendly on the voyage home. They even visited the engine room together and Langmuir enjoyed explaining to Bobby how the turbines worked.

In July Bobby came to Schenectady. The Italian astronomer Giorgio Abetti and his wife — who had extended their hospitality to the Langmuirs earlier in the year at the Observatorio Arcetri near Florence — had returned the visit, and were just leaving Schenectady when Bobby Crum arrived, on July 17, on the overnight sleeper from Pittsburgh. "He plays his composition based on the first 2 themes I gave him on the steamer," Langmuir's diary reads. "We ask AG Davis and Polly to listen to him after lunch. He has repertoire of 368 pieces (plus) learned since March. We listen to him all evening."

The next day, July 18: "Bobby works on composition. In the evening go to the Playhouse." July 19: "At Lake George: We all climb Shelving Rock and pick Blue Berries in the afternoon. Evening at Ranger Island." July 20: "Up Buck Mtn. with Bobby." July 21: "Bobby plays 1/2 hr Brahms, Rhapsody No. 2. Also his own composition. At home."[1]

Then, on July 23: "New York: Buy clothes for Kenneth. Then I go to see Aylesworth and AG Davis at the National Broadcasting Co. offices on 5th Ave. I give them my plans for 5 Groups of men to work on research for RCA Victor, to:

1. Perfect Loud Speaker.
2. Study of Ear and its ability to hear various sounds.
3. Perfect method of recording sound.
4. Methods of creating and recording *new* sounds of any desired character.
5. Musical Talent to utilize and to create new music."

---

[1] There is no further mention of Bobby Crum in Langmuir's diary until the year 1946. The Crums had disappeared, and now Bobby, aged thirty, reappeared playing at the Town House Night Club in Albany, playing five performances a night, seven nights a week. He came to see Langmuir on January 19 on the 4:30 train, and the Langmuirs drove him back. Langmuir was naturally quite distressed to see that the young musical genius who had demonstrated such marvelous potential had come no farther in the intervening years than drudgery in an out-of-the-way night club. But he didn't know what he could do about it.

It was Aylesworth who put Langmuir in touch with Stokowski, who was also very much interested in improving the quality of sound recording. "I was very happy to receive your letter," Stokowski wrote, on August 14. "I hope to be able to go to Schenectady about August 21. I have read with great interest your letter and am eagerly looking forward to talking over with you some of the problems we both have in mind. I have planned, in any case, to go to the laboratory of the R.C.A. in Camden, so I hope we can both be there at the same time to discuss the questions which interest us all.

"I forgot to mention in my previous letter that I am very interested in Light, Color, and our reactions to color in the home and to colored light in theaters and concert halls."

Stokowski did get to Schenectady toward the end of August, but Langmuir was too busy with experiments, with flying lessons, and with negotiations for the Crown Island property, to make any diary entries that week. Right after he had soloed in his Waco, Langmuir wrote Stokowski again, and Stokowski promptly replied (on October 9). "When you come to Philadelphia," he wrote,

---

On January 23 Bobby came back again. He had gone to the studio of Carl Lamb in Albany after finishing his stint at the Town House the night before, and had stayed up from 3:00 a. m. to 10:00 a. m. recording his own music about Langmuir, for Langmuir. Langmuir was of course much moved by this tribute. His diary entry simply reads: "Robert Crum comes over from Albany and brings me 4 two-sided records . . . based on the themes that I gave him when we met on the *Georgic* in 1928 (returning from Europe). There is an Introduction (our meeting) and the story of music in the future etc. Marion and I take him back to Albany at 6 and stay until midnight."

(Langmuir's memory was inaccurate on this occasion; he had the wrong trip in mind. His own diaries of the period show that he met Bobby on the *Minnetonka* in 1930, not on the *Georgic* in 1928.)

Over a year later — on November 28, 1947 — the Crums turned up again in Schenectady. "We find the Crums (Bobby and his mother) are at the Mohawk Hotel," Langmuir wrote. "Broke and half starved. Bobby has an engagement in Des Moines, Iowa but doesn't have the money to get out of the hotel or travel. Mrs. Crum has been locked out of her room. Bobby sick in bed. I see Mr. Blodgett [a lawyer] re what to do about helping them. We wire Des Moines and get an OK for him to arrive late. I give them enough money to complete the trip."

Langmuir never heard from the Crums again. They disappeared without leaving a forwarding address. This experience affected Langmuir profoundly. To him there was no tragedy more tragic than the waste of genius.

after some preliminaries, "I hope you will come to stay with me as my guest. I have an apartment which is on the edge of Fairmount Park, so that in two minutes one can be walking in quite wild and untouched nature, and it only takes fifteen minutes to drive into town — with plenty of taxis always to be had. If you could stay here with me you would have complete privacy, because you would not be actually in my apartment, and we would only be together when we would both have free time. There would probably be much we would like to talk over together, and then I would like to take you to a rehearsal or two with the Orchestra if you would have time, so that we could study certain questions of tone. But above all I want you to feel absolutely free to do whatever you like because that is the only way I can live myself, and I imagine that everybody who is doing much work has the same feeling."

"I had a talk with Mr. Aylesworth," Stokowski went on, in that same letter, "which was — in the main — satisfactory, and I should like to tell you about it when you come here. The chief point was that he told me of his conversation with you, and assured me that he absolutely intended to carry out your plans. And that he hoped I would cooperate — which I of course told him I would be delighted to do."

Langmuir came to Philadelphia on October 28 and went directly to Stokowski's apartment. He was charmed by Stokowski, and delighted by his interest in, and ability to grasp, rather complicated technical matters. Stokowski, for his part, was fascinated by Langmuir's description of his World War I research and his ideas for new research, and was pleased and surprised at Langmuir's knowledge of music and his keen ear for musical tone. The following day they went to the Academy of Music, where Langmuir heard Stokowski conduct Stravinsky's *Sacre du Printemps.* "Wonderful," he wrote. Then he and Stokowski had lunch at the Art Club with E. W. Kellogg of the RCA Victor Laboratory. After lunch Kellogg took them over to the laboratory — in Camden, New Jersey, across the Delaware River — for a long visit. Langmuir had many good words to say about the research going on at RCA Victor, but also suggested a number of ways in which research might be improved and expanded. In his typically blunt way, too, he took issue with Kellogg regarding some views on the acoustical design of auditoriums which Kellogg had expressed in a paper published in the *Journal of the Society of Motion Picture Engineers* earlier in the year. Kellogg took it well, even discussed Langmuir's criticism in some detail in a closely-typewritten nine-page engineering memorandum he wrote as a result of the Langmuir–Stokowski visit.

"I believe it would be very desirable to set up a double channel listening system," Kellogg wrote in his memo, "similar to the one we used during Dr. Langmuir's visit, in a place where it could be used for demonstrations and tests at any time. It would serve as a valuable means to interest visitors and would be available for our own education, and whenever anyone has an inspiration in regard to some new test, it could be used." Kellogg outlined four lines of research — inspired directly by the session with Langmuir — which he recommended might be fruitfully pursued by the laboratory. The long memo is indicative of the manner in which a Langmuir visit always stimulated research people in laboratories everywhere, and why laboratory directors always encouraged the friendly scrutiny of his restlessly probing curiosity.

That evening Langmuir went back to Philadelphia and spent a stimulating evening of talk and music with Stokowski. The next day he attended another rehearsal of Debussy and Stravinsky, made another brief visit to Camden, then caught a train for New York. He stopped to see Mama, who had had a heart attack a week earlier but was now feeling better, then took the overnight train to Schenectady because the next morning Lindbergh was due back for his second visit and Whitney was scheduled to return after two months in Europe. After Lindbergh had gone, Langmuir wrote Stokowski about some research in sound reproduction he was planning to initiate at GE. Stokowski's reply was a bit delayed because he was now at his New York apartment on East 88th Street, and the letter had to be forwarded. "I am delighted at the prospect of the new research in your laboratory that you mention," he wrote on November 29. "I shall, of course, not speak of it to anyone.

"I am working on the new research possibilities in Philadelphia and if we are able to obtain the necessary financial support for this I will do as you suggest and try to persuade Fletcher to head it, and put this organization in close touch with Schenectady and the telephone laboratory in New York."

There are some who believe that the stimulus thus provided by Langmuir for new research in several laboratories ultimately led to a number of important advances in man's knowledge about sound — all the way from better understanding of how the human ear hears to the development of stereophonic sound recording. Langmuir was often given credit by his loyal friends for germinating ideas that led to important developments to which his name has never been attached in any way (radar was one, for example). But Langmuir himself never had any patience with this sort of credit-claiming. He believed that the free cross-fertilization of ideas constituted the lifeblood of science. "Either consciously or unconsciously," he once said, "I must make use of other people's ideas in my work. Why then shouldn't other people make free use of my ideas?" The only instances where Langmuir was careful to document his claims to priority for an idea or discovery was when it might mean patent rights for his GE employers who so generously and unquestioningly supported his free-wheeling and often expensive work. In the case of his sporadic sorties into the field of sound, he felt quite adequately rewarded by the fun he had playing with the ideas, and by the friendship that resulted from it with that civilized gentleman, Leopold Stokowski.

"I am so happy that you and Mrs. Langmuir can come to New York next Saturday," Stokowski wrote in the letter just quoted. "I enclose the tickets for the evening concerts. Mrs. Stokowska and I both hope you will come home with us after the concert for supper so that it will give us an opportunity to talk over the new plan. We shall, of course, be most informal and probably nobody else will be there.

"I am so glad you will make a record of the *Sacre* range volume.

Could you do it in the concert, because we do not rehearse that day? I would make a special rehearsal that day for this purpose but the union will not permit it. Would you like Mr. Marvin to come to the concert? He could set up the microphones before the concert and then control the measuring work either from behind the scenes or in front of the house, whichever would be more practical.

"Thank you for the information of the capacity of telephone wires. This is very valuable to me.

"After Christmas I will go up to see Prof. Hardy, if he is willing, to study his electrical organ."

That Saturday, December 6, Langmuir's diary reads: "Christmas shopping in NY. Dinner with Dean & Ethel, Herbert & Edith at Sherrys. Then to Carnegie Hall in Stokowski's box to hear concert. Finlandia, Sibelius Concerto for Violin. Then Sacre du Printemps by Stravinsky. In box with us was Mrs. Stokowski, Miss Adams, a famous Astrologer, Deems Taylor, a Miss Parkhurst, Mrs. Zimbalist (nee Alma Gluck). (Zimbalist was the soloist) and in the next box was Josef Hofman. Afterwards to Stokowski's apartment for supper (Deems Taylor)."

The next day, December 7: "Breakfast in room with Dean who also stayed at the Commodore. To Englewood. Mother is much better. Edith tells me that Herbert has serious (incurable!) disease. At first thought to be Angina Pectoris. Now in bed (for 10 days)."

Herbert's trouble was cancer. He had already had a malignant intestinal tumor removed earlier in the twenties. He would soon be going under the knife again, and recurrences were to plague him for the remainder of his life. Though his stretches of hospitalization might be years apart, with apparent good health in between, the threat of surgery hung constantly over Herbert's head. After fourteen more years of chronic anxiety and gradually diminishing vigor, Herbert finally succumbed to the ravages of the disease in 1944.

Chapter 17

"Do what you love. Know your own bone; gnaw at it, bury it, unearth it, and gnaw it still."

HENRY DAVID THOREAU

A FAIR amount of space in the last few chapters has been devoted to a by-no-means exhaustive account of Langmuir's activities in the period from 1920 to 1930 — his family affairs, his travels, his hobbies, the people he met, the conferences he attended, the awards and honorary degrees he received. All this is simply to indicate the bustling, many-splendored eventfulness of a sample decade in the life of Irving Langmuir. One might well wonder — while Langmuir was climbing the Matterhorn, or skate-sailing across Lake George, or attending the Como Congress, or getting a degree at Edinburgh, or showing Paris and Göttingen to his wife, or instructing his nephews in chemistry and the calculus, or flying with Lindbergh, or sitting in Stokowski's Carnegie Hall box with Evangeline Adams and Deems Taylor, or involved in any of the myriad other activities not even mentioned in these pages — when, for heaven's sake, did he ever have time to do any of his scientific work for General Electric? Obviously he must have found ample time for it. Otherwise he could not have turned out such an outstanding quantity and variety of work that was not in any sense superficial; nor could it have been sufficiently high quality to win him such a quantity and variety of honors. With it all, what is perhaps the most important work Langmuir did throughout much of this period — work which he had begun earlier and was to continue later — has so far not even been discussed at all. This was his work in surface chemistry, the work which won him the Nobel Prize.

How did he manage to get it all done?

Well, Langmuir's fantastic output was accomplished in large part, of course, by dint of his own phenomenal energy. Whether in the laboratory or out of it, whether in Schenectady or elsewhere, he always had work with him to which he could turn, between other activities. With his formidable powers of concentration he could, in a hotel room or on a steamer deck chair, perform complex calculations and organize prodigious amounts of raw data into intelligible form. It should be pointed out, however, that Langmuir, like most scientists who have achieved any status, was saved a great deal of his personal time by having assistants perform much of the painstaking laboratory routine for him. Langmuir was fortunate in selecting wonderfully competent assistants from among the younger scientists and technicians in the laboratory. He possessed both the faith to trust them and the capacity to inspire them with great loyalty and devotion to himself and his projects. "Watching him," says Kenneth Kingdon, "you would say to yourself — this is what science can be like."

Much of his early research at GE, for example, was done with only a single assistant, Samuel Partridge Sweetser. Sweetser was to Irving Langmuir what Everett had been to J. J. Thomson and young Faraday to Sir Humphrey Davy. A small, shy, quiet Englishman, Sweetser was a talented craftsman, a careful experimenter and a meticulous taker of data. Langmuir would outline to Sweetser exactly what he was trying to do. The two would go over the design details of the experimental apparatus — usually austerely simple — which Langmuir wanted built, and Sweetser would supervise its construction. Then, once the experiment got under way, Langmuir would leave Sweetser to watch the experiment for the required periods of time while he went off to do something else. Sweetser would ultimately bring him the results, which Langmuir would then interpret. The essence of a piece of Langmuir research was a very simply set up experiment and an elaborately sophisticated analysis.[1] Naturally, Langmuir would often, in his fascination with what was happening inside a lamp, say, peer into it himself for hours at a time. But the point was that he could leave it any time he wanted, while Sweetser could not. His job was to stay there and be watchdog of the experiment. Langmuir often gave Sweetser explicit credit for his help in the text of his published papers, and, though Sweetser was a technician rather than a full-fledged scientist, Langmuir — a man quite unconscious of rank — treated him not as an underling but as an equal, whom he saw socially with some frequency. The reason he did not see more of Sweetser after hours was simply that Sweetser was not the vigorous outdoor type, and the two men had very few interests in common outside the laboratory.

It should also be mentioned that Langmuir had many higher-level scientific collaborators and assistants. Most of them — people like Albert W. Hull and Kenneth H. Kingdon, Katharine Blodgett and Lewi Tonks, H. A. Jones and J. B. Taylor — were fine scientists in their own right who also did important research of their own; but Langmuir could not have done nearly as much as he did without their help and interest. Most of them, of course, would be the first to add that neither could they have done nearly as much as *they* did without *his* help and interest. But that, of course, is what makes a laboratory a laboratory. These scientists, when they collaborated with Langmuir, were listed as co-authors of the published papers, and thus became better known than the anonymous Sweetsers. "Langmuir certainly knew how to make the best use of people," Kingdon recalls. "He let them do the things they could do best, and he never tried to make anybody over."

Though Langmuir's Nobel Prize came in 1932, he was a can-

---

[1] Reviewing a series of Langmuir papers on the dissociation of hydrogen into atoms, Bridgman commented: "I have the impression that few physicists would have been able to keep their eyes on that distant goal through the intricacies of an analysis as complicated as this."

didate for it at least as early as 1927. On November 27 of that year, in England, he noted in his diary: "Cambridge: Arrive 9:50 . . . See Lord Rutherford and have tea at his home. He tells me that he has proposed my name for the Nobel Prize and expects me to get it next year." There was another rumor in 1929, but nothing came of it.

But on November 10, 1932, Langmuir was able to note: "H. Lundbergh (at 1 pm) a representative of a newspaper in Gothenberg telephoned me of rumor that I had received the Nobel Prize in Chemistry. Later another Swedish rep of a paper in Stockholm said that it has been confirmed. At 5 pm got a cable, 'Nobel Prize for Chemistry awarded to you. Please wire whether you can be present at Stockholm on Dec. 10.' Signed Secretary, Academy of Sciences."

Langmuir had paid little attention to the first call, thinking it might be just another false alarm. But when the later confirmation came through, he went to the living room, where Marion and the children were sitting, and announced, "Well, we've won the Nobel Prize, and we'll be going to Stockholm."

"Can we go too?" Kenneth and Barbara asked, not quite in unison.

"Yes, you can. We're *all* going," said Langmuir emphatically.

"But what about school?" asked Marion.

"They'll learn more on a trip like this than they would learn in school," said Father. "Besides, they can take their lessons along to do in the evening."

There is a wide choice of achievements for which Langmuir might have been awarded a Nobel Prize in either physics or chemistry. As it turned out, his work in surface chemistry was singled out for the honor. "Numerous scientists are at the present time working industriously and successfully in this field of research," said Professor Söderbaum of the Swedish Academy in citing reasons for the Nobel committee's choice. "It would seem, however, that the greater honor is due the first man, the pioneer, who has broken new ground, than to the cultivators of ground already cleared, however industrious they may be. The prize is awarded to Langmuir for his outstanding discoveries and inventions within the field of surface chemistry."

Surface chemistry is a science whose esoteric details are extremely difficult to explain non-technically to a lay audience. Langmuir, a man with considerable expository gifts, tried to do exactly that himself just before he left the country to accept the Nobel Prize. The occasion was the Chemists' Club dinner in New York, the same dinner where Arthur made the speech quoted earlier at such length. Langmuir's talk at the dinner was carried over the NBC radio network. Its purpose was to bring to the public an understanding of the behavior of atoms when spread on a surface, and the reasons why this was important. But when the talk was over, George C. Lewis, president of the Chemists' Club, soothed the public by assuring them that even some of the chemists there didn't understand what it was all about. It was not that Langmuir had done poorly; it was just that he had taken on a job that was too tough even for him. He did a much better job of popularizing surface chemistry later, in 1935, in a lucid article written for the *General Electric Review*. Since the work was so ingenious, and of such significance — not only to physics and chemistry, but to biology as well — and since it is now better understood than it used to be, an attempt will be made here, not to *explain* surface chemistry, but to give some glimmering of the nature of this monumental Langmuir achievement.

It all began, as so many lines of Langmuir research did, with those early experiments with the incandescent lamp. Though scientists from Franklin to Faraday, and from Lord Rayleigh to Sir James Dewar, had been interested in surface phenomena, the amount of sure scientific knowledge which existed on this subject at the time Langmuir went to work for General Electric in 1909 was so minimal that Sir Eric Rideal considers it quite proper that Langmuir "be called the founder of the subject" since he not only revealed all manner of new facts about surface chemistry, but "first formulated with clarity and precision" its principles.

To Langmuir a surface was not only the visible "top" of something; it was also "the boundary between two phases." A surface might be "the interface between two liquids which do not mix" — oil and water, for example. Like any curious physical chemist, Langmuir was bound to wonder about the familiar but mysterious phenomenon known as adsorption, which he defined as "the condensation of dissolved or gaseous substances on a surface." (When something is *absorbed,* it passes through the surface and disappears into the body of the substance; but when it is *adsorbed,* it remains on the surface and goes no farther.) When Langmuir first began prying into the nature of adsorption, a fair amount was already known about how gases were adsorbed on porous materials — charcoal, for example. "When Sir James Dewar found that charcoal, cooled to the temperature of liquid air, was capable of taking up large quantities of such gases as oxygen and nitrogen," Langmuir wrote, "it was explained that these gases were condensed upon the surface of the charcoal. The very fine state of division of the charcoal which should give it an enormous surface thus accounted for the large amount of gases adsorbed under these conditions." Langmuir knew how valuable this knowledge became in designing gas masks during World War I.

"An example of adsorption with which everyone is familiar," he pointed out, "is that of the action of soap on water. Water is a liquid that possesses an unusually high surface tension. If a finger is dipped into clean water, the drop that hangs from the finger on removing it from the water is much larger than it would be in the case of any other ordinary liquid. The force that holds the drop of water against the force of gravity is the surface tension . . .

"If the merest trace of soap be dissolved in water, the surface tension of the water is greatly lowered . . . This naturally results in smaller drops being formed. Anyone may demonstrate this affect to himself by merely dipping a finger of one hand into a glass of clean water and a finger of the other hand into a glass of soapy water. It will be seen that when the fingers are withdrawn the drops of pure water are several times larger than those of soapy water."

Willard Gibbs had been much intrigued by soap bubbles, and

had shown "by theoretical reasoning that any substance which lowers the surface tension of a liquid always does so by being adsorbed at the surface of the liquid." Gibbs even worked out a formula containing an adsorption factor to account mathematically for surface tension.

"Prior to 1910," Langmuir wrote, "many different theories of adsorption had been proposed, but none of them had been very successful. In most of these theories the increased concentration of the adsorbed substance near the surface was thought to be analogous to the retention of the earth's atmosphere. An adsorbed gas was thus regarded as a kind of miniature atmosphere extending out a short distance from a solid substance. In general, such theories were called upon to account only for qualitative aspects of the adsorption of gases on solids. Most of the knowledge of adsorption was empirical. Even Gibbs' law had not been verified experimentally."

It will be recalled from an earlier chapter how Langmuir, looking for the hydrogen that had capriciously disappeared from the confines of his tungsten-filament lamp, found that it had firmly attached itself to the inner surface of the lamp bulb in its atomic form. Another thing which Langmuir discovered at the time — a discovery with revolutionary implications — was that the hydrogen atoms clung to the glass surface in a layer that was only a single atom in thickness. He never came upon the kind of sheath of compressed gas that Faraday had envisioned, nor the several layers — diffusing and diminishing in density — predicted by Bodenstein and Fink. The layers were never even as much as *two* atoms in thickness, let alone atmospheric (even miniature-atmospheric) in depth.

Langmuir was not really as surprised as he might have been had he not already been prepared to find surface atoms behaving in this fashion. Much influenced by the Braggs' work in X-ray crystallography — which also influenced his octet theory of the atom — Langmuir already suspected that, in any given solid mass, the crystals at the very surface might be open to combination with a layer of impinging atoms or molecules that would, in a sense, extend and complete its own crystalline lattice. Along with his observation of hydrogen layers on glass, Langmuir began studying other adsorption phenomena inside his lamps — including the way oxygen, or caesium, or thorium, coated the surface of a tungsten filament[1] — and here again, the layer was invariably one atom thick. The atoms were always packed tightly on the surface, and the surface would take only a fixed quantity of atoms and no more — just as a certain amount of oxygen would combine with only a fixed quantity of hydrogen and no more. And the atoms formed such a stable film on the surface that it took a lot of force to get the atoms to evaporate once they had been absorbed; one remembers Langmuir baking the glass bulb in an oven to get the hydrogen atoms loose. These considerations and others led him to conclude that adsorption was a chemical bond rather than a physical attraction[2] (though he had always considered the distinction between chemical forces and physical forces rather dubious anyway). In Langmuir's first papers on the subject, says N. K. Adam, "the theory of adsorption was at one stroke lifted from indefinite obscurity into clear definition."

The new theory was radically different from any that had gone before. "According to the new theory," Langmuir later wrote, "the surface of a tungsten filament is to be regarded as a surface lattice or checkerboard which can hold adsorbed atoms and the atoms of the underlying metal. If a second layer of atoms could be formed on top of the first, the forces holding these atoms would then be quite different from those that hold the atoms in the first layer. In other words, the structure of an adsorbed film is considered from somewhat the some point of view as that of the

---

[1] These layers of atoms on a filament can have radical effects on the filament's electrical behavior, too, Langmuir discovered. Coating a pure tungsten filament with a single layer of thorium atoms, for example, makes it emit, when heated, a hundred thousand times as many electrons! Almost every bit of research Langmuir did threw light on some other line of research — or opened up a new one. In this case he was really studying thermionic emission from the thoriated tungsten filament, with the surface studies, at first, only incidental.

[2] This same conclusion was reached independently, and at almost the same time, by W. D. Harkins.

organic chemist when he derives the structure of the molecules of organic substances."

Langmuir, at this point in his article, then took advantage of the opportunity to make known some of his views on the nature of chemical, as opposed to physical, forces: "The older views on adsorption are now often referred to as constituting a physical theory of adsorption, whereas the newer ideas are described as a chemical theory. I think this distinction involves *not so much the nature of the forces involved as the traditional attitude of mind of physicists and chemists.* [Italics supplied.] The physicist, probably ever since the time of Newton, has been inclined to consider forces which vary as some power of the distance between the bodies acted upon by the forces. He has also had many occasions to consider fields of force which extend throughout space, such as gravitational, electric, and magnetic fields. The chemist, on the other hand, has nearly always considered that chemical action between molecules or atoms takes place only when they are in contact. It is a natural tendency for the physicist in considering the problem of adsorption to think of the behavior of the adsorbed atoms or molecules as being in a field of force produced by a solid or liquid surface. It would be more in accord with the tradition of the chemist, however, to think of an atom on the surface as being attached to one or more atoms of the underlying surface.

"In very recent years this distinction between the attitudes of physicists and chemists is fast disappearing, for the physicist has become convinced that the great majority of the forces involved in the structure of matter have such a short range of action that the forces became practically negligible unless the atoms from which they originate are nearly in contact.[1] The difference between physical and chemical theories is thus becoming of merely historical interest. It should, however, be emphasized that the older methods of the chemist by which he derived the structure of

[1] To indicate just how short-range is the force of a chemical bond, when the surfaces of atoms or molecules are as much as one hundred-millionth of a centimeter apart the attractive force between them virtually disappears.

chemical compounds should be looked upon more favorably than ever, and that they now receive support and justification from modern physical theory. The simple, chemical pictures of phenomena are particularly well suited to those who wish to consider such problems as adsorption from the practical point of view rather than to go into elaborate mathematical calculations for which adequate data are rarely available." (One will here recall Langmuir's "chemical picture" of the atom as a case in point.) Langmuir documented his case for chemical adsorption so convincingly that it soon received widespread acceptance, and the phenomenon was simply called "chemisorption."

Langmuir's intensive studies of surface phenomena took him into a whole new world of "monolayers" (layers one atom or one molecule thick). He reasoned out the mechanism of the forces that held molecules on a surface upon which they impinged. He worked out the "Langmuir isotherm" — the relation between the pressure of a gas and the quantity of it adsorbed. He also worked out formulas to show that the rate of evaporation from metal surfaces was roughly analogous to the half-life of radioactive elements. He studied those rare and peculiar sets of conditions where a second layer of atoms was not only adsorbed but actually had stronger bonds than the first layer — such as, for example, the special case where mercury or cadmium atoms gather upon a glass surface which has been pre-cooled down to a temperature of $-50°C$. When this occurs, the bonds holding the second layer of atoms to one another are stronger than the bonds holding the first layer to the surface of the glass. Meanwhile, as he tried all sorts of variations of gases adsorbing on solids, he was getting interested in "an entirely different set of experimental facts which throw a new light upon the structure of adsorbed films. I refer to monomolecular films on the surface of water. Interest in these phenomena was first aroused by the work of Lord Rayleigh and Miss Pockels about 1890. Lord Rayleigh pointed out that the properties of certain oil films on water could best be explained by assuming that they consisted of a single layer of molecules." J. G. Crowther tells us that Benjamin Franklin carried out similar experiments on a pond at Clapham in London, and came to similar conclusions.

"Devaux and Marcellin, between 1903 and 1914," Langmuir went on, "devised some beautiful, yet simple, experimental methods for measuring thicknesses of oil films, and considered that this thickness gave the diameter of the molecules. In reading of the work I became interested in these monomolecular films because of the close analogy to the monatomic films on solids. I thought that a further study of these insoluble oil films should throw light upon the nature of the forces involved.

"It was known that some oils spread on the surface of water while others do not, but no adequate reason had been given for this difference." Langmuir soon began to find out some of the reasons as his laboratory became more and more cluttered up with trays and troughs (including the new Langmuir trough, which he invented) full of water coated with a variety of films. "Langmuir," Kingdon wrote, "made a tremendous extension of this technique [the Rayleigh–Pockels–Devaux–Marcelin technique] by the introduction of a surface balance method [the Langmuir film balance] for measuring the spreading force of the films and showed that these films were truly monomolecular. In collaboration with Katharine Blodgett and V. J. Schaefer, a whole series of techniques were developed for working with surface films and used to study gaseous, liquid and solid films, including such complicated molecules as proteins."

In the course of these experiments Langmuir observed that, in molecules on the water's surface, it was always certain atoms — and always the same atoms — and only in certain positions in the molecule, that held onto the water. These atoms seemed literally to turn downward to provide the "hook" that attached the molecule to the surface. If the molecule consisted of a short chain of atoms, the attraction of the "hooking" atoms might be strong enough to drag the molecule into the water after it — i.e., it would dissolve, and there would be no surface film at all. In the case of a large, long-chain molecule of oil, the attraction was enough to maintain a stable film, but not strong enough to pull the long, heavy chain down into the water. Some oils — pure mineral oil, for example — have no chemical hooks at all; hence they do not react with the surface but simply sit around in solitary little globs, never forming a film. Some ends of some molecules turned down, others seemed to stand up; some molecules seemed to lie down on their sides, depending on the nature of the chemical hooks. Langmuir gradually found out quite a lot about the size, shape, structure and chemical behavior of a variety of molecules, and ultimately developed his Principle of Independent Surface Action — which permitted him to predict chemical behavior from his knowledge of molecular structure, and vice versa. While finding out about molecules on water, Langmuir also found out a great deal about water itself — its structure, the nature of its chemical bonds, its rates of evaporation under various conditions. He learned, for example, that with certain kinds of films on its surface, water evaporated very slowly. This finding has been put to great practical use in many water-scarce areas of the world — from Texas to Israel to the U.S.S.R. to Austria — where monomolecular films are spread on ponds, lakes, reservoirs, and irrigation ditches, thus saving enormous amounts of water that would otherwise have evaporated away.

A nineteenth century English clergyman and educator named Edwin Abbott once wrote a little book called *Flatland,* a fantasy which envisioned a population of beings who lived on a plane surface, in two dimensions only, with no concept of a third dimension. It was exactly this kind of world that Langmuir found in his monomolecular films. The molecules could move only on a plane surface, as if there were a solid floor and ceiling hemming them into their narrow world, with no up-place or down-place to go. George W. Gray, visiting Schenectady to interview Langmuir for an *Atlantic Monthly* article shortly after the Nobel Prize award, was given a striking demonstration of this by Langmuir:

"He laid a strip of paper across the water surface," Gray wrote, "and by pushing the strip forced the oil to one end of the tray. If the agitated particles had any freedom to leave the surface, they surely would have used it. Instead, under the pressure of the paper barrier, the film condensed into a two-dimensional film of liquid. Further pressure converted it into a two-dimensional solid. The thin crust, measuring only one twenty-millionth of an inch in thickness, was invisible, but by blowing on the surface one could prove its rigidity. On the release of the barrier, the pressure dropped, and instantly the two-dimensional solid melted into a two-dimensional liquid, which in turn evaporated into a two-dimensional gas and diffused all over the surface, as the freed molecules darted about in wild abandon." And it was the affinities between the chemical hooks in the molecules and the chemical hooks in the water that was responsible for all this bizarre behavior.

The experiments grew even more interesting when Langmuir and his colleagues figured out ways to transfer the films to solid surfaces for study. "By dipping a polished metal strip into . . . a floating monolayer," Rideal explains, "one monolayer at a time could be transferred to the metal. Multilayers could also be built which gave graduated optical interference colors, depending on the number of layers deposited. A simple thickness gauge was thus formed, and the actual length of a molecule could be measured with extremely simple equipment."

Langmuir studied more and more complicated molecules. Very early in the game the importance of surface-chemistry techniques in biological studies became apparent, and he was soon studying the structure of chlorophyll, enzymes, and — with the British scientist, Dorothy M. Wrinch — proteins. Though there were obvious limits to what Langmuir's methods at the time could accomplish with the prohibitively complex molecules of biology, he did carry them to the limit, and he did point the way for the studies that are still being carried out today. "Langmuir," writes Harry Sobotka, "during his almost meteoric appearance in the field of organic monolayers, created a whole body of novel techniques and enunciated ideas which had been foreshadowed to some extent by himself and by others, but which he . . . spelled out with courage and originality."

The importance of Langmuir's invention — it can almost be

called that — of surface chemistry can scarcely be exaggerated. It provided significant clues to the structure and electrical behavior of all matter, including the giant molecules of life. And it is more, even, than a basic key for opening doorways to new scientific knowledge. Over the years, the ability to manipulate atoms and molecules in accordance with the principles laid down by Langmuir and his successors has resulted in a steady stream of ever-proliferating new products and processes which have a multitude of applications in agriculture and aviation, in mining and medicine, and in virtually every facet of our technology, civilian or military. To understand this — without understanding the complexities of Langmuir's mathematics and terminology — is to understand why the Swedish Academy of Sciences rated this new science, and this pioneer scientist, as great.

Chapter 18

"And pomp, and feast, and revelry,
With mask, and antique pageantry,
Such sights as youthful poets dream,
On summer eves by haunted stream . . ."

JOHN MILTON

AFTER the news came of the Nobel Prize award, the Langmuirs began preparing for Stockholm and a subsequent European tour. Arrangements were made with the school authorities for Kenneth and Barbara to be absent, and they were supplied with plenty of homework to do in the evenings so they would not fall behind the rest of their classmates while they were gone. And when they came back, Kenneth, who was then sixteen, and Barbara, who was fourteen, would have plenty to tell their classmates, including what the champagne tasted like at the Nobel Prize dinner.

On November 27 they all arrived in New York and checked in at the Hotel Windermere, where Mama was then living. Then they all drove out to Englewood, where Herbert and Edith were host and hostess to a triumphal gathering of the clan. Many speeches were made, including Herbert's about why the Nobel Prize should come to the Langmuir family; it was here, too, that Herbert dug out and read his old letter to Irving in Göttingen urging him to choose a life dedicated to scholarship in preference to one devoted to commerce. (Irving had actually done even better; he had chosen scholarship, and demonstrated how to make it pay big commercial dividends.) Later in the day the Langmuirs — the Irving Langmuirs — went over to Brooklyn for tea with more relatives; then to Dean's for dinner, where the topic of conversation, according to Irving's diary, was "more family history," and Dean no doubt reminded him of the days in Paris when Irving would back him up against the apartment wall and try to force him to learn some arithmetic and chemistry.

The next day Irving met Arthur at the office of the Chemists' Club to talk over plans for the dinner to be held the following evening in Irving's honor. Late in the morning he had a brief session with Gerard Swope, than president of General Electric. From there he went to lunch with the editors of the *New York Times* and was interviewed for two hours by their science reporter. Then dinner at the Windermere and the evening reminiscing with Mama, who said how proud Papa would have been to be here now and see the world paying homage to the great scientific achievements of his terrible-tempered little boy. The next day: "Spend a.m. preparing 11 min radio talk over NBC net work. Dinner in my honor at the Chemist Club. Speakers: Lamb, Swedish Consul General, Arthur, Prof. Bogert, AG Davis and Lewis (pres of Chem Club). I talk on Surface Chemistry." Arthur, near the close of his speech about Irving, said: "He is leaving us this midnight on the *Bremen* en route for Stockholm. Let us wish him a rough trip, for both Irving and his wife are good sailors. I am quite sure you will find him tomorrow on the bridge, stop watch in hand, following the course of the great waves of the Atlantic." After the dinner, Herbert drove Irving, Marion and the children to the boat, scheduled to sail at a half hour past midnight.

The sailing of the *Bremen* was held up for an hour awaiting the belated arrival of actress Clara Bow, but the "It" Girl never showed up. Among the passengers aboard was Hattie Carnegie — and, it turned out, so was Marilyn Miller — as a stowaway, a discovery which held up the boat again when it arrived at Cherbourg. On the way over, Langmuir did indeed keep track of wind, waves and temperatures, as usual. On the first day out there was some engine trouble. "A bolt got mixed up with bearing of a turbine and the shaft to one turbine had to be disconnected," he explained. Two days later Arthur and those who may have joined him in wishing the Langmuirs a rough trip got their wish. After a few stormy days and a day of calm, they arrived, on the sixth day out of New York, at Cherbourg, where Dorothy Mersereau — who was already in Europe — joined them before the boat proceeded to Southampton and Bremen.

What happened during the ensuing weeks is best told by a pair of letters from Irving Langmuir to his mother. The first, dated December 18, 1932, was written on the stationery of Niels Bohr's Institute for Theoretical Physics in Copenhagen. "I know you will all be disgusted with me for not writing sooner about the wonderful events of the last week," he wrote. "But never have I had such a busy week. Our time has been occupied by many official functions and by dinners from friends and sightseeing trips arranged for us, and what time we could get alone has been too short for necessary shopping and attending to acknowledgements of pressing social letters, etc.

"But today we arrived in Copenhagen and all five of us [Irving, Marion, Kenneth, Barbara, and Dorothy] are visiting the Bohrs in their palace-like home. The house could accommodate 30 to 40 people, I think, and is surrounded by a 10 acre garden with conservatories, Pompeian courts, fountains, etc. It was the home of Jacobsen, a multimillionaire who left all his property including his home to a scientific foundation, which supports most of the scientific work in Denmark. Bohr and his family, including 5 sons, live here in this beautiful estate kept up for him by the foundation. Bohr has made us at home and suggests that we would like time alone to rest and to write home, etc. — a very welcome suggestion.

"When we arrived at Stockholm we were met by a Dr. von Euler, a Nobel Prize winner and a member of the Nobel foundation who escorted us to the Grand Hotel where we had three rooms facing the King's Palace across the beautiful body of water. The next day, Dec. 9, after purchasing a silk hat, and evening clothes for Dorothy, we attended a formal dinner given by the American Ambassador Morehead in his very beautiful home. Other guests were H.R.H. Prince Wilhelm, brother to the King, Baron and Baroness Rudebach (whom I escorted to dinner), Vice Admiral Lindberg, Prof. Svedberg (Nobel Prize man in chemistry living in Upsala) and others (Counts and Countesses, etc.) — in all 24 people. After a very delicious dinner with many kinds of wines and champagnes we retired to three large connecting rooms on an upper floor where after about an hour of conversation we were entertained by good music, piano and an opera singer (Olsen, I think).

"The Award of the Nobel Prizes took place the following day, Dec. 10, at 5 P.M. in the large Concert House holding about 2000 people with every seat filled. It was the most impressive ceremony I have ever attended. At exactly 5 P.M. the King and the Royal Family, etc. (in all about 25 people) entered the hall and were seated in the front row of the auditorium. The stage or platform (without curtain) had about 50 seats with members of the Nobel Foundation, University professors and all Nobel Laureates present. The platform was decorated with Swedish flags in the center with one huge American and one British flag on each side. The King's arrival was announced by trumpet calls with trumpeters on each side of huge columns on the platform: — trumpets 6 ft. long like in Aida, pointed upwards by trumpeters in silver and black uniforms of medieval type. All the foregoing was told me by Marion for I was not then present but was waiting for a signal back of a large velvet curtain at the back of the platform with the President of the Nobel Foundation and the other two prize winners for this year: Adrian and Sherrington. Unfortunately Galsworthy was not present as his doctor forbade him to leave home.

"After the entrance of the Royal party, the Royal hymn was played by a large orchestra hidden in a concealed balcony back of the audience near the roof. Then with more trumpet calls the prize winners entered the platform from the curtain at the rear and took their seats. After the President of the Foundation, I entered first, then Adrian and then Sherrington. Marion says (but I did not see this) that far over our heads from little stone balconies, a large American flag was lowered in a salute as I entered and a British flag when Adrian and Sherrington entered.

"After a beautiful musical selection the President of the Foundation gave a 15 minute speech in Swedish about Alfred Nobel and the Nobel Prizes. Then another selection and a talk by Prof. Söderbaum, Secretary of the Swedish Academy of Sciences (in Swedish) about my work. Then in English he addressed me for 2–3 minutes while I stood and as soon as he was through I went down the steps from the platform with more trumpet calls and flag lowering, to stand in front of the King while the whole audience arose. The King presented me with a gold medal and a large hand decorated diploma and assignation for the prize. He said a few words and shook my hand (but I was not called upon to reply at that time) and I then returned to my seat at the platform. After another musical selection and address, Adrian and Sherrington together received their medals, etc. from the King (as they were given the Nobel Prize jointly). In a similar way the Prize was awarded to Galsworthy, the British Minister appearing for him.

"At the end of the ceremony (about 6:30 P.M.) the King and Royal Family left first and then those on the platform and finally the audience. Marion, Kenneth, Barbara and Dorothy had seats in about the fourth row just behind the Royal Party.

"At 7 P.M. there was a dinner in the Banquet Hall of the Grand Hotel for about 220 people. At first the Nobel Laureates and their families (including Barbara and Kenneth and Dorothy) formed a line in the reception room and the Royal Family (except the King who did not attend the dinner) filed by us. This seemed a queer arrangement as if we received the Royal Family instead of their receiving us, but it is the universal custom here and a very practical one, for we are the ones who have to wait until the Royal Family are ready to present themselves.

"At the banquet Marion had the place of honor at the right of the Crown Prince. On his left was Mrs. Adrian. Beyond her was the Crown Prince's brother, H.R.H. Hertigen an Sodermanland, and then Mrs. Sherrington (then another prince). On the other side of Marion was the Crown Prince's son, Heir Apparent, who has just recently married Princess Sybilla. I sat right across the table from the Crown Prince's son between the wife of the Crown Prince and the wife of Prince Carl, brother of the King. I escorted the latter to dinner.

"I have a printed booklet giving the seating arrangement of all 220 guests showing where Dorothy, Barbara and Kenneth sat. After the dinner there was a reception lasting until about 11:30. Since the death of Emmanuel Nobel last year, the supper at 1 A.M. has been discontinued.

"The whole affair was very delightful, giving us an opportunity not only of meeting all the nobility of Sweden but all the university people. The children were thrilled beyond measure in being included at the dinner (for we had not expected that) and of meeting the Crown Prince and Princess, etc. They were all very cordial and had long conversations with all of us. At the dinner the wife of Prince Carl even waved her hand to Kenneth who was sitting some distance away.

"The next day (Sunday the 11th) we spent the day at the summer home of Mr. Egnell (a wealthy instrument manufacturer of Stockholm and a friend of Prof. Berg of Schenectady). They have a beautiful home surrounded by 4000 acres of forest along the shore of one of the numberless inlets of the sea. We had two good walks through the woods. The weather was delightful and mild. They have had no snow so far this winter.

"That evening we dined with the King (just Marion and I). About 80 people present. The Bohrs are ready for dinner so I'll stop this letter and continue when I get the next chance."

It was January 3, 1933, before the "next chance" arrived. The letter was from St. Moritz, on the stationery of the Kulm Hotels. "We have been here at St. Moritz now about 10 days," he told Mama, "being out of doors every day on skiing trips. There is not very much snow (about 1 foot) and that fell several weeks ago. As a result many of the slopes that face the afternoon sun are bare grass. Still there are a good many trips, in valleys among the higher peaks, which afford some perfect skiing conditions.

"We had intended to go to Arosa after a few days at St. Moritz, but we hear that there is still less snow there so we now plan to stay here until we have more snow. The weather is far too perfect — every one of the ten days (except one) has been practically cloudless and windless with the same temperature every day, minimum about 10 degrees F., max. about 25 degrees F. Not once has the temperature risen to 32 degrees. The one cloudy day we had brought 1/2 inch of snow at St. Moritz and about 2 inches on the surrounding mountains." (Who else but Langmuir would complain about the weather being too perfect?)

"In my last letter," he continued, "I told you of the ceremonies of the Nobel Award but did not tell you of the dinner at the King's Palace. The dinner was at 8 P.M. and in accord with the invariable custom of the punctual Swedes we arrived 5 minutes before this time. There were about 60 people present. We all gathered in a reception room and were arranged in definite order around a circle and then the King and the Royal Family entered and passed around this circle shaking hands with each person and saying a few words. After this we passed thru several rooms of royal style (like rooms of palace at Versailles) into the huge dining room called the 'White Sea.' When entering the Palace each man took from a silver tray held by a footman in medieval costume a small card (I enclose mine) on the back of which was the name of the lady whom he was to escort to dinner. There was also a map of the long dining table with an arrow to indicate the place of entrance to the dining room, a red cross to mark the seat to be occupied and a small black dot to represent the King. My partner was Selma Lagerlöf. I have a copy of the complete seating arrangements, but it is packed up in a suit case which we have sent to Cook's.

"Dr. Lagerlöf is a woman of about 70 who speaks English moderately well. She is now writing her autobiography — the first part dealing with her childhood has just been published. The lady on my left was one of the ladies in waiting. After the dinner we all returned to the reception room and talked for about $1/2$ hour. At 9:30 according to fixed custom the King leaves with other members of the Royal Family, and the party soon broke up. Marion was talking to one of the court attendants (?) at the dinner, who said that as usual after such functions the King played bridge until 12 or 1 o'clock and for that evening he had been 'summoned' to play bridge with the King altho he would far rather go to bed.

"These ceremonies at Stockholm were most impressive. According to all reports the Swedes specialize in formality and have reduced it to a perfection seen nowhere else. In their language they never use the pronoun *you*, but always say in addressing Prof. X, 'Does Prof. X wish to imply that Prof. X would like to visit the museum,' etc. It's so troublesome to the Danes who speak nearly the some language but use '*you*', that Prof. Bohr says he always speaks English or German to Swedes.

"For several days at Stockholm we were very busy with dinners and luncheons and being shown the sights of the city by people we met. The Egnells, friends of Prof. Berg at Schenectady, were particularly nice to us.

"We left Stockholm on Saturday Dec. 17th and took the night train to Copenhagen where we were met by Prof. Bohr and one of his sons. We were with them 3 days in their beautiful home. They are the most ideal family I have ever visited. Mrs. Bohr is a delightful woman. They are going to be in America this summer and will spend a few days with us in Schenectady and Lake George.

"In many ways Bohr is I think the greatest living scientist. His point of view in regard to all scientific problems is unique and is based on a power of analysis that is extraordinary. He has just published a paper on the application of his philosophical viewpoint to the biological problem of the nature of life. He points out that the usual chemical and physical methods of sciences are fundamentally not applicable in an investigation of vital functions. I believe his views will ultimately have a profound effect on the attitude of biologists and particularly of psychologists.

"After Copenhagen we again took a sleeper to Berlin where we spent only 24 hours requesting to be allowed to remain incognito. We were however met at the station by a party of about 6 people and were escorted to a suite de luxe at the Esplanade Hotel and had a limousine put at our disposal for the time we were there.

"I have promised to return to Berlin near the end of January for about 4 days to give two lectures and to be entertained etc. by the physicists and chemists of Berlin. I am also to give a lecture in Vienna on Feb. lst. Marion and I will take this trip to Berlin and Vienna leaving the children in Arosa with Dorothy. After that we will return for a week or so to Switzerland and then go to Paris with the whole family.

"We are having a fine time here at St. Moritz. We are all taking daily skiing trips, but in nearly all cases we take the Funicular to the Corviglia Hut (8500 ft.) and choose one of about 4 routes down to St. Moritz. We had a delightful skiing trip of about 10 miles from the Berminar Hospitz to Pontresina with descent of about 1800 ft. Dorothy doesn't ski but takes long walks on the excellent trails. We are impatient for more snow so that we can take a wider variety of trips.

"The Nobel Prize money I converted gradually into dollars retaining about $3000 in a Swedish bank until I return to America. In all it amounted to about $30,600, about a $1000 more than I expected from the exchange rate when I left home. Our expenses here are about $10 a day apiece as compared with Arthur's estimate of $20. Rates in Switzerland are 30% less than 3 yrs ago. At Arosa we will stay at a much simpler hotel where we don't have to dress for dinner (which we all regard as a nuisance). We got a whole bunch of letters on Christmas eve which delighted us."

Langmuir did get back to Berlin, as promised, toward the end of January, and he was indeed royally entertained — not "royally" on the Stockholm scale, but as royally as his Berlin scientist friends could manage. He and Marion had lunch one day with Professor and Mrs. Nernst. One cannot help wondering if Nernst remembered how negligent he had been of his old graduate student back in Göttingen days and, remembering, felt ashamed; or whether he simply convinced himself that it was he who started Langmuir on the road to greatness, and therefore felt very proud and pleased with himself. At any rate, the older and younger Nobel laureates did seem to enjoy their lunch together.

In the gaps between luncheons, cocktail parties, opera and the theater, Langmuir lectured and visited a number of the Berlin laboratories. Among the scientists he met at the Siemens Laboratory was young Dennis Gabor, who was passionately interested in a series of experiments Langmuir had performed — during those busy twenties — with Harold Mott-Smith in low-pressure mercury discharge tubes, where he and Mott-Smith had discovered the existence of plasmas. This was important work wich almost everyone else had ignored. Gabor felt especially challenged by what he called "The Langmuir Paradox." The paradox was that certain phenomena in the discharge tubes — phenomena well established as existing today, though not in Langmuir's day — were unquestionably where they had no theoretical right to exist at all. Gabor was finally able to solve the paradox — but not until 1955, after a five-year stretch of hard work. "There is another of my papers which stems immediately from Langmuir's work," says Gabor, writing in the year 1960, from the University of London. "This is the 'Wave Theory of Plasma,' *Proc. Roy. Soc.* 1952, which is really a straightforward realization of a mathematical programme sketched out by Langmuir in his wonderful *Proc. Nat. Acad. Sci.* paper of 1928. He could not carry out the programme, because even the necessary mathematics (the Wiener-Khintchin Theorem) was not available in 1928 — but by ingenious order-of-magnitude arguments he reached the same conclusions as I!"

It was while Langmuir was in Berlin — on January 30, 1933 — that Adolf Hitler was made Chancellor of Germany by President von Hindenburg. Langmuir made a passing note of it in his diary, but if he attached any special significance to the event, he did not mention it. On the other hand, Leo Szilard — who was there, at the University of Berlin, at the time — recalls that he was unable to convince his German colleagues — even the Jewish professors — that a civilized nation like Germany would really permit itself to be taken over by the Nazis. If even the German scientists refused to take Hitler seriously, there is no reason why a visiting American, enjoying himself in this festive atmosphere, should get upset about it all.

Szilard, incidentally, left Berlin right after the Reichstag Fire. He had foreseen what seemed to him to be the inevitable course of events, and had, as a matter of fact, been living for some time with two suitcases packed, ready to go. He announced that he was going on vacation — a vacation from which he had no intention of returning — and boarded a train for Vienna, where Langmuir met him again, at a tea at Professor Abels'. Langmuir lectured in Vienna,[1] then went on to Budapest, with Szilard on the train for company.

Langmuir's lecture in Budapest became famous, not for its content, but for its introduction. As Gabor and Szilard — both Hungarians, by the way — tell the story, the audience at the university was packed with high-ranking Hungarian nobility and at least one member of the Hungarian royal family. Each speaker, before beginning, turned obsequiously to the formidable assemblage of aristocrats, addressing each of them in turn by his full title, so that the normal ladies-and-gentlemen kind of introduction turned into a long-winded speech all by itself, before the speech ever began. It was all very tiresome, naturally, but protocol was protocol. When it was Langmuir's turn to speak, he got up and, with the characteristic bluntness of a man who had never learned the art of smalltalk, began: "If you take a tungsten wire and —" Before he could finish the sentence, a brief

[1] A letter home said: "In Vienna we stayed at the house of Prof. Ehrenhaft and were protected from newspaper men, who did not find out where we were. The lecture there was one I promised to give two years ago if I visited Europe again. It was in the largest lecture hall in the University and so many people applied for tickets that they connected up a second lecture room with loud speakers. There were over two hundred in this second room."

burst of spontaneous applause broke out among the delighted scientists, who then repeated all over Europe the story about the straightforward American.

Chapter 19

"He delighted to wander in unknown lands, to see strange rivers, his eagerness making light of toil."

OVID

THE Nobel Prize tour was of course the highlight of the thirties for Langmuir. But perhaps even more interesting, in its way, was another travel experience — a round-the-world trip which began in October of 1934 and ended in March of 1935. Invited to give the 1934 Iwadare Lectures in Japan, he decided he might as well avail himself of the opportunity to see some of the Orient — which neither he nor Marion had ever visited — and come back via the Suez Canal.

Walking through the lobby of his hotel in Seattle, before their departure on the *Empress of Japan,* Langmuir was amazed to find himself in the middle of a mob of shoving-and-elbowing teenagers holding up books and pieces of paper and shouting, "Can I have your autograph?" Teenagers, after his autograph? And in such numbers? Impossible. Looking around, he soon spotted the cause of the furor — the great home-run hitter, Babe Ruth. "The Babe" was also going to Japan, and Langmuir later met him on the boat. The two men could hardly have been more unlike in temperament. And since Langmuir, great outdoor sportsman though he was, knew about as much about baseball as Ruth did about science, one could hardly expect their conversation to have been memorable.

In Japan Langmuir gave his lectures, was given the Order of the Rising Sun, and made an honorary member of the Japanese Institute of Electrical Engineers. He toured the country extensively, the Japanese arranging accommodations all the way. From Beppu, Marion wrote home to Arthur's wife, Alice: "Irving's lectures are a great success and he makes wonderful after-dinner speeches so that we feel we are making many good friends ... We have been complimented on our management of chop sticks ... 'Doctor,' as Irving is called, is just about worshipped. He likes the people and has made them realize he does."

And Irving wrote to Mama: "In some of my many after-dinner speeches I have told of your many trips to Japan and they have always expressed profound regret that you should have visited Japan without having been entertained as the mother of the 'world's foremost scientist, etc.' I am sure if you will only take another trip to Japan you'll have the keys of every city in Japan presented to you."

The Japanese even arranged part of his China tour, and at various points around the Far and Middle East, representatives of International General Electric saw to the Langmuirs' comfort. Langmuir occasionally complained that all this arranging — none of which he solicited — often kept him and Marion from doing what they wanted to do, and made it very hard for them ever to get a day alone to themselves. At times, of course, it was nice to have an arranger on hand. In Sendai, for example, staying at the Hotel Hori Kyu where a fish breakfast was served on the floor, Langmuir noted in his diary: "Guide takes us along road which is not finished. We return 4 miles in dark. Only fruit at hotel for dinner. Then Hot Japanese Bath for 2, but by special request of Dr. So, reserve for ONLY 2. Beds are queer, but comfortable, on the floor."

Throughout the grand tour the Langmuirs saw all the standard sights — Fujiyama and the Geisha district, Angkor Vat and the Emerald Buddha, the Pyramids and the Taj Mahal. But Langmuir, while appreciating the tourist attractions, always had his senses alert for the sights and sounds and smells of living, the people he saw and met, the social scene, and the natural phenomena that he observed as a matter of habit anywhere in the world. He could easily have expanded his diary notes of the trip into a very readable travel book, had he been so inclined. A few random excerpts:

In Tokyo: "We nearly buy dried fish, thinking it candy." ... "Japanese baths said to be 42–45°C (107 to 113°F). I believe it!"

"Terribly fast and agile taxi drivers in Osaka."

"Inland Sea — Kobe — Tokyo. Up at 5 am to see islands. Note under the door from Takahashi saying he can explain. We find him suffering from delusions that he has been hearing us talking about him all night even though he changed his stateroom twice. We are scared for his safety and sanity (which is temporarily gone). He can't sleep. But we finally quiet him and he seems better. Tenabe and others meet us in Kobe (Thank heavens)."

"Mrs. Yamaguchi brought Japanese costumes for Marion and me ... to the Manchurian Legation."

In Mukden: "Taken to Yamato Hotel and have breakfast (Beef a la mode altho I want Kippered Herrings but we are powerless) ... Palace is *very much closed;* armed soldiers, why?"

In Shanghai: "Coolies carry 360 lbs 1/4 mile for .2 ¢ each load. They sing."

In Saigon: "After dinner to the theater at Cholon (Annamese). 'Reductio ad absurdum.' Bedlam. Whole audience talking and orchestra (?) drown out voices of actors completely. Children (part of audience) crowding the actors on stage."

In Phnom-Penh: "Present King of Cambodia — Sisowath-Monivong — descended from heaven. This is believed by our guide who took us through the palace."

At Lake Srah Srang: "See sunset and boys shooting fish with arrows."

At Angkor: "See ants following definite trails. I disturb them and watch them adopt new trails."

In Bangkok: "See Siamese Prize-fight (kicking, knees and elbows — permitted." Then: "After lunch to Pasteur Snake Farm. See a King Cobra and a Banded Krait. Poison extraction and forcible feeding."

In Penang: "See women collecting rubber. Only about 5 ¢ per tree . . . Our chauffeur takes us to the wrong steamer & leaves us in driving shower."

In Rangoon: "At 5 am we saw the Southern Cross. Magellanic clouds and the Star cloud in Saggitarius. Also fine 1st magnitude star Cadeus (?) half way from Sirius to S pole (Decl 52°S RA 6°)." . . . "At 12:15 pm we go to Ceremony of Ear Piercing (2 girls 7 or 8 yrs) and Head Shaving (2 boys 8 to 14 yrs)."

In Calcutta: "Boatloads of Pilgrims going to the mouth of the Ganges. Our Captain (on his last voyage) tells us that the place the Pilgrims go is infested with Cholera and also tigers. Marion and I walk the streets of Calcutta. We see many beggars minus toes and fingers (Leprosy?)."

In Darjeeling: "Men do the washing (swinging clothes against flat stones). Women do the heavy work; carrying dirt and stones."

In Benares: "River not dirty; only refuse we saw was flower wreaths."

On the Red Sea: "Many porpoises . . . As many as 6 at the bow sometimes, swimming upside down or on side so they can look at the ship. No motion of tails or bodies."

In Marseilles: "See remarkable cloud vortex, horseshoe shaped at about 3000′ altitude nearly overhead."

In a Spanish cathedral crypt: "4 echoes per second from sound made ½ way out along the radius of the vault. Faint and more rapid at center."

On the S.S. *Roma*, coming home: "Ground swell 15 sec. period. Under bridge with 10 sec. period, my weight on spring scales varies from 120 to 240 lbs; this corresponds to a vertical movement of plus & minus 27 ft." (There were no baseball stars aboard the *Roma* but songwriter Irving Berlin made up for this lack, and Langmuir also met Nathan Hayward, a professor at the Franklin Institute.)

After being away for so many months, there was a complicated series of meetings in order to see everybody. When the *Roma* docked at 10 a.m. on March 9, 1935, Alice and Edith — the wives of Dean and Herbert — were waiting, and so was a Mr. Glasser of IGE. Irving and Marion had lunch with Dean and Herbert at the India House, then dinner in the evening at Herbert's New York apartment, after which they caught a train for Baltimore so they could see Barbara, who came over from her school — Oldfields — to spend the next afternoon with them and was delighted with the gifts they brought, especially a white coat from Peking. By prearrangement they met Arthur, who was returning from Washington, on the train and rode back to New York with him. Then they took the night train to Schenectady, where they were met at the station by Kenneth, Dorothy, and Katharine Blodgett.

In between his more ambitious trips, Langmuir was always ready to go on shorter jaunts at a moment's notice — to a conference, to help out with a patent suit, or merely to go flying, skiing, sailing, or mountain-climbing. A flight to Minnesota? A cruise to Nova Scotia? If the proposal sounded like fun, why not? Once, in the summer of 1933, his nephew David, then a graduate student at M.I.T., and two of his room-mates decided to go on a boat trip. They knew a fellow who had a 38-foot yawl, which had a motor and would sleep six, and which he was willing to rent for sixty dollars a week. It sounded like a wonderfully cheap vacation to David and his friends. But David did not trust himself to handle a boat of that size. One of his room-mates had never been on a boat before in his life... The other knew a great deal about boats — but mostly from reading. Obviously, if they wanted to make the trip, they would need a skipper with some experience and seniority. So David wrote to Uncle Irving and asked him if he would like to come along.

In a couple of days Uncle Irving telephoned and said, "I got your letter. Yes. When are you planning to leave?"

"On August 21."

"All right. I'll be there."

And he was. The Nobel laureate appeared with the blue serge suit and black dress shoes he was wearing, and that was all. "He had no luggage with him," David recalls. "He had been too busy to think about the trip or make any preparations for it. When the time arrived, he grabbed the plane and flew up to Boston, just as he was."

It took quite a while to get all the supplies stowed away and the boat ready to go, since the party that had used the boat before them had left it full of bilge water and in a general state of disarray. It was nearly sunset before they took off from the Cottage Park Yacht Club in the rain. Almost immediately they began to have engine trouble, but the wind took them as far as Nantasket Point. While David and his friends shivered miserably in the chill dampness of the night, Uncle Irving seemed not the least bit cold. And while they tossed uncomfortably through the night, fifty-two-year-old Uncle Irving stretched sleepily, and, still wearing his blue serge suit, lay down on a wet mattress, covered himself with an oilskin, and slept the sound sleep of the innocent.

The next day, sailing when it was windy enough and starting up the motor when the wind died down, they limped along as far as the Cape Cod Canal. During the morning, on a rough sea, one at a time — first MacAdam, then Chapman, then David — got seasick and lost their breakfasts. But Uncle Irving, incorrigibly hungry, left the tiller every so often and went down to get some biscuits to chew on. It all reminded him, he said, of the time on the *Margaret* in 1918, during one of the submarine-detection tests, when the captain and the whole crew got sick. "I went down to the galley," he said, "and even the *cook* was sick. I had no choice except to fix my own lunch."

They had dropped anchor in the Cape Cod Canal about dark. When the light turned green, they started up again, but they were only making four knots against a three-knot tide. A power boat pulled up from behind, and, after towing them the last two miles through the narrow canal, cast them off at the head of Buzzard's Bay, where they sat, becalmed, in the dark and driving rain. "What do we do now?" asked David.

"Get me the chart," said Uncle Irving. And he was finally able to thread his way slowly, following the barely-visible channel lights, to a safe anchorage at Buzzard's Bay. The next day the sea got really stormy. Though they did not know it at the time they were getting part of a tropical hurricane whose eye had just passed east of Cape May. Now the wind blew mightily up Vineyard Sound, and their yawl was getting nowhere. They were stuck right where they were until the tide changed. In the thickening fog, the boat heaved and tossed, water and spray came over the side, the bilge pump quit working, the engine drained a lot of oil — in short, things were in a mess, and the morale of the cold, tired and hungry M.I.T. sailors hit rock bottom.

"Here," said Uncle Irving to David. "Take the tiller."

David did. Uncle Irving left, and came back shortly with four spoons and a big pot full of steaming-hot baked beans. He had put some Sterno in a can, nailed the can to the galley shelf, lit it, braced himself securely and held the beans over the Sterno. Then he fed everyone a hot lunch. Surprisingly, they all held it down. It warmed their innards and made them all feel much better. Gradually, as the wind's fury lessened, Langmuir took the boat on past Woods Hole and into Martha's Vineyard, where Herbert and Edith — David's parents — were vacationing at their summer place. The boat got into Gay Head, on the island, at 9:30 that night.

Next day, at the Vineyard, the winds were still blowing with gale velocity, but Langmuir insisted on a beach picnic. "I love weather," he said, and went for a swim in the lashing surf. All day, while David and his exhausted friends rested, Langmuir kept vigorously busy. He wanted to spend more time with Herbert, but the boys had to get back. That evening they drove back to Gay Head and spent the night on the boat. They got up at 6:00 and were on their way by 7:00. Though the day was bright and sunny, there was a strong head wind that wet everybody thoroughly with blown spray. They took the boat into Newport without serious incident that evening. The next morning they went to Providence, and then by train to Boston.

When they arrived in Boston, David, MacAdam and Chapman were speechless with amazement and disbelief when Uncle Irving told them he was now going to fly back to Martha's Vineyard to talk with Herbert some more. He went directly from the train station to the airport, got his plane, and, for the fun of it, followed the same route they had just covered in the boat. He was pleased to note that he could fly in fifty minutes the same distance that had taken the boat thirty-two hours. He spent that night, August 26, with Herbert and Edith. His diary the following day reads: "Swim at Beach Club with Herbert and see his Lot. Fly home in 3 hrs 15 min. Going against the wind. Explore a cloud. Then on to Lake George. Aunt Anna and Otis Haven there." And the day after: "At Crown Island: Aquaplaning. Out in sailboat but no wind. NE Squall in the afternoon. Get wave data with Otis Haven." And that is the way it went with Irving Langmuir, who believed in living every minute.

In 1935, not long after his return from the Far East, some of his Schenectady friends persuaded him that he ought to *do* something about the city government which he had lately been so critical of. The persuasion led to Langmuir's one brief fling in politics. His diary of August 31, 1935, reads: "I accept nomination to the City Council under Manager Plan (Plan C) under Charter League."

As November drew nearer, Langmuir campaigned quite actively, and he was giving as many as three speeches a night, attending political rallies, and talking on the local radio station. But despite his best efforts, Schenectady was not interested in honoring — at least, not in this particular fashion — its most-honored-by-the-world citizen, and Langmuir, on November 5, wrote: "I fail in election for City Council. I am 10th with 11,453 votes. At one time it seemed as though I might be elected with 6 Republicans. I was much relieved to see English go ahead of me. The City has lost a great opportunity of breaking away from the rotten . . . Political Machine."

In the thirties, Kenneth entered Dartmouth. David graduated from Yale, and Alex from Harvard — both cum laude, and then went on to their respective graduate schools, David to go into physics, Alex into medicine. (Langmuir even went to a Yale-Dartmouth football game with Kenneth and Alex, and watched Dartmouth win, to Kenneth's great delight.) Robert, too, had decided to become a physicist. Barbara had her coming-out party. Six months later, at the Langmuirs' 1937 Christmas party, she and her neighbor, Harry Summerhayes, Jr., announced their engagement. On November 5 of the following year they were married in the Union College Chapel.

One Langmuir automobile gave way to another, then another, then there were two at a time. One airplane was sold, another bought. Dogs died or got lost, and new ones were adopted or purchased (the Langmuirs always had at least one dog, sometimes two). Maids and handymen came and went at the big house on Stratford Road, and Langmuir noted their comings and goings in his daily entries. There were engagements and commencements and weddings. There were births and christenings — and there were deaths. Marion and Irving both lost their mothers in the thirties. Marion hurried back from a European trip in 1931 after receiving a cable from Dorothy about her mother's illness, leaving Irving — feeling "much depressed" — to complete the tour alone. Mrs. Mersereau died, at seventy-nine, in 1931; and Mrs. Langmuir, at eighty-seven, in 1936.

And there were illnesses, of course, slight and serious. Irving worried about Herbert's cancer, and about Arthur, who began to have heart trouble. And Alex, now a physician, was increasingly called upon to appear — even if only to lend moral support — in medical emergencies. In June of 1939, Herbert's trouble suddenly became Irving's, quite literally. Pains, an examination, and Dr. Hans Rozendaal — the General Electric doctor — gravely advised Irving Langmuir to go to Boston for an operation of his own.

His diary of June 17 reads: "Marion and I are driven to Boston and the New England Baptist Hospital and, as prearranged, we meet Dr. Cattel (who will perform the operation) at noon. I am put to bed."

On June 21: "Given dope at 8 am. Conscious when taken to the operating room. Spinal injection. Tilted head down. I am conscious during the operation. I heard Dr. Cattel describing his findings, etc., 1 hr and 17 min plus time to close the wound. No pain. No nausea. No gas pains."

The diagnosis was cancer of the large intestine and more surgery would be necessary; but the news was restricted to such a small, intimate circle, that even many Langmuirs may be reading of it here for the first time.

On September 1: "We are in Boston for a second expected operation . . . At 7 A.M. I am given dope and at about 8:30 I am taken down to the operating room. Spinal anesthetic. I am conscious but half asleep. Operation lasts about 45 min. At 9:30 I am back in my room perfectly conscious & comfortable. Numb from upper chest down. No discomfort." Alex, who was on hand, recalls that Uncle Irving offered free advice to the doctors until the anesthetic took effect, than resumed as soon as it started wearing off.

The operations apparently were successful in removing all traces of the malignancy. Irving Langmuir, fifty-eight at the time, continued to live a full life for another eighteen years, with no hint of the cancer's recurrence.

As he lay in Boston on September 1 waiting to go down to the operating room, Langmuir heard, over the radio, that German troops had invaded Poland at six o'clock that morning. Two days later England and France declared war on Germany. Just about one year later, Langmuir was in Detroit for the one hundredth meeting of the American Chemical Society. On September 9, 1940, he noted: "Have lunch (Detroit) with Conant who asks me to come to Washington for some special work."

Though the United States was still more than a year away from Pearl Harbor, the "special work" was war work. Irving Langmuir had lived to serve his country — and serve it well — through another war, the direct outgrowth of the event he had taken so little notice of that day in Berlin in 1933.

Chapter 20

"MR. MCCORMACK: What is your opinion as to the importance of research and development work in connection with our military organizations?

"MR. QUARLES: Well, as you can imagine, Congressman, I would tend to put that near the top of the list..."

Transcript of 1954 hearings, House Subcommittee on Military Operations.

CLOSELY associated with Langmuir in all his work throughout World War II and thereafter was Vincent J. Schaefer, who also became one of the closest personal friends Langmuir ever had. Langmuir first met the younger man at Apperson's camp, which was next to his own at Lake George. Schaefer, who worked for General Electric as an apprentice machinist, was another tall, husky lover of the out-of-doors. He was particularly fond of the Adirondacks, and was quite active in Apperson's never-ending conservation battle. He now and then made a documentary movie for the cause (Langmuir was especially impressed with one he made to point up the dangers of carrying on timbering operations in the thin, glaciated soil of the Adirondacks), and he usually edited his film in Apperson's Lake George camp. Katharine Blodgett also had a camp there. She was Apperson's next-door neighbor, too, on the other side, and she got to know Schaefer around the same time Langmuir did. She and Langmuir were then hard at work on their surface chemistry studies, and back at the laboratory they began more and more to call on young Schaefer — who was fascinated with their research — to help build their apparatus. He showed not only an ingenuity and meticulousness in equipment-making that almost — but not quite — matched Sweetser's but also a remarkably inventive imagination. He was constantly suggesting good experimental ideas, and showed such a quick understanding of what the work in monolayers was all about that Langmuir began to see in Schaefer the same kind of promise that Sir Humphrey Davy had seen in his unschooled laboratory assistant, young Faraday. Schaefer was soon looked upon more as a fellow researcher than as a mere technical hand. Still, he had no official status; nor, he felt, could he hope for any. Though he had picked up quite a lot of scientific knowledge from prodigious reading, night study, and home experiments, he simply had none of the formal educational credentials which he knew were a *sine qua non* of advancement in the laboratory. He had reached a point, in fact, where he was seriously considering going into the nursery-and-gardening business, where his work would at least have the advantage of keeping him out of doors.

When the time arrived for Sweetser (who was, incidentally, Schaefer's next-door neighbor in Schenectady) to retire as Langmuir's assistant, Katharine Blodgett suggested to Langmuir that Schaefer was the natural replacement for him. Langmuir agreed. He went to Schaefer and offered him the job, which Schaefer instantly and enthusiastically accepted. For a while there was great reluctance on the part of Langmuir's superiors to hire as Langmuir's assistant a man who had no college degree at all — in fact, not even a real high school diploma. But to Langmuir any considerations other than a man's proven capabilities seemed quite irrelevant. He insisted on Schaefer, and Schaefer got the job.

His first assignment was to continue investigating the mechanical properties of monolayers. "I am still amazed," he says, "at the amount of freedom Langmuir gave me to carry out the work in my own way — even when it meant neglecting or postponing some specific chore he wanted me to do for him." In the laboratory and out, he and Langmuir spent a great deal of time together, and Langmuir — always an eager teacher — found in Schaefer an equally eager pupil, keen-eyed and keen-minded, with a curiosity as restless as Langmuir's own. Educated at what he likes to call "Langmuir University" — of which he is of course not the sole alumnus — Schaefer later became one of GE's best known scientists. The former apprentice machinist, journeyman toolmaker, and landscape gardener even became "Dr. Schaefer" by virtue of an honorary degree from Notre Dame. Schaefer, a dedicated amateur naturalist, was delighted to discover that there were things which he could teach even Langmuir about the out-of-doors, especially things about plants and animals; and this may have been one of his great attractions for Langmuir — whose teaching tendencies did not keep him from remaining a perennial pupil himself.

When Langmuir made himself available once more to the United States government as it started mobilizing its research resources for World War II, well before its own direct participation in the war, Langmuir was naturally put right to work. In 1940 the Chemical Warfare Service of the Army was worried that the Germans might use poisonous smokes against the combat troops of its enemies. If they did, the Allies would be caught completely off guard, since the conventional gas masks would afford no protection against such attacks. Gas masks, as Langmuir well knew from his surface chemistry studies, used charcoal to soak up poison gases. The surface of charcoal could adsorb (or a mass of charcoal could *ab*sorb) gases only. So if a smoke were volatile, a gas mask would work. But if a smoke, instead of vaporizing into a gas, remained suspended in the air in the form of extra-fine dust particles, a gas mask could do nothing to keep them out. What was needed to stop such particles was a new kind of filter. The National Defense Research Committee asked Langmuir if he would undertake a study of the smoke-filtration problem.

"With characteristic energy," Schaefer — who joined Langmuir at the very start of the program — writes, "he set about to develop a basic physical theory of filtration mechanisms and within a few weeks had developed a number of ideas that needed testing. Meanwhile, as was his custom, he had asked me to start experimenting with fibres of various types so that time would not be lost in testing out ideas which might arise as the result of experiment or theory."

Now Langmuir, a man strong on theory, had often heard the argument — and agreed with it, up to a point — that a lot of time can be wasted on experiments if the experimenter does not know where he is going or exactly what he is looking for. But he was altogether impatient with the dogmatic theory-first-*then*-experiment school of scientific research. Langmuir held that it was dangerous to theorize too much in advance of plunging into the experimental work. In so doing a scientist was likely to generate too many preconceived notions about what he is going to find, and thus be unprepared to take advantage of the windfalls of serendipity. A man can become so completely focused on some specific result that he virtually brainwashes himself into expecting nothing else. Then he tends to look so hard for what seems to him the relevent factor in an experiment that he is in danger of overlooking facts which may turn out to be much more significant. Even worse, too much theorizing can talk a man out of performing an experiment altogether. Remember Willis Whitney's trouble trying to get any of his scientists to find out whether bugs could live in a vacuum? They all *knew* that no organism could live without oxygen. Why do the experiment then? But Whitney did the experiment and found out that an insect could seem to be dead in a vacuum yet come quickly to life again once an oxygen supply became available.

Langmuir's philosophy of research made him doubly grateful for an assistant like Schaefer. They made a perfect team. Once Schaefer understood the problem, Langmuir had absolute confidence in his experimental instincts. He would turn Schaefer loose to start experimenting, unfettered by any theoretical preconceptions. Then he, Langmuir, could retire to his study and theorize contentedly, knowing that Schaefer would serve as his experimental *alter ego* and not let him miss any bets. All this is what Schaefer meant when he talked about the "usual" custom they followed on the smoke-filter program. By the time Langmuir had worked out the theory, Schaefer had done just about all the necessary testing, especially with glass wool asbestos fibers, which not only seemed to have the desirable dimensions, but were also plentifully at hand.

Before they could adequately test their filters, of course, they first had to have something to filter. And the something — if the tests were to help the Army — had to be a smoke consisting of the kind of submicroscopic aerosols that would be very difficult to filter — in brief, the kind of smoke the Germans might be likely to use. So Langmuir and Schaefer had to learn how to generate that kind of smoke, since no available type of smoke generator was capable of doing it. And the smoke particles would have to be stable enough so that their size, concentration and distribution could be measured. "It then took a lot of preparation," Langmuir said, telling the National Academy of Sciences about the project after the war was over, "to make particles of uniform size, determine how to measure them, and to learn how much of the material went through the filter.

"That work lasted for about one year. We obtained fairly successful theoretical results and a better understanding of how to build a good filter. But notice what we did incidentally: we acquired a great deal of detailed knowledge as to how to make a smoke which would be non-volatile, which would consist of very, very small particles, far smaller than those of ordinary smokes, and we learned much about their optical properties. We studied such things as the passage of gases through small spaces and around fibers and studied the trajectories of little particles carried by those gases."

Langmuir had an ulterior motive in telling his audience about the smoke-filter project in such detail. Yes, his theme again was serendipity. He wanted once more to drive home his favorite message that no amount of planning can predict where a given line of research might lead; that overplanning can severely inhibit creative research, since it builds fences around the researcher and strictly delimits his sphere of activity; and that the best research planning, in Langmuir's view, is to "put ourselves into a favorable position to profit by unexpected circumstances."

Just as Langmuir and Schaefer were finishing up the smoke-filter project (having assured adequate protection for Allied troops in the event the enemy did decide to use poisonous smokes) in August of 1941, a form letter came around. It was sent out, said Langmuir, "probably to everybody working in that field," and it conveyed the information that the Germans were using light colored smokes on a rather large scale for smoke-screen protection of their industrial plants. The smoke screens had been observed from the air only, and no one knew how the Germans generated them. The letter appealed for ideas on how to create artificial fogs or white smoke screens that could render large areas invisible to enemy aircraft, or, at least, to make it harder for enemy planes to find their targets.

Well, now here were Langmuir and Schaefer with a new smoke generator in hand, the one they had just had to design in order to generate the fine-particled smoke necessary to test their smoke filters. From their studies of both liquid and solid particles of various sizes they had become quite familiar with the optical properties of these particles. Langmuir already knew, then, when the form letter arrived, that the smaller particles would be best for smoke-screening purposes. Long ago Lord Rayleigh had worked out the laws of light scattering (such as the scattering of light from the molecules of the atmosphere, which is what makes the sky look blue), and it was known that the scattering depended, measurably and calculably, upon the size of the particles doing the scattering.

"In other words," said Langmuir, "there must be a definite particle diameter which gives the most effective screening. This optimum diameter was found to be practically equal to the wavelength of the light which it is desired to scatter." For scattering visible light, he calculated, the ideal particle diameter would be six-tenths of a micron.

These were much tinier particles than had ever been made by any previously existing smoke generator (in the United States, at least), but it so happened that the particles Langmuir had just been generating for his filter tests — the size most difficult to filter — measured *five*-tenths of a micron in diameter, even a tiny bit tinier than the ideal size. Thus, by sheer accident — or call it serendipital force — he already possessed a generator that was close to being able to do the screening job. Of course a much larger generator would be needed for practical use in the field. "When the quantities of smoke needed were established," Schaefer recalls, "it became apparent that a radical change in our method of making smoke was needed if we were to meet the required objectives. Where a hundredth of a gram per second had been used for our smoke filter testing, the generator needed for producing a suitable artificial fog would be required to convert at least 10,000 times more material into smoke.

"With this in mind, Langmuir, as was his custom, retired to his home study, leaving me to approach the problem experimentally. It occurred to me that a modified version of Langmuir's vacuum pump might work, using oil instead of mercury. When I showed him how effective such a unit could be (I used an oil can as a model) he became very enthusiastic and excited, and encouraged me to build a much larger generator embodying my basic idea.

"When I next saw him," Schaefer continues, "a week or so later, after I had made, abandoned and redesigned a number of versions of such smoke generators, he announced with quiet satisfaction that he had worked out a theoretical design he was confident would work efficiently, using the quantity and type of material we had previously agreed upon. My more successful experiments had shown that a practical design depended on the use of a flash boiler operated so as to boil oleic acid or S.A.E. No. 30 auto oil at about 10 pounds of pressure with an escape orifice of 3/16 inch and a boiling point for the liquid greater than

400°C. He grinned when I gave him these findings as he showed me the results of his theoretical computations. They showed that a flash boiler operated at 9.4 pounds per square inch, using an oil having a boiling point of 425°C with an escape orifice of 0.187 inch was indicated!" They could hardly have come to a closer agreement, one pursuing pure theory, the other following the experimental road. (This design, by the way, is quite close to the design still used by the Army for its smoke generators.)

Now, to field-test their generator, they needed a wind tunnel. A big wind tunnel. Bigger than any the Air Force possessed at any of its research facilities. As they talked about the problem, they suddenly remembered a really big wind tunnel — a wind tunnel a mile wide and ten miles long. And it was only twenty miles from Schenectady. Since they were both outdoorsmen, their imagination would not be restricted to considering what kind of research facility might be *built*, at great expense of time and money. They looked to nature's facilities, and found their wind tunnel in the Schoharie Valley — near Middleburg, New York — a site familiar to both Langmuir and Schaefer from years of trekking around the region. The valley had a nice flat-bottomed flood plain with high hills on one side and a cliff on the other. And from one point — known as Vroman's Nose — on the cliff's Ice-Age-smoothed summit, there is an overhang right where the valley bends, affording an excellent view in both directions. "We decided to make smoke in that valley," said Langmuir, "and see how long it lasted and how far it traveled." The first tests were made with their own still-too-small generator that could boil only ten gallons of oil per hour. Once they had convinced themselves it worked, they wanted a much bigger one for a really convincing demonstration — a real working model that would boil a hundred gallons of oil per hour.

The General Electric laboratory did not have the facilities to build the huge smoke generator to Langmuir's specifications, so Langmuir decided it might be sensible to try an oil company. He went to the Standard Oil Company of New Jersey. "The generator was assembled," said Langmuir, "by the Standard Oil personnel from things they could manage to obtain in three weeks from their scrap piles and other places." They built "a large workable unit which was finished and ready for operation within a month."

Meanwhile Langmuir and Schaefer had acquired several assistants to speed their task, and had established a test site for the smaller generator in the Schoharie Valley. On Vroman's Nose, Langmuir set up a time-lapse camera, and was thus able to document photographically what they observed. Langmuir learned a lot about how to use the generator. He also learned a lot about the daily climate patterns of the Schoharie Valley, which was important to the success of the work. They had not been there long when the Army sent them some of their own smoke generators — the best then available. These burned the same amount of oil, ten gallons per hour, as the Langmuir–Schaefer test model. The smoke they emitted was black, sooty, and greasy stuff. For comparative testing, the Army's best was set up side by side with the new generator — still the small field-test model. The new generator gave out not only an incomparably superior quality of smoke for the purpose — but gave it out in quantities that covered an area *four hundred times as great.* Langmuir could hardly wait for the big Standard Oil model to arrive, and — once it had been tested — to demonstrate it for the big brass of the Defense Department.

Such a demonstration was finally set up for June 24, 1942. The day before the scheduled test — on June 23 — Langmuir ran through what he calls in his diary a "dress rehearsal" of the demonstration. Everything came off to his satisfaction. When the brass arrived that evening, Langmuir was distressed to learn from their aides that no one was in favor of starting for the valley much before nine o'clock in the morning. Langmuir had counted on everything — including the observers — being ready to begin the performance before sunrise. He hurriedly called together the party of some thirty or forty officials and gave them a straight-faced briefing, announcing the prearranged schedule (up at 2 : 30, breakfast at 3 : 30) and explaining that everyone had to get to the summit of that mountain, with only a jeep road going most of the way up — and after that only foot paths, before dawn. Everyone followed the schedule obediently, even cheerfully, since Langmuir had infected them with his own enthusiasm for what they were about to see, and had described in detail what would happen, hour by hour, from sunrise to eleven o'clock.

"We all arrived half an hour before sunrise," Langmuir recalled later. "There were no casualties. The sun rose, there was not a cloud in the sky, there was very little wind, and the valley was completely filled with smoke in a short time. After we had run for about one hour and the whole valley to a distance of six or eight miles was filled with smoke, the wind started up as we hoped it would, and it blew the smoke out, to show what happens when you do not have quiet conditions and the smoke is carried into the sky. We were glad this happened since it was important to show how an allowance must be made for the effects of winds when screening operations are carried out." Another reason he was glad it happened, of course, was that he had predicted it would. "To this day," says Schaefer, "I am not sure whether the job was sold on the effectiveness of the fog demonstration, or the perfect weather and atmospheric behavior forecast given by Langmuir the night before!"

Less than a week later — with the Army already cancelling its orders for the old-style generators — Langmuir gave a report in person to the high brass of the Chemical Warfare Service in Washington, and was ready to go on to other matters.

What Langmuir did not learn until long after the war's end was how widely the Allies had used his smoke generators. Many cities overseas protected themselves with a blanket of artificial fog to reduce the hazards of enemy bombing. The Canadians used the generators extensively as a cover for troop movements in Holland. For three successive days before and during the Allied crossing of the Rhine in the war's final phases, smoke screens were laid down along a sixty-five mile front. Troops in North Africa, invasion forces in the bays and on the beaches of Italy, engineers throwing pontoon bridges across German rivers — all were protected by the Langmuir smoke screens. There is no way to estimate the number of soldiers' lives they saved.

Even the Navy in the Pacific, which at first thought smoke generators unnecessary, changed its mind when the Japanese suicide pilots with their explosive-laden *kamikaze* planes began to take such a high toll of American naval vessels. After the Navy finally did get the smoke generators into operation, never again was a single ship lost, or even damaged, in a *kamikaze* attack!

One more thing about the Langmuir–Schaefer smoke generator: It was capable of producing, every second of its operation, 10^{17} smoke particles — that is, a hundred quadrillions of particles. It would also, when the time came, be able to produce an equal number of particles of silver iodide — and silver iodide particles, it was soon to be learned, had a strange effect on clouds . . .

But before Langmuir and Schaefer could make the next stop along Serendipity Road, another chore intervened — the resumption, for a while, of the submarine detection work Langmuir had done so successfully in World War I. "As soon as our field demonstration [in the Schoharic Valley] was over and we had all indulged in a couple of days of sleep," says Schaefer, "we tidied up the loose ends of our field project and entered into a new and entirely unrelated project concerned with the use of binaural sound for the detection of submarines — an interesting sequel to work done by Coolidge, Langmuir, Hennelly and Ferguson during World War I."

Actually Langmuir had already gone to a few conferences on the submarine detection problem back in June of 1941 and had been consulting right along. Very little progress had been made in the field since the advances the GE group had achieved in 1917 and 1918. Now, in World War II, Ed Hennelly and Vaughn Ferguson again went to work on the project. Hennelly remembers the group's first meeting — a big dinner meeting at the Parker House in Boston — called to discuss the next steps to be pursued in the antisubmarine research. He was astounded to hear Langmuir, after a lapse of more than twenty years, describe and reconstruct all their World War I experiments in voluminous detail — the apparatus, the procedures, the ideas, even the specific data. "It was as though it had all just happened that morning," says Hennelly, "and he had written it all down and was now reading it, verbatim, from the paper. I've always been amazed at Langmuir's memory. It is phenomenal in two directions. He can remember every detail of something that might have happened a long time ago; and he can forget what happened five minutes ago, if what happened didn't particularly interest him. He can remember every handhold and crevasse of a mountain he climbed as a teen-age boy. Yet I've gone to the movies with him, and had him not realize until the picture was half over that he'd already seen it before."

When one of the Navy men present commented on his feat of memory, Langmuir said he believed that how well you remember something depends largely on how interested you were at the time you experienced it. "That may be true," said the Navy man. "But to remember in such *detail*. You really do have an incredible memory."

Hennelly, who liked to twit Langmuir about his long-standing unwillingness to admit the existence of a supreme deity — or of anything else whose existence could not be proved — offered an explanation: "It's a gift of God."

"Haw!" snorted Langmuir, then quickly changed the subject back to the detection of submarines.

In December of 1942 Langmuir did get out — again off Boston — to sea on the *Beverly* with Hennelly and Ferguson, to test a new device called the KC tube. While waiting in the harbor, aboard a tug, for one of the tests to begin, Langmuir, leaning over the side with another GE man, noticed the usual oil scum floating on top of the water. "He started to point out some of the properties of the oil film on the water to the other GE man with him and his conversation was so interesting that, one by one, young sailors crowded around. He sent to the galley for some vegetable oils and put on a demonstration of surface film effects. The sailors were spellbound by his interesting talk and demonstration."

For the most part, however, Langmuir left the sea testing to the others, and contented himself, this time, with watching the antisubmarine project from the sidelines. Leaving the Navy under water, he began, on behalf of the Air Force, to tangle with the clouds.

Chapter 21

"There is really no such thing as bad weather – only different kinds of good weather."

JOHN RUSKIN

EARLY in 1943, the Secretary of War asked Langmuir to look into the problem of electrostatic precipitation on aircraft flying through snowstorms. The problem had suddenly become important in the war plans against Japan. "It was believed," Langmuir said, "that the invasion by Japan would have to come through the Aleutian Islands, across Alaska and from the North. That led to a tremendous development of air transport and airplanes through the Aleutians.

"The difficulty in flying aircraft in the Aleutians is very, very serious. One of the great difficulties was icing of aircraft," he later recalled, "but even more baffling was the complete loss of radio contact when these planes flew through snow storms. In Alaska the planes become charged, sometimes, with 250,000 volts or more and this electric field produces corona discharges from all parts of the plane. This caused such electrical disturbances that radio sets could not be used to receive messages. Particularly, pilots had difficulty in finding their bases and getting down through this foggy bad weather."

Langmuir had no ready-made theory to apply to this problem.

nor any solutions to offer. Obviously he would have to set up some sort of experiment to duplicate the conditions that caused the electrical discharges to occur. Only then could he investigate the reasons for the trouble, and suggest a remedy. But how to duplicate, in the laboratory, the condition of a plane sweeping through a snowstorm without setting up something elaborate, costly, and time-consuming? Might nature provide the ideal facility again, as it had in the case of the smoke generator? It might at that. And Langmuir believed that Mount Washington in the White Mountains might be just the place.

Langmuir had come to know Mount Washington during his early days in Schenectady. In fact he, in the company of his rugged friend Apperson, had been among the first ever to make a successful winter ascent of that formidable peak. "Mount Washington in winter has a wonderful climate," said Langmuir, with great enthusiasm. Only Langmuir would think it was wonderful. "The average temperature," he gloated, "is 4 or 5 degrees below zero Fahrenheit. The wind velocity is about 60 miles per hour average, day and night, and most of the time with this high wind velocity clouds are sweeping over the summit.

"We thought that, with this drifting snow, all we would have to do would be to take different kinds of surfaces such as aluminum, put different coatings on these surfaces, expose them to the drifting snow, and in the well-equipped laboratory of the Mount Washington Observatory, with power equipment and so on, measurement could be obtained of the electrical charges which develop from the impact of snow on the exposed surfaces.

"We sent a lot of equipment up there before the road closed in the middle of October," he went on. "We got it up there just in time. Then Mr. Schaefer went up there several times to conduct experiments during storms and found the results to be very disappointing. We found, much to our surprise, that anything exposed on the summit of Mount Washington during the winter when clouds were there, as they are most of the time, immediately becomes covered with ice. This was due to the presence of supercooled water droplets. We had heard about rime, we had seen it, but we did not know it occurred all the time at a place like Mount Washington. There are very few winter days without it. This puzzled us a lot."

"Since we were primarily interested in the charging rates of snow on metal rather than snow on ice," Schaefer remembers, "it appeared that much of the intensive effort to build and install equipment on Mount Washington before the winter storms of 1943—44 blocked the road was likely to be wasted." As it turned out, most of the information on electrostatic precipitation did have to be gleaned from laboratory work indoors, using icelike powders and Mount Washington's natural snowfall.

Meanwhile Langmuir grew fascinated with the icing phenomena. He wanted to know why and how the ice formed on the metal surfaces. He wanted to know more about those supercooled water droplets and how they formed in clouds. "It so happened," said Langmuir, "that the Secretary of War's office was just as much interested in problems of aircraft icing as precipitation ice static. So we started on a study of the icing of aircraft."

Langmuir was luckier in World War II than in World War I in being able to follow the research that intrigued him most. In 1917 and 1918, he could not drop the antisubmarine work in favor of projects which promised no contribution to the war effort. But in 1943 and 1944 the further research that he wanted to do was directly applicable to war problems. He had, in any case, gone just about as far as he could with the precipitation-static studies. As the indoor laboratory work progressed and a B-17 flying laboratory went to work on the problem, Langmuir was free to — and, in fact, urgently encouraged to — proceed on the icing problem. The water droplets that froze on aircraft wings could be — and often had been — deadly.

"Thus," says Vincent Schaefer, "without losing time or effort we quickly shifted our objectives and were soon actively involved in basic studies of the physical and chemical nature of icing clouds sweeping over Mount Washington. Few places in the world surpass Mount Washington in providing better conditions for such studies. No existing facility in the United States remotely approached the Mount Washington Observatory in providing better research conditions and facilities. Accordingly for the next two years intensive studies were carried on with the hearty co-operation of the Observatory research personnel led by Victor Clark.

"Langmuir visited the Observatory a number of times in 1944 and 1945," Schaefer goes on. "Although then over sixty years of age he climbed the mountain on skis several times with the writer. We would go the short steep route by way of Tuckerman's Ravine and Lion's Head. His climb was a steady slow pace interspersed with pauses during which all manner of natural phenomena would be discussed. The presence or absence of ice nuclei under varying conditions, the properties of the snow, sky and clouds, the appearance of timber line trees, the behavior of ice boring pebbles, the use of stereophotography to determine the depth of snow in the ravine — these and numerous other aspects of the atmosphere and its interaction with the mountain made such a climb a stimulating adventure in understanding.

"Upon arrival at the summit work would really begin as his searching mind probed all aspects of the many interacting phenomena going on outside the door."

While these experiments were in progress, John D. Langmuir, Arthur's son, received a letter from his Uncle Dean, dated May 2, 1944. "Irving came down a week ago to see Herbert," Dean wrote. "I have never seen him look better nor has his mind ever been keener. During the winter, Irving has been directing some research work done on the top of Mt. Washington, in connection with some war work of his. A few weeks ago, he decided that he wanted to get some firsthand information on what they were doing so he skied up and skied down — quite an accomplishment for a man of 63 who has had very little exercise in the last year or two.

"As a matter of fact," said Dean, in his letter, "he didn't ski up the mountain but had to climb Tuckerman's Ravine by using crampons since the side of the mountain at that place was solid ice and there was no snow. It must have been an undertaking as he said there was a 43° slope."

Langmuir was doing more than just a job on Mount Washington. He had become utterly absorbed in the data being procured. He felt he was on the trail of some really basic knowledge about the weather, and he was finding clues to what made clouds form, why it rained, why it snowed or failed to. The scientific crew on the mountaintop caught some of Langmuir's own impatience to acquire as much information as possible, and to acquire it as rapidly as possible.

"During our visits which lasted generally for three or four days," says Schaefer, "many of the crew would literally work around the clock gathering data, trying out new ideas, devising new and crude but workable equipment to test out theories which were continually being made or abandoned as we explored the nature of the subcooled clouds that engulfed us most of the time. Occasionally when the skies would clear Langmuir and I would don our skis or crampons and explore the summit cone and its environs. Every such excursion would be an adventure with nothing ever quenching his enthusiasm for exploring and trying to solve the mysteries of water and ice and their role in the atmosphere. Typical of his observations and studies were his reports on the growth of particles and his pioneering studies of water droplet trajectories. Another result of his enthusiasm were the voluminous reports issued by the Mount Washington Observatory during this period including the highly useful monograph 'The Multicylinder Method' used by many research groups since that time establishing cloud droplet size, size distribution and liquid water content.

"A tangible result of his regard for the mountain as a place to do icing research was the increased use made of the mountain by the Navy and Air Force and aircraft engine manufacturers for testing out anti-icing characteristics of airplane engines, airfoils, flight instruments and components. This eventually led to the construction of the multimillion dollar Air Force Icing Research Laboratory near the summit and used for a number of years for aircraft icing protection studies."

As Langmuir learned more and more about what goes on in

clouds, their structure, the formation of water droplets and ice crystals, the effects on them of air currents and changing temperatures, he began to devise a number of theories — making extensive use of his knowledge of surface chemistry, and the knowledge of particle behaviour picked up during his smoke-generator studies. If any of the theories even approximated the truth, their proving-out could revolutionize the very inexact science of meteorology. He was extremely eager to test out his fundamental theory covering at least the partial reasons why particles of moisture accumulated into various kinds of clouds. "However," he wrote, "the conditions on Mount Washington are complicated. The wind blowing over the irregular surface of the mountain gives turbulence and complicated wind structures. It would be far better to study cloud-particle growth in airplane flights except that then, to measure the vertical air movements, new instruments would have to be devised. The velocities are higher and there are many other difficulties.

"Schaefer and I gave a lot of thought to instruments that we could devise and put on airplanes to get the needed data. On a certain flight through a cloud, we would want to measure how much water there is, how big are the particles, and how they compare in size. What is the vertical velocity? How long has it been since that air entered the base of the cloud? How fast is it rising into the cloud?

"Those were the things we wanted to measure. That meant an accelerometer or something to measure the bumpiness of the air. To get such data meant a lot of work.

"The war had about ended at that time so we had no more Army contracts, or at least the war-time contracts were over, and I couldn't see why the General Electric Company should go into meteorological work. It seemed however that we should understand something about clouds from a national defense standpoint.

"We took the question up with the Army Air Forces and the Signal Corps. We were led to think that perhaps somebody might furnish aircraft for experimental purposes of this sort. We did not get along very fast. We carried the research along on our own to a large extent, testing instruments on Mount Washington, but we never got tests in aircraft."

This was one time, then, when it was impossible to take advantage of the laboratory nature provided. They would have to think of some meaningful way to find out what they wanted to know with indoor experiments. And obviously the set-up would have to be reasonably simple. If they could not afford an airplane to go up in, they could certainly not afford any elaborate ground facilities. "There must be something in the atmosphere that causes water to change to ice only at certain times and under various conditions," Langmuir insisted. The problem was how to find out what the something was without flying again and again into clouds to observe what went on inside them. As other matters more and more occupied Langmuir's attention, it was Schaefer who did most of the fooling around with the postwar experiments.

There had been many other things to occupy Langmuir during the war years of course — including a brief sortie into salvaging a war effort of a different sort in Schenectady. He interceded on behalf of *The Folks Back Home,* a small newspaper put out for Schenectady boys who were overseas, and edited by Marion Langmuir. When the paper was about to go broke, Langmuir talked the local War Chest Board into providing the additional few hundred dollars that were needed to keep it going.

One of the Schenectady boys overseas, by the way, was Captain Kenneth Langmuir of the Antiaircraft Artillery, who was in Italy. He had gone into the Army as an enlisted man, come out of officers' candidate school at Camp Davis, North Carolina, as a second lieutenant, and had been promoted twice since. On Christmas day, 1944, Kenneth sent flowers from Italy. On May 7, 1945, Langmuir wrote in his diary: "Pres Truman announces that the German Armies have surrendered unconditionally... Kenneth is now out of the war!" And on September 17, 1945: "At 9 AM Kenneth telephoned from Camp Kilmer. He arrived in US yesterday. He will go to Fort Dix today and will come up to Schenectady soon. I have to go to Chicago tonight for Conference on Atomic Bomb at the Univ. of Chicago."

Japan had already surrendered, too, by the time he made that last entry, and the two atomic bombs had been dropped on Hiroshima and Nagasaki, catapulting an ill-prepared world into a new era. Langmuir had visited Lise Meitner's laboratory in Berlin on his 1931 European trip, and had come away very much impressed by that lady's work with radioactive elements. When he later heard of her work on uranium fission, brought successfully to its conclusion in a classic experiment by Hahn and Strassman after she had fled Nazi Germany, Langmuir recognized the tremendous significance of the possibilities and, like so many other scientists, began to feel a sense of foreboding about the future. Unlike many of the others, he did not participate in Project Manhattan, and may not even have known about the existence of the project until he heard the public announcement of the Hiroshima bomb. But when he heard it, his fears were confirmed. From then on he participated in most of the activities of the atomic scientists designed to alert the public to the dangers inherent in the atomic age.

His desire to do something about awakening the American public to the hard choices that lay ahead had already been stimulated by another experience — before the bomb fell on Hiroshima — which had a profound effect on him. This was a trip to Soviet Russia, which came about very unexpectedly as a result of an invitation to attend the celebration of the 220th Anniversary of the Academy of Sciences of the U.S.S.R., lasting from June 15 to June 28, 1945. He tells about this trip and the impressions he absorbed while in Russia in two long articles which appeared in *Chemical and Engineering News* and *Scientific Monthly* in 1946. Though his stay in the U.S.S.R. was brief, he was able to gather a voluminous amount of information. Langmuir was a superb reporter, as these articles show, and one can only wish he had found the time to write similarly descriptive and penetrating articles about some of his other trips to Europe, Asia, Canada, Mexico, and Central America.

Packed as these articles are with interesting information, however, they naturally leave out a great deal about the background of the trip, and the circumstances under which it was made. His brother Dean, who was very close to him at this time, wrote a fascinating series of letters about Irving's Russian journey, to his niece (Arthur's daughter, Ruth Van de Water), and to his own daughter, Evelyn Harmon. Dean was able to tell in his letters what his brother could not, for obvious reasons, include in his published articles. The eye-opening Russian journey was so influential in shaping Langmuir's attitudes and utterances in world affairs after his return to the United States that it seems well worth the space to quote at some length from Dean's previously-unpublished epistolary account.

Chapter 22

> "'Some people,' said Mrs. Gamp, again entrenching herself behind her strong point, as if it were not assailable by human ingenuity, 'may be Rooshans, and others may be Prooshans; they are born so, and will please themselves. Them which is of other naturs, thinks different.'"
>
> CHARLES DICKENS
> *Martin Chuzzlewit*

"IRVING phoned from Schenectady on Monday, June 4," Dean wrote to Ruth Van de Water on June 18, 1945. "He gave me the startling news that he had been invited by the Russian government to go to Russia for a month, and that he would spend the next night (Tuesday) in New York and would leave the morning after (Wednesday) from LaGuardia Field on a Russian plane for Moscow via Alaska and Siberia. I had a cot put up in my room for him because hotel rooms in New York are now scarcer than ever...

"The day after arrival, on Wednesday, Irving heard that the plane wouldn't take off until late in the day so I stayed at the apartment until noon for a long farewell talk though we had talked until 1 AM the night before. He showed me the invitation he had received and I thought it rather curt..."

There was a P.S. on the invitation (signed by N. Novicov, Charge d'Affaires of the Soviet Embassy in Washington) which read: "Travel expenses and expenses of the sojourn in U.S.S.R.

will be paid by the Academy of Sciences of the U.S.S.R." The invitation had been addressed to "Prof. Irving Langmuir, Shenektady, N.Y."

After quoting the invitation, Dean wrote: "The following comments pertain to the above letter:

"(1) The error in calling Irving a professor and in mis-spelling Schenectady was typical of all his dealings with the Russians. The official list of the 25 other guests contained so many errors in spelling that in several cases, we couldn't identify them until Irving obtained the correct names elsewhere.

"(2) I thought it significant that the Soviets are celebrating any anniversary as old as 220 years. I thought their memories went back only for the last 25 years. Since then a friend who has visited Russia tells me that in the great hall of the Kremlin, there is a huge picture of Lenin at one end and of the last Czar at the other end and that the Russians won't listen to any criticism of the Czars.

"(3) I asked Irving about his drinking capacity and warned him about the 'festivities.' Eric Johnston and others who went to Russia on strictly business trips found their time taken up almost exclusively with series of banquets with interminable toasts each of which require leaving the glass bottoms up, with a Russian companion on each side who immediately filled all glasses. In the case of Irving's trip, there wasn't even any pretense of a business or scientific trip for he was notified at the outset it would be solely a matter of 'participating in festivities' to 'celebrate' an anniversary. I asked him if under these conditions he could expect anything less than an uninterrupted series of drinking orgies.

"(4) Irving said that never in his life had he been asked to take a trip with so inadequate a picture of what the trip was about. Usually there is at least a list of speakers and a description of the conferences to be held, a program, etc." (Langmuir had said Yes to this short-notice invitation just as he always had to almost any invitation which sounded interesting — like the sailing trip with David.)

"(5) When Irving called up the State Department upon receipt of the invitation, he was told that the postscript did not mean what it seemed. He was told that the Soviets never pay expenses to Russia. Originally there was no thought of traveling by a Russian plane and the postscript meant only that travel expenses to the U.S.S.R. would be paid by the Academy and also the expenses of the sojourn in U.S.S.R. This matter assumes considerable importance since foreigners are not permitted to travel over Siberia and the only other airplane route now available is via Teheran, where Russian planes pick up Americans entering Russia. Unfortunately the cost of a round trip from New York to Teheran is $2,500.

"Irving was so eager to visit Russia that he decided he would put up the $2,500 himself. But most scientific men and college professors are usually not affluent and, after learning from the State Department the true state of affairs, the great majority of those invited declined their invitation. It was only on Monday, June 4th, just before Irving telephoned me, that the Russian government telegraphed him that a Russian plane would pick up the guests at LaGuardia Field.

"Late Wednesday Irving learned that, because of weather conditions, the plane which was to bring one guest from San Francisco and another from Chicago, before leaving New York for Canada and Alaska, had been delayed and wouldn't leave until Thursday.

"When I got home Wednesday I found he had spent the day making final arrangements for the trip with the Soviet Consulate and had had interesting talks with Mr. Minor, President of International General Electric, and with other GE men who were intensely interested in his trip.

"Mr. Minor told him that the Russians were shrewd and difficult negotiators, who often changed their minds and resorted to bluff. But he said that once the Russians signed a contract, they lived up to it more scrupulously than those of any other nationality . . .

"Irving telephoned me at the office Thursday afternoon that the trip would be delayed several days. When I got home, Irving told me that so much had happened during the day that he hardly knew where to begin the story.

"Soon after I had left in the morning," Dean continued, "two army officers, representing a certain Major General, called on him and advised him that the Army requested that he not make the trip on the ground that they would prefer that a man who knew so many secrets about our war effort should not visit a foreign land. Irving was infuriated at their coming to such a decision at so late a date and he denied that he knew as much about the war effort as they thought he did. He asked if they wanted him to lie to the Soviet Embassy and tell them that he was sick and he pointed out that the Soviets might deeply resent a refusal to go following his formal acceptance." (This was all at a time, remember, when the U.S.S.R. was still the wartime ally of the United States, and before the start of the Cold War.) "They replied that it was up to him to excuse himself in any way he preferred, that they did not order him not to go, but they requested him not to make the trip and they gave him the name of another guest who considered a similar request as final.

"After they left, Irving got in touch with a Vice-President of General Electric who, in turn, telephoned the Major General, and the request that he not go was finally withdrawn.

"By this time many of the guests about to take the trip had gotten together at the Harvard Club here and they were joined late that morning by the two guests who had just arrived on the Russian plane, one from San Francisco and the other from Chicago. Their story of the plane and of their trip was disconcerting.

"It seems that it was not a passenger plane, but a freight plane in which nine seats had been installed. Since 18 Americans proposed to go, half would have to take turns standing up at any one time. I meant literally standing up, for the plane was so full of gasoline tanks and packages that there was no place to sit except on the nine seats. The plane was not heated and there were no facilities for warming or for serving foods. The toilet facilities were nothing more than zero. There was not a single blanket on board. These inconveniences, hard enough on a short trip, were insurmountable on a five or six day trip over Siberia, well within the Arctic Circle. The passenger from Chicago, who was not in good health, actually thought he was going to die [on the way to New York] for they climbed to a high altitude and his legs got so cold that circulation stopped.

"There were other disadvantages. The Russian plane was not equipped with radio to pick up our radio beacons or to communicate with landing fields. By law, the plane had to carry from San Francisco an American aviator, although little was gained thereby since he couldn't talk Russian. This man said he had flown well over 3000 hours but that this trip was by far the most hazardous he had ever taken. Since radio beams and the beacons meant nothing to the Russians, they flew across the continent just as we would across Asia, i.e., by map and regardless of rules and regulations.

"After landing in Denver, they took off from the field there under weather so bad that every American plane was grounded. As they landed at the field in Chicago without communicating with the tower, the American pilot was horrified to see a big four-motored American plane bearing down on them from the side. Not knowing Russian, the American pilot pointed to the plane the Russian pilot had not observed. The pilot swerved and avoided a disastrous collision, but the planes did hit each other and both planes had to stop and survey the damage before proceeding.

"Furthermore, the plane landed in Chicago at 1:30 AM and the Russians had made no hotel reservations. They were hungry on arrival but the restaurants were closed and hotel reservations were impossible to get. Altogether, the two scientists who had traveled on the plane advised their confreres not to travel by it over the Arctic wastes of Siberia.

"Most of the group knew one or more government officials and between them all, they had contacts with almost everyone in Washington, so they joined forces and tried to get an Army plane to take them to Teheran. One of the first obstacles was to make sure that the Russians would not be insulted if all the guests, refusing to go by their plane, went instead by an American plane. The Russian Embassy assured them that they would be delighted to have them go by an Army plane and that the Russian plane, instead of returning empty, would pick up a full load of Russians. Finally President Truman said he would order an army plane put at their disposal providing Acting Secretary of State Grew requested such action, but they couldn't reach Grew.

"The Russian plane was due to leave at 8 PM (Thursday) and some of the hardier members of the party (including a man of 75) said they would go by the Russian plane if they couldn't get an American plane. Since they expected to hear from the White House at any moment and it was getting late they asked the Russian consulate if the departure of the Russian plane couldn't be held up for 15 minutes. They were told that that would be impossible, but they learned that the Russian plane had run into a truck at LaGuardia Field several hours before and that the necessary repairs delayed the departure many hours. At 7:30 PM they learned that President Truman had ordered an Army plane put at their disposal.

"Friday and Saturday were spent marking time, waiting for final plans. They had to get new visas to provide for stopping at the various countries where stops were to be made on the way to Teheran. The Washington authorities had to figure out what appropriation was legally available for the trip. Irving packed up and left the apartment Saturday morning, expecting to leave late that day.

"He was back again for dinner, however, and it was only at 8 PM that evening that the final plans were divulged. They were to go on one of the President's own planes, a C-54, the largest American transport plane, and the expense would come out of the President's own budget. I gather that it is this plane which on its return trip brought back General Eisenhower.

"The final plan was that they were to meet in front of the Harvard Club at 4:30 AM on Sunday morning, with the departure from LaGuardia Field scheduled at 6 AM.

"Oversleeping would have meant that Irving would miss the trip, so I put in a call at the desk downstairs for 3:30 AM, set two alarm clocks for 3:20 AM and had Western Union call me at the same time. Irving wanted time to take a bath, his last for many days, and I got him some hot coffee and fruit. Prof. Shapley also phoned at 4 AM to make sure Irving was on time.

"At LaGuardia Field they were to submit their baggage and papers to outward censorship, a regular procedure, to make sure they were not taking secret documents with them. Papers and baggage not needed on the trip were to be sealed until arrival at Teheran, so as to avoid examination at the stops on the way. They traveled light, for the Russian Embassy had told them they could carry only 'from 20 to 30 pounds,' whereas they learned at the last moment that on the C-54 they could take 65 pounds.

"The scheduled stops are Newfoundland, the Azores, Casablanca, Cairo and Teheran. At Teheran, they expect to be entertained by the Shah of Persia. When I said good-bye to Irving, he was as eager to go as a little boy...

"No arrangements have been made for the return trip but Irving says the entire group is anxious to return by Siberia and Alaska if the Russian Government can be persuaded to put a plane at their disposal, i.e., a regular passenger plane, even though the Russian Government would furnish transportation only to Fairbanks, Alaska...

"Incidentally, I should have said above that Irving's final decision was that he and one or two others of the group have agreed not to have any drinks at all while in Russia."

Dean wrote Ruth again on June 20, 1945: "I might add some further observations about Irving's Russian trip. I told Irving that I thought that the Army officers who opposed the visit to Russia of certain members of the party had more to their side of the case than he originally admitted. It is a fact that an invariable feature of Russian hospitality is the prolonged and repeated drinking bouts. Apparently the Russians have a far greater capacity than those of any other nationality and their sense of propriety requires that their guests drink toast after toast, draining the glass in each case.

"It is also a fact that there is a certain percentage of people who, in any event, drink more than they should and it is also undeniably a fact that a certain percentage of people who drink become talkative. The State Department and War Department might examine in detail the record of achievement of each of the scientists invited to Russia but they would have no possible way of telling which ones of them were given to going on occasional benders and which ones become too talkative under such conditions...

"The entire procedure relating to the trip is subject to criticism. I do not believe the Russian Government should have been allowed to approach directly individual American citizens. They should instead have approached the State Department directly. Certainly the Russians would have had a fit if we had approached independently a group of twenty of their key men and asked them each separately to come to this country on a mission..."

On July 23, 1945, Dean wrote to his daughter Evelyn. "I spent the weekend in Schenectady," he told her, "arriving in time for dinner on Saturday and leaving before dinner on Sunday. This time I stayed at Irving and Marion's.

"The purpose of this trip was to hear Irving tell about his experiences in Russia. He had telephoned me the week before and suggested that I come up. We talked until 2 AM Saturday night and resumed the conversation at 9 AM on Sunday. Until Robert and Lee arrived around 3 PM on Sunday, the conversation dealt exclusively with his Russia trip.

"Irving's story was most impressive in the favorable picture which he gave of the Russians and of the possibility and probability of effective and satisfactory cooperation between Russia and the U.S.

"He certainly had excellent opportunities for observation. He walked alone for many miles around Moscow. He spent many evenings in the homes of various college professors. He attended a banquet at the Kremlin facing Stalin at a distance of only 100 feet. He attended a Victory Parade in Red Square where 300,000 picked troops paraded. On the last day he attended the trial of the sixteen Poles. He had innumerable conversations not only with scientists but also with Ambassador Harriman and with others of the U.S. Embassy."

Most of the other details of this letter are very similar to those contained in Irving Langmuir's own articles. But there were some interesting sidelights. "Irving was flattered," wrote Dean, "to find that they considered him not only a great scientist, but the greatest scientist in the world. They knew much more about his work on surface tension than he did, and they have a huge organization at work to study further Irving's findings in that and in other fields...

"Irving says that the top scientist, whom he became well-acquainted with, lives on a scale comparable to that of a $25,000-a-year man in the United States and the best opera tickets are available to him at any time he chooses to go. He has an attractive summer home and he also told Irving that if, for any reason, he would want a second home, the Government would unquestionably provide one for him...

"I asked Irving what I thought was a significant question. Had he come across any case where people were pushed around or treated brusquely by policemen or government officials, or had he seen any instance on the part of anyone in authority to take advantage of his position to treat others in an autocratic fashion? His answer was an emphatic negative.

"The policemen treated the people with the greatest courtesy and in a spirit of good fellowship. No one in the hotels, on the trains, or in the streets ever seemed to order anyone around in a disagreeable manner. No one in Russia appeared to him to be unhappy or disgruntled.

"The reception at the Kremlin, which was attended by Stalin, was the high spot of the trip. Contrary to the advices given him by a rabid anti-Soviet man in the American Embassy, he found that it was not at all necessary to drain the glass even when it came to a toast to Stalin. Half of the Russians would drink toasts of lemonade, carbonated water or even with an empty glass much as is done at similar functions in the U.S. There was no drunkenness on the part of anyone during the entire trip.

"Irving returned by Siberia and in his round-the-world trip by airplane, he covered 21,000 miles. They did not travel by night so he saw all of the scenery. However, since the Arctic nights are so short and he wanted to see everything he only slept three or four hours a night for long stretches of time. He was greatly puzzled to find that he felt perfectly normal and well even through his sleeping hours were cut to a fraction of the usual amount.

"The trip ended with very much of an anti-climax. A special Russian plane left them at Fairbanks, Alaska and a special Army transport delivered them to Minneapolis, which is the terminus of the Army transport lines in the U.S. They had wired from Fairbanks asking that transportation be furnished back to New York. Upon arrival at Minneapolis, however, they were met by the Colonel in charge, who, while very courteous, told them that he had received instructions from Washington to furnish no transportation from that point on.

"They asked if the Army could not arrange to give them some kind of priority back on a commercial airplane even though it were only second or third class priority. The Colonel replied that he had no authority to give them any priority whatever, and he informed them at the same time that it would be impossible to secure any airplane reservations for weeks to come.

"They asked if Pullman reservations had been made for them and the Colonel said he had no authority to make such reservations and added that it was impossible for any civilians to get such reservations without waiting for a period of days.

"This treatment was at such variance with the treatment they had received within Russia and it was in such contrast to the courtesies shown by our government at the point of departure, that the trip ended on rather a sour note. In Russia the pure scientist enjoys a position which is at the top of the social structure and he is treated with considerable deference. It was a shock to find that this was not the case here. Since they were all busy men, they had to get back quickly. Some returned by day coach, some had to stand up but they got back as best they could. Irving had fairly good luck, and, although he had originally been kept off the Zephyr train to Chicago, he stumbled on to an empty seat and he was also lucky enough to get an upper berth back from Chicago. The others did not fare so well.

"Irving lost seven pounds during the trip but he seems in the best of health. He attributes the loss of weight to the lack of sleep and to the fact that on the long airplane trips only light lunches were usually served."

One wonders how Dean happened to write about all this in such exhaustive detail. Well, the Langmuirs — especially Irving and his brothers — were all trained from childhood to write long, descriptive letters to one another. In Dean's case, he may have been doing this for his own record, since he was apparently planning to write a book about Irving some time. He never did get around to it, which is too bad, since the rigorous early training forced on him by Mama and Papa gave him a keen eye for detail and a certain narrative power.

Later events forced Langmuir to revise downward his opinion of the Russians, but he came back from this trip very stimulated and full of hopes and warnings. He was especially impressed by the state of science in Russia. Of the researches at the Russian Academy, he wrote: "They were all clearly working on problems that had been planned by scientists who were free from undue political control." Langmuir had always assumed that in a Communist society, the scientists would be regimented, like everyone else; and that the regimentation would inhibit creativity and therefore stifle progress. But somehow the scientists of Russia had achieved a special kind of privileged status. "In fact," Langmuir went on, "they had been able to carry on during the war scientific work of a kind that would have been impossible in the United States."

"The progress in science in Russia during the war was greater than we had expected. In some fields the Russians are leading the world." Langmuir was quite explicit, in his articles, about which fields these were, and about the fields in which the Russians were still far behind. But the fact that they were ahead in *any* of the sciences was an eye-opener for Langmuir. He had had free access to their institutes, a wide-open first-hand look at the experiments, and was given apparently complete answers to all his questions — and they did not ask him any in return. Langmuir said flatly at the end of his first article: "I believe they have already planned a postwar science program greater than that contemplated by any other nation . . . If we continue, through the effects of government policies and labor legislation, to stifle the incentives upon which our progress has depended, *we may expect a period during which Russia forges ahead far more rapidly than we do* [italics supplied]." (The remark about the "effects of government policies and labor legislation" reflects Langmuir's violent anti-New Deal philosophy. Anyone who was at all acquainted with this rock-ribbed old Republican conservative must have grinned broadly at the hints occasionally dropped — because of his favorable comments about Russia — that he was probably a fellow-traveler.) If Americans had listened to Langmuir back in 1945 and 1946, they would not have been so astonished when Sputnik I appeared in the skies in October of 1957 to jolt them out of their complacency.[1]

After his Russian visit and the advent, soon thereafter, of the atomic bomb, Langmuir got very interested in science legislation, disarmament, the international control of atomic energy, and re-

---

[1] It is only fair to point out that, by 1950, Langmuir himself changed his mind about how well the Russian scientists were doing. He said that in 1945 "I was over-optimistic in hoping that the Russians could cooperate with the rest of the world. I believe that at that meeting it was the intention of the leaders to make a gesture to the world that they intended to cooperate, and I also think that they sincerely thought they could. The atomic bomb which was first tested in New Mexico only about two weeks after our party left Russia probably was the turning point in the Russian plan to cooperate with the scientists of the world. Shortly after that, it must have appeared to the Russian government that their own scientists had deliberately chosen to work on such things as the liquefaction of helium and the use of oxygen in blast furnaces rather than study atomic energy. As a result, I believe that the scientists were no longer trusted and were no longer left in charge of their programs. Instead of that, the scientists are now controlled politically, as we see in the case of T. D. Lysenko in the field of biology, with similar control of the arts such as music. This change of attitude on the part of the Russian government toward its scientists will, I believe, force future scientific developments in that country to follow lines which promise foreseeable advantages to the politicians but seriously discourages all work which might lead to fundamental discoveries."

lated matters. He knew we underestimated the Russians' scientific capacity and wanted us all to know that we were in danger of being overtaken in at least a few important areas of science. He wanted us to drop any illusions that we could maintain for any length of time a significant degree of scientific superiority, including our monopoly of atomic energy. He wanted to change attitudes in this country toward our own science to provide the incentives that would step up our scientific progress once more. He felt strongly that, while there was still a breathing-space after the war during which our relations with Russia — on the surface, at least — were still good, and since he was convinced, from his visit, that the Russians' feelings of friendliness for us were sincere and that they would be willing to co-operate with us, we should take advantage of this period to cement the relationship, to establish mutual confidence, and especially to set up international co-operation in such matters as the effective control of atomic energy. To these ends Langmuir attended meetings, wrote articles, spoke on the radio, and testified before Congress.

All this semi-political activity did not keep Langmuir from attending to all sorts of other matters — from family doings to the Boy Scouts to the Lake George Protective Association to accepting the Faraday Medal. It did, however, cut somewhat into his research, especially the atmospheric studies he had become so engrossed in on top of Mount Washington. However, he was soon to become absorbed in these studies once more thanks to a fortuitous discovery by Vincent Schaefer who, all this time, had never stopped serendipiting along as ever.

Chapter 23

"I wonder if it's theirs or ours?"
One clergyman to another, as they look out at the rain, in a *New Yorker* cartoon.

EARLY in 1946, the Langmuirs took a long, leisurely tour of the Southern and Western United States, during which they visited friends and relatives all over, went sightseeing, climbed, skied, and took all sorts of side trips. In the course of it Irving lectured, picked up honorary degrees, went to meetings, stopped to visit scientists and laboratories, and, in passing, met celebrities as varied as Wernher von Braun (at Fort Bliss, Texas) and Norma Shearer (whose husband was a ski instructor at Donner Pass, California). They were away, in all, nearly four months.

On his return to Schenectady in June, Langmuir found that Vincent Schaefer, still trying to duplicate in the laboratory the formation of ice crystals in clouds, had been performing some experiments which, for elegant simplicity and ingenuity, matched almost any of Langmuir's own. Langmuir was of course delighted and excited, and pronounced them "beautiful." As Langmuir described the now-celebrated work, Schaefer "had taken a home freezing unit, which is used for food storage, about four cubic feet capacity and lined it with black velvet, directed a beam of light down into it, in order to see what happened in the chamber. He then breathed into it and the moisture condensed and formed fog particles which were just like ordinary cloud particles, although the temperature was about −23°C. No ice crystals formed. He tried many different substances dusted into that box to get ice crystals to form, and practically never got any. He got just enough to convince him that, if he did get them, he could easily see them. However, the number was totally insignificant.

"Finally, one day the temperature of the chamber was not low enough. He wanted it somewhat lower so he took a big piece of dry ice and put it in the chamber to lower the temperature. In an instant, the air was just full of ice crystals, millions of them.

"He then took the dry ice out, and the ice crystals persisted for a while. Then he found that even the tiniest piece of dry ice would fill the cloud with crystals. Then he took a needle which he dipped into liquid air and he let that pass once across the box. The result again was the production of hundreds of millions of ice crystals by just one brief contact with the needle. The effect rapidly spread throughout the entire box. It is a wonderful experiment ... It is very easy to do. It has been done by some high schools. One young girl student in Rhode Island made a chamber out of wash boilers cooled with brine. The effects to be seen are wonderful to look at and it is a simple matter to duplicate all the conditions of an actual cloud in the sky.

"Well, that discovery changed the whole situation. What was discovered first was that the dry ice had no direct effect on the supercooled cloud but rather its temperature was the important thing ... Anything can be used having a temperature less than −40°C.'

Langmuir went on to describe further experiments with the velvet-lined icebox which showed that "there is a quite critical temperature of about −39°C, the temperature of freezing of mercury, where a spontaneous reaction occurs to produce natural nuclei. This can be proved quite conclusively by covering the box with a sheet of glass and continuing to supply moisture into a cold chamber having a temperature of −40°C. The ice crystals continue to separate out, fall on the bottom of the chamber, and new crystals form from moisture produced by evaporation of ice."

Creating artificial snow in the cold chamber was all well and good, but did its innards *really* duplicate the conditions in a cloud? Could the new knowledge be applied to stir up real clouds in the sky? Meanwhile, Langmuir was so pleased with Schaefer's icebox, and what could be done so simply inside it, that he had Schaefer bring it to a meeting of the American Meteorological Society in Boston, where it was installed, for demonstration, in the Georgian Room of the Hotel Statler; and GE gave a cocktail party for the occasion.

On November 13, 1946, Schaefer took off in a small, piloted plane from Schenectady, carrying with him six pounds of granulated dry ice. He was looking for a likely cloud to sprinkle it on. Drifting across the New York state line into Massachusetts, he spotted a fleecy, supercooled, strato-cumulus cloud which he estimated to be about four miles long. He told the pilot to fly over it. Then, scattering the dry ice on the cloud at the rate of about a pound and a half per mile, he dropped all six pounds of the ice granules. Then he directed the pilot to fly back so they could watch what happened. What happened was described later in *Time* magazine: "Almost at once the cloud, which had been drifting along peacefully, began to writhe as in torment. White pustules rose from its surface. In five minutes the whole cloud melted away, leaving a thin wraith of snow. None of the snow reached the ground (it evaporated on the way down), but the dry ice treatment had successfully broken up a cloud."

Langmuir described it more briefly and less dramatically in his report: "The whole supercooled cloud was converted to small ice crystals." But in his diary at home that evening, he permitted himself more emotion: "It worked!"

But dry ice turned out to have many disadvantages. It could disturb a cloud only for the brief period of time the granules were falling through it, and the ice crystals created by the presence of the dry-ice particles had to react instantly, or they would evaporate. Often dry ice seeding simply created a compact cloud of ice crystals, not bulky enough for the snow to begin falling. Langmuir wanted a more stable and permanent kind of particle that would have the same effect as dry ice without its disadvantages. He turned the problem over to another of his brilliant young assistants, Bernard Vonnegut.

Meanwhile seeding was continued, often with dramatic results. "In one case," Langmuir related, "I happened to be driving an automobile under a cloud which was being seeded. I never saw such heavy rain in all my life. It came down in torrents for about fifteen minutes. The wind was so strong that it looked as though it was going to blow over several trees, and a few trees were blown over. Fortunately, it did no harm. We drove up to the side of the road, my wife and I, because we did not know what was going to happen. Then there was a little hail, small pieces about a half inch in diameter, after the rain. Usually, the hail comes first, but here it had been raining for five or ten minutes and then came some hail.

"It then let up a little, so I drove on, less than half a mile. The rain stopped. I got out and looked, and the road was dry. It had not rained there at all.

"We expect such thunderstorms to go to the east in our region. That storm did not go to the east, it just ended, completely. At that time, five minutes after it stopped raining, there was no rain to be seen anywhere. The whole thing disappeared. Now that is a quite unusual type of thunderstorm."

One day in the winter of 1946, a mass of clouds near Schenectady was seeded with dry ice, and it began snowing very shortly thereafter. The snowfall turned into a storm, and the storm into a blizzard — not a blizzard of disaster proportions, just a normal winter blizzard. But it caused all the usual inconveniences that blizzards cause; and, more than inconvenience, blizzards always result in expensive clean-up programs, a drop in city business, an increase in respiratory ailments, and even a few tragedies — the old man who drops dead while shoveling snow, the drunk who goes to sleep in the snow and freezes to death, the driver whose car skids on the ice and wraps itself around a tree. GE officials began to worry about the legal implications. They were not at all sure the dry ice had caused the blizzard; it might have snowed anyway. And they were certain they could not be proved responsible in court. Just the same, a big corporation is always an eminently suable entity, and GE felt quite uneasy in the possession of the newest Langmuir–Schaefer discovery. Soon they were to own the patents to other methods of cloud-seeding. As a possible force for good, rainmaking and snowmaking had tremendous potential, and the owner of those patents ought to have a large, steady income from the royalties. Yes — but suppose you made rain for a rancher, and the rain soaked a field of hay drying in a nearby field; couldn't the farmer sue you for the loss of his hay? Or suppose you made rain in order to fill New York City's reservoirs during a dry summer; couldn't the owners of mountain and seashore resorts whose weather and business you ruined hold you accountable? (This exact set of circumstances later actually came to pass.) GE decided to divorce itself from cloud-seeding in every possible legal manner. The company threw the patents open for public use and waived all royalty rights, and there was much relief when the government took over the work of Langmuir, Schaefer and Vonnegut under Project Cirrus, in March of 1947. The contract was with the Signal Corps, with the Navy and Air Force participating.

In turning the patents loose and thus solving its own legal difficulties, GE compounded everyone else's legal difficulties. As legions of rainmakers went to work seeding clouds everywhere, even state legislatures and the United States Congress got involved in the consideration of bills to regulate cloud-seeding operations. Did California have a right to steal Arizona's rain? Should Ohioans make rain on Pennsylvania without Pennsylvania's consent? Later, when Langmuir came to the conclusion that the *overseeding* of clouds could *prevent* rain that might have come down had there been no seeding at all, the problems got even more complicated.

GE's disclaimers of legal responsibility did not altogether relieve the Company of worry. For a while GE officials were quite anxious about what Langmuir and Schaefer would do — and what they would say in reporting their results. For the first time in Langmuir's long career at GE, officials occasionally wanted to know in advance what he was going to say in his public reports. And quite understandably. On October 10, 1947, Langmuir's diary reads; "Meeting in NY of the Steering Committee of Project Cirrus ... A new Hurricane is reported NW of Jamaica and we plan to seed it. Much attention given to avoidance of any publicity." The report on the hurricane-seeding operations, carried out on October 13, 1947, was submitted by Commander Daniel F. Rex, Chairman of the Operations Groups for Project Cirrus. The operation was carried out by three aircraft based at Mac-Dill Field, Tampa, Florida, and the seeding itself went on for about thirty minutes. "During this thirty-minute period," Commander Rex wrote, "80 pounds of solid carbon dioxide was dispensed along the 110-mile track. In addition, two mass drops of 50 pounds each were made into a large cumulus top at 30.7 degrees North, 73.4 degrees West... No attempt was made to penetrate through the wall of the storm into the eye... Visual observation of the seeded area showed a pronounced modification of the cloud deck seeded."

Now, this hurricane had crossed the Western tip of Cuba, gone Northeast over the Southern tip of Florida, and was already a good way out into the Atlantic, still headed Northeast, at the time the seeding took place. After the seeding, the hurricane's path made a sudden, erratic, 108° turn to the West, headed back to the mainland, and slammed into the coast and inland, with the usual amount of hurricane havoc. No wonder then, that GE was worried when Langmuir scheduled, only a month later, his first major report on cloud-seeding and Project Cirrus before the National Academy of Sciences in Washington. Langmuir's diary of November 17, 1947, the day he was due to give his address, reads: "A hectic day — preparing for talk 'to-night'... The legal dept of the GE and all are afraid of what I will say. Finally I get OK."

In his talk, as presented, Langmuir was careful to point out, in his account of hurricane-seeding: "These experiments were made under the control of the Operations Group of Project

Cirrus. I was not present at any of them. Mr. Schaefer and one General Electric man were each on one of two planes as observers." And he also found a hurricane which, in 1906, had followed a course — without benefit of cloud-seeding — just about as erratic as the one which was seeded. It, too, had gone out to sea, then swerved suddenly back into the Florida coast. So it *could* have happened quite naturally again.

In any case, Langmuir's diary reported that "the newsmen present don't show any interest at all in the seeding of the 'hurricane'; nor the data." And since Weather Bureau officals were soon scoffing at the efficacy of rainmaking anyway, and saying that the sudden change in the hurricane's course had been mere coincidence, there were really no further legal problems to worry about.

Long before all this, meanwhile, Bernard Vonnegut had gone to work to find a substitute for dry ice in cloud-seeding experiments. He had pored through many a weighty tome in crystallography before he found what looked like a promising substance — silver iodide. Though silver iodide molecules do not look like water molecules, silver iodide crystals do look very much like ice crystals. It was worth a try. The try — at least the first try — did not work. But Vonnegut thought that its failure might be due to impurities in the commercial grade of silver iodide he had employed. He used an old Langmuir technique, and, heating a wire with an electric current, succeeded in evaporating off enough pure silver iodide for another test. This time it worked as effectively as dry ice ever had. And it took only a tiny bit of silver iodide to fill the cold chamber with snow; in fact, it was hard to get an amount that was too small to work.

"You can make this experiment," said Langmuir, suggesting a simple laboratory test of silver iodide. "Take a silver coin out of your pocket and while you hold it in your hand, make a high frequency spark from a Tesla coil jump to it." This would provide enough silver for the experiment. "At the moment the spark passes, you blow once down into the box which is open on top and full of cold air. Then a moment later you open a bottle of iodine and blow some of its vapor into the box. You soon find that the air becomes full of ice crystals, perhaps less than a millimeter apart, which means that something like 100 million snow crystals have been formed in 100 liters of air, from the silver iodide particles that were caused by the vaporization of the silver coin as you held it in your hand."

Obviously Vonnegut had found the potent and stable substance Langmuir had been looking for as a dry-ice substitute. "Electron microscope pictures of these particles," said Langmuir, "indicate that from one gram of silver iodide about 10^{17} nuclei can be produced." Ah, the magic number! It was exactly 10^{17} particles that Langmuir had been producing every second in his smoke generator. "This suggests," he said, "that a few pounds of silver iodide would be enough to nucleate all the air of the United States at one time, so it would contain one particle per cubic inch, which is far more than the number of ice nuclei which occur normally under natural conditions." Then, talking about the smoke generator, he said, "If you make silver iodide smoke that way, it would cost five dollars an hour for the materials. The proper distribution of particles is more difficult. If the particles retained the activity that they have in laboratory tests a wide distribution of them in the atmosphere might perhaps have a profound effect upon the climate."

There had been no extensive silver-iodide seeding at the time Langmuir gave his 1947 report to the National Academy of Sciences. That was to come the following year in New Mexico. Meanwhile Langmuir had become fascinated with the idea of causing a "chain reaction" in the atmosphere. Just as a chain reaction of atom-splitting can be caused by the impingement of a single slow neutron on a critical mass of uranium, so, Langmuir thought, could a single ice crystal or water droplet impinging on a critical cloud mass, under the right conditions, set off the entire cloud.[1] "The chain reaction," he explained "is one where you start out with one snow flake and by some mechanism

[1] Langmuir was a firm believer in what he called divergent phenomena, of which this kind of chain reaction would be an example. A divergent phenomenon is one in which a very small occurrence – which happens, however, to

it becomes two. Then those two become four, and those four, eight, and so on, and the thing propagates rapidly, in exactly the same way as does a haystack when you light it with a match. It starts burning. It does not make any difference where it is ignited, in three places or one place, it spreads through the whole haystack. The heat produced by burning one particle of hay has to be enough to heat the next particle."

Later, from data which came out of some cloud-seeding operations in Hawaii, he worked out a fairly comprehensive theory for his chain-reaction ideas. "Out in Hawaii recently," he wrote, "there was an extremely interesting flight, by Luna B. Leopold and Maurice H. Halstead, where dry ice was dropped on some clouds at a temperature of + 10°C, and they got rain. The cloud started to grow from 8000 feet up to 15,000 feet and then rose above the freezing level when it was again seeded with more dry ice. It grew to 26,000 feet and kept on raining and spread and traveled out across the sea and went from one island to the other and rained all night.

"The results of the experiment made me think a lot, because I have been interested in the growth of rain ever since 1944 when I started to develop a mathematical theory of the growth of particles in clouds." His thoughts led him to the conclusion that a chain reaction occurs when there is an updraft of air through the cloud that keeps carrying rain droplets back up before they reach the bottom of the cloud. The raindrops blown back upward create more raindrops until "the whole cloud simply goes over into heavy rain."

---

occur at the right place and under the right conditions — can cause a quite impressive series of events. Because it acts as a trigger, the events it sets in motion are out of all proportion to the size of the triggering incident itself. A favorite example of Langmuir's is what happens in a Wilson cloud chamber, where a single quantum event — like the disintegration of a radium atom — produces countless thousands of water droplets. The writer has already pointed out the work of a single man, Langmuir, and its phenomenal impact on all subsequent science and technology, not only in America but abroad as well, as a fine example of a divergent phenomenon at work in society. For a fuller explanation of Langmuir's theories of convergent and divergent phenomena, see "Science, Common Sense, and Decency," which appeared in *Science,* January 1, 1943.

"Now if there are no rising air currents," he held, "all those drops fall until they reach the bottom of the cloud. That is no chain reaction." He expressed the belief that the kind of chain reaction he described was what must have taken place in the Hawaiian seeding operation. "It was done by us every time we seeded a cumulus cloud. I have worked it out mathematically in a theory which will be published soon." Langmuir was writing in 1947, and the theory was published, as promised, in 1948. "It is simple," he said. "It tells you that the conditions that have to be met in order to bring about that chain reaction in rain formation are a vertical velocity of five miles per hour and a liquid water content such that there is at least a tenth of an inch of rain available. The cloud particles have to be rather large, about twenty microns in diameter; very small ones will not do. When you meet those special conditions, then *only a single large drop of water will set off a whole cumulus cloud* [italics supplied] and bring down most of the moisture in it."[1]

During 1948, in between eye surgery for the removal of cataracts, Langmuir made several trips to Puerto Rico, Central America (he arrived in Costa Rica in the middle of a shooting revolution), and South America — where he studied trade winds, sought the causes of "blow-down" storms in the banana plantations, and also had a chance to try out some water-seeding experiments, but with inconclusive results. "As might be expected," wrote Schaefer, "Langmuir returned from these field expeditions with much data based on visual evidence, photographic records and with intense enthusiasm."

The year 1949, however, marked the beginning of a series of

---

[1] Langmuir gave a paper in January, 1948, on his theory of self-propagating storms at a meeting of the American Meteorological Society at the Hotel Astor in New York. Later he was to meet Marion and Kenneth at Le Bistro for dinner; but, with time on his hands, he went to the Museum of Natural History (where the meetings were to continue the following day) to look around. There he got so engrossed in the exhibits that he stayed past closing time, and the lights went out. He spent a scary half hour or so trying to find his way through the complexities of the darkened museum. When he finally found an exit, fortunately, someone was there to let him out.

experiments that were to attract worldwide attention and to set off a controversy that was to continue throughout the rest of Langmuir's life, and even after his death. With Schaefer and Vonnegut, he arrived on July 5, 1949, in New Mexico, where they were planning to work on the next phase of Project Cirrus — cloud-seeding from a ground-based silver-iodide generator. They were to work with E. J. Workman — who became, along with Schaefer, one of Langmuir's best pals — and his staff at the New Mexico School of Mines in Socorro. It seemed an out-of-the-way place, but the School of Mines had an impressive research program already under way in weather — and particularly on the nature of thunderstorms. Besides, New Mexico was ideal for other reasons. The clouds were sparse and easy to pick out. And in that dry country any rain or snow, from whatever source, was looked upon as an unalloyed blessing. The white man prayed for moisture, the Indian danced for it, and anyone who complained about it was considered virtually treasonable (or some dumb Easterner passing through).

A B-17 flying laboratory, based at Kirtland Field, near Albuquerque, was put at Langmuir's disposal. Most of the scientists stayed at a ranch near Albuquerque called the New Mexico Experimental Range, which had been used for secret wartime work in developing the proximity fuse. Seeding from the ground-based generators began almost at once. On July 14, Langmuir's diary reads: "We split a big cloud at Albuquerque." And on July 15: "Vonnegut made a thunderstorm..."

An account of the two storms which later appeared in *Time*, begins: "Near Albuquerque in July, 1949, Langmuir performed an experiment that is still debated heatedly in meteorological circles. He started his silver iodide generator early on a morning when the Weather Bureau had predicted no substantial rain. Then he watched developments by radar.

"At 8:30 a.m., a cloud started growing 25 miles away downwind. When the cloud reached 26 miles, it suddenly spurted, bulging upward at 15 m.p.h. Soon a radar echo showed that the cloud was full of rain or snow. Heavy rain fell near the Manzano

Mountains. A short while later, a second cloud showed a similar convulsion and also produced a heavy rain.

"Langmuir insisted that both these thunderstorms formed in the trajectory of his silver iodide particles and at about the time when the particles must have been entering their bases. He therefore took credit for the rain they dropped as well as for other rain from later storms."

Langmuir calculated that the Cirrus-caused storms over this two-day period produced hundreds of billions of gallons of rain and believed there was only one chance in a million that the storms would have come about in the natural course of events without being artificially stimulated by the silver iodide particles.

On January 25, 1950, Langmuir wrote in his diary: "New York, Hotel Taft: I spend the morning preparing paper for this PM. Lunch at the Hotel Astor with Steve Reynolds and Workman. I read the most important paper that I have ever given at the afternoon session of the American Meteorological Society, about 1½ hrs. Reichelderfer is Chairman. Wexler and Lewis out on a limb." Reichelderfer, Wexler and Lewis were all Weather Bureau men who had been — and who still remained — skeptical of Langmuir's results. They and other meteorologists found his theories incredible and his statistics unconvincing. The Weather Bureau itself carried out some seeding experiments in Ohio — experiments which Langmuir considered altogether unsatisfactory — with negative results.

Despite continued rebuffs from the people he was most trying to impress, Langmuir was certain he was working on revolutionary discoveries that would prove to be the high point of his scientific career. He finally hit upon what he considered a real cause-and-effect experiment, something which, if it worked, would be quite conclusive, and could not fail to convince even the doubting Thomases of the Weather Bureau that small seeding operations could have very large effects upon the weather. He carried out his experiment for nearly a year, and, in his view, it worked beautifully.

Now, just what was Langmuir's grand experiment? "Langmuir figured," wrote Francis Bello in *Fortune,* "that if the weather were as capricious as his critics suggested, he would try to make it behave periodically by releasing, every week, about 1000 grams of silver iodide. Initially Langmuir planned to run the Cirrus generator every Tuesday, Wednesday and Thursday. The experiment had barely started in December of 1949, when heavy rains, concentrated chiefly on Mondays and Tuesdays, began drenching the Ohio Valley, causing near floods ... Langmuir cut generator operation to Tuesday and Wednesday. Still the rains came. By April, 1950, the rainfall over the entire Eastern half of the United States had assumed a striking weekly periodicity. Every Tuesday it rained from Alabama to Minnesota. One or two days later the storms had usually marched to New York and the New England coast. In subsequent months the periodicity became sporadic — upset, according to Langmuir, by commercial cloud seeders who had begun to work in earnest. Nevertheless, an analysis by the Weather Bureau confirms that a strong tendency to periodic rainfall existed for the entire eleven months of weekly seedings."[1]

Throughout the weekly seedings Langmuir, with the help of Meteorologist Raymond Falconer, collected voluminous amounts of data, from which he made elaborate statistical computations. Later he did more complicated experiments to prove a "phase shift" in the relationship between seeding and rainfall — but the results here are something that only a professional statistician can follow. Langmuir never did offer a physical explanation for what happened in the atmosphere to cause this seven-day periodicity over such widespread areas; all his arguments were based on statistics, which he felt proved his case overwhelmingly. The

[1] When the news of all this got around later, Senator Moody of Michigan wrote a complaining letter to the Defense Department, in which he said: "The tourist and resort industry is the second largest industry in Michigan, exceeded only by the automobile industry ... It would appear, therefore, that Dr. Langmuir's cloud seeding in New Mexico on Monday, Tuesday and Wednesday is going to have a serious effect on the economy of my state [because it made it rain there on weekends] ... We would like to have Dr. Langmuir change his schedule." By the time that letter was written, the seedings had long since ceased.

whole problem was made even more difficult when Clyde Harris, a young mathematical physicist on Workman's staff in Socorro, determined that silver iodide was destroyed by sunlight after a short period of time; hence, it would seem impossible that it could linger in the atmosphere for days at a time as it drifted eastward to cause further storms. Yet — perhaps the first seeding triggered some kind of larger chain reaction. No one knew what happened, if anything. Some said there had been such periodicities in weather in earlier years.

Confusing though the situation became, and still is, interesting things undoubtedly had begun to happen after Langmuir started his grand experiment, and there remains a nagging uncertainty about the possible correlation between the happenings and the experiment. Francis Bello quotes Meteorologist Henry Houghton as saying, "It's the most mysterious thing I have ever run up against. How could one lonesome generator in New Mexico have the effect Langmuir says it had? If it wasn't chance, it was a totally new effect."[1] And he quotes another meteorologist who said, "The whole experiment was a great tragedy. If Langmuir actually influenced the weather, no one will believe him. If the periodicities were mere coincidence, nature played Langmuir a dirty trick." Langmuir and others have urged that his grand experiment be repeated, but so far it has never been done.

The whole matter is perhaps best summed up by Horace R. Byers: "The weather effects which Langmuir related to periodic seeding in New Mexico were fantastically great. The whole North

---

[1] The writer should here admit built-in bias in favor of Langmuir. Once in Albuquerque the writer, at the time a *Time-Life* correspondent in the Southwest, received a private, hour-long lecture from a bubbling and bright-eyed Langmuir, in which he explained the experiment and the seemingly overwhelming statistics proving the correlation between the weekly seeding and the weekly rainfall; and the writer came away absolutely and utterly convinced of Langmuir's rightness. The writer, of course, is neither a scientist nor a statistician.

It should perhaps be mentioned here, too, that many of the critics of Langmuir were meteorologists who would have been less than human not to resent this two-fisted invasion of their field. If Langmuir were right, it obviously meant that many things they had believed all their lives were wrong.

In the long run, of course, any honest scientist will — when the facts are all in — face up to them.

American continent and even the greater part of the northern hemisphere seemed to be responding to the weekly releases of silver iodide from a single ground generator. The statistics looked good; the giant atmosphere appeared to be reeling under the influence of man's puny infusions. Figuratively speaking, Langmuir fought and bled with these statistics. At the hands of the statisticians who must pass judgment on such matters his claims found no grounds for acceptance. One has only to ask that someone in the Southwest repeat this ridiculously simple experiment to see what vindication can be found for Langmuir." Langmuir's New Mexico colleague, E. J. Workman, feels that the experiment could no longer be carried out meaningfully in the American Southwest because of the hordes of commercial rainmakers who continually seed the clouds all over the West, and whose operations would seriously interfere with the results. Workman does believe, however, that the experiment should be repeated somewhere else in the world, and the sooner the better. "Science owes it to Langmuir," he says, "to do this. What's more, science owes it to itself."

Whatever the ultimate outcome, there is no doubt whatever that Langmuir contributed vital new ideas to meteorology and started a good many meteorologists on paths they would otherwise not have thought of following. In giving an intellectual hotfoot to what had been a relatively dozing science, Langmuir performed a great public service. The whole concept of weather control has become feasible, millions of dollars — which, without Langmuir's successful capture of the public imagination would not have been available — have been poured into meteorological research, and a vast amount of new knowledge about the weather has resulted. It will take a good many years before the extent and value of Langmuir's contributions to meteorology can be adequately assessed, but — whatever the verdict on Langmuir's more extravagant claims — the value placed on his overall contribution cannot help but be great.

Meanwhile, for the best scholarly summary of the state of the "rainmaking" art as of the late 1950's, Horace R. Byers recommends an eight-page review article by James E. McDonald (1958) in Volume 5 of *Advances in Geophysics.* For a more popular account, Byers' own 1959 size-up, contained in *Science and Resources,* which was published for Resources for the Future, Inc., by the Johns Hopkins Press, would be as helpful as any.

Chapter 24

"Strong men are made by opposition; like kites, they go up against the wind."

FRANK HARRIS

ONE of the unpleasant side effects of The Great Rainmaking Controversy was that it brought into the open a great deal of smoldering hostility toward Langmuir. He had made many enemies over the years — more than he had realized. Enemies may be too strong a word, since it perhaps exaggerates the degree of animosity they felt. Nevertheless he *had* antagonized quite a few scientists in his time. Langmuir's temperament was not the sort to follow the course which Isaac Newton once prescribed to a young friend: "Seldom discommend anything, though never so bad, or do it but moderately, lest you bee unexpectedly forced to an unhansom retraction." Langmuir had jumped mercilessly on other scientists' pet ideas and theories in public. He was, as Gabor pointed out, "unbelievably impatient with fools." He had made it a special point to sniff out and expose cases of what he liked to call "pathological science," where the data did not, in his view, support the conclusions.

There was, for his example, his celebrated paper on "The Speed of the Deer Fly." This was occasioned by a report Langmuir saw, claiming that the flight speed of the deer fly had been clocked at 800 miles per hour. The scientist — a perfectly reputable researcher — who had made the report said he had timed the deer fly over a measured course with an automatic camera. Another equally reputable scientist said he considered the reported speed excessive; it was, he thought, more like 500 or 600 miles per hour. Langmuir calculated that, in order to attain velocities of this order, the tiny insect would have to eat one and a half times its own weight every second, and would have to develop nearly half a horsepower — in which case its delicate head would be crushed by the pressure of the onrushing air it churned up. He did some extremely simple experiments of his own, proved conclusively that the deer fly was doing very well if it made 60 miles per hour.

There were many instances where Langmuir looked into doubtful experiments, often at the request of some scientific society, and found errors. The fraud was seldom deliberate. Usually the mistakes were inadvertent.

Langmuir, in some of his talks on pathological science, used as examples the celebrated case of the N-rays in France, and the flying-saucer sightings.

In April of 1937, attending an American Chemical Society meeting at the University of North Carolina in Chapel Hill, he went over to Durham one day to visit the extra-sensory perception (ESP) laboratory of Professor J. B. Rhine at Duke University. His diary of April 15 notes: "Afternoon with Prof. JB Rhine and we talk of his work on 'Extra Sensory Perceptions.' I am not convinced."

On April 16: "I spend 3 hrs with Prof Rhine and his wife. I tell him of my 5 symptoms of Pathological Science & try to find possible source of error without success. I still suspect unconscious selection of data (after results obtained). For example: He said that some 2000 trials recently have been made (in 3 yrs) which have given *negative* departures. These have not been published. He hints of other data which he has been 'too busy' to work up. He thinks that such negative departures *support* the theory of ESP; showing that the state of mind of the recipient is important. Possibly! but a very dangerous conclusion as *wishful thinking* in this way may influence results! After all the net effect of all results is only 7.1% correct out of 2.5 instead of 5.0% on chance basis."

In a later diary entry — in 1941 — he lists his five symptoms of pathological science:

"1. Effect is of magnitude which remains close to threshold of detectability despite attempts to increase it.

"2. Fantastic conclusions and lack of reasonable theory or one which starts as reasonable theory but gradually becomes more and more unreasonable.

"3. Magnitude of Effect Independent of Intensity of Causative Agent.

"4. No useful applications or developments.

"5. Interest (and doubt) at first intense, but with gradual waning of interest or decrease in the number of believers even if no *disproof* has been possible.

"Examples: N-Rays; Mitogenetic Rays; Davis-Barnes Effect; Allison Effect; Rhine ESP."

In addition to his critical scrutiny of other people's work, Langmuir had often burst bumptiously into fields outside his own — like biology and meteorology — with very upsetting and unorthodox concepts. This was merely the robust expression of the wide and untrammeled range of Langmuir's scientific interests. As Coolidge put it: "He was very open-minded, and in nowise bound by tradition. He felt, seemingly, as free to think things out for himself, in any field, as did the immortal Greeks of the Age of Pericles." But there were those who looked upon Langmuir as an outsider who had invaded their territory. And there were those who felt that he occasionally, in his enthusiasm, pushed his own ideas too hard and too fast. So when the experts refused to accept either his theories or his results on cloud-seeding, there were many to enjoy his discomfiture.

During those petty-backbiting days, when a few scientists who had never liked Langmuir got together, one of them might remember the time, at a seminar, when Langmuir had been making rapid calculations on the blackboard. When he came out with an answer he didn't like, he erased it and started over again, saying vehemently, "By golly, we'll *make* it work!" And that might remind somebody else that he had once heard some people from the GE lab joking about what they called the "Langmuir Correction Factor."

Then someone might bring up the occasion when Langmuir published "proof positive" — which turned out to be a big mistake — that he had induced the evaporation of thorium from tungsten. The next recollection might be Langmuir's erroneous "proof" of Dorothy Wrinch's cyclol theory of insulin structure; and everyone would snicker. "Maybe old Langmuir ought to be looking closer to home for examples of 'pathological science', hm? Now, this periodic rainfall business — isn't that the payoff? You think he's getting senile?"

On one occasion Langmuir arrived at a certain university to consult on a piece of research, and was given such a rude reception that he turned right around and left.

"Why did this sort of thing have to happen to Langmuir in his declining years?" it was asked. "Isn't it a pity he has to spend so much of his time and energy defending this fool theory of his?" Actually Langmuir enjoyed defending his "fool theory." He had always enjoyed a good fight, and he really didn't care terribly who won, so long as the truth came out. He didn't even seriously mind all the carping. He welcomed and respected his honest critics — like Glenn W. Brier, the Weather Bureau's chief statistician, who disagreed quite firmly on the interpretation of Langmuir's statistics. As for the petty backbiters, he had only contempt for them — and some sympathy for their sensitivities. He knew he had often irritated people by his bluntness, but that was the only way he knew how to operate.

Langmuir also knew he had often been wrong. "But if I have a theory about some facet of the physical universe," he once told Workman, "I have to believe it and everything it implies, and I feel obliged to speak up strongly in its favor. How else can I get the ideas criticized and tested?"

"It was because Langmuir was so unafraid to be wrong," says

Workman, "that he was able to be right so often. Had he been a more cautious type, he could not have achieved nearly as much." And when Langmuir was proven wrong, he took it graciously and was the first to admit it — even publicly, even in a written publication, as in the case of the induced evaporation of thorium. In the case of the induced rainfall, he never admitted he was wrong because it was never proven to his satisfaction that he was anything but right.

And he was far from downcast about all the criticism. In its cover story on Langmuir and rainmaking in 1950, *Time* wrote: "At 69, he is a stocky man of middle height with plentiful white hair and an air of semi-polite skepticism. But he can also blaze with indignation and laugh like a kid — all within a few minutes. In the presence of his gentle-voiced, humorous wife, he smiles like a man who is happy."

And why would he not be happy? He was still in good health, and still enjoying all the things he had always enjoyed. The fact that a few scientists were down on him did not negate the fact that the science world at large still looked upon him as one of the greats of his time. He was still respected, even adulated, in most places. He still was asked to lecture, he still received awards and honorary degrees, and he was still asked to consult on problems as varied as how to improve the efficiency of guided missiles, how to get rid of smog in Los Angeles, and how to raise better cotton in Arizona. In 1947 he even had a mountain in Alaska named after him. He kept in touch with all the numerous Langmuirs, and enjoyed putting cousins in touch with other cousins they never knew they had. He still traveled a great deal, still went often to Lake George, and still stayed in the middle of various research projects at the GE laboratory.

And he dreamed and talked of the new wonders that science would bring into the world. "I can conceive," he said in one speech, "of an orchard operated entirely without workers in which the fruit-bearing trees can be cared for and cultivated and the fruit picked by machines operated and controlled by electronic devices... There is no fundamental reason why we could not travel at a speed of 2000 or even 5000 miles an hour in vacuum tube. Such a tube extending from New York to Chicago, or to San Francisco, could be constructed in which the air-tight vehicles are magnetically suspended in space while moving forward at high speed. The intricate operations would be controlled throughout by electronic devices... We must plan on building our cities on a two-level street plan throughout, with traffic on any highway never moving except in one direction and with no grade crossing." No wonder he appreciated one of the favorite aphorisms of his favorite inventor, Charles Kettering: "I object to people running down the future. I'm going to live all the rest of my life there."

On January 12, 1950, there was a dinner at the Schenectady Golf Club in honor of three GE scientists who were retiring: Albert Hull, Langmuir's long-time friend and associate, companion on early river outings, collaborator in developing radio power tubes; Gorton Fonda, the handsome young man all the Schenectady girls were so struck with the night Irving met Marion at the church supper; and Irving Langmuir. But Langmuir's official retirement did not slow him down at all. In fact, it was only two weeks after the retirement dinner that he gave his first controversial Project Cirrus paper. He never stopped his field work, and he still appeared frequently in his old office at the laboratory. As always, his door remained open, with no appointments necessary, and his mind remained as keen and alert as ever. He was approached much less frequently than in the old days by the new young researchers, however. Langmuir was looked upon with too much awe to approach easily. He had become a legend.

Part of the legend was that he was a "cold fish," aloof and unfriendly. Those who knew Langmuir well were always astonished to hear this. The undeserved reputation was probably due to a combination of poor eyesight and preoccupation with the problem at hand. He often simply didn't *see* people as he went by. And of course, though he got to be quite an impressive public speaker, he never did learn the art of smalltalk. Anyone who came in to see him, however, found him warm, friendly, helpful, and sympathetic.

Another part of the Langmuir legend was his absentmindedness. And he *was* absentminded, up to a point, like all preoccupied gentlemen. Everyone has at least one story to tell about Langmuir's absentmindedness. Hull remembers the time his own laboratory assistant, a young lady, was out sick, and Mrs. Hull came in to pinch-hit for her. Though she was there all day and Langmuir came in several times to talk to Hull, he was surprised later to learn that Mrs. Hull had been there.

Others recall the day Mary Christie, Whitney's secretary, looked at her watch and said to Langmuir, "Dr. Langmuir, it's almost time for your appointment with the dentist."

"Oh," said Langmuir, looking up from his work, "is he here already?"

A GE painter remembers the time he was painting the hall of the lab, and Langmuir, his mind obviously somewhere else, kicked over a paint can in the hall. Though the paint spilled all over, he walked right through it, never slowing his pace or noticing what he had done.

There are any number of versions of another story: Mrs. Langmuir had gone shopping and Langmuir was supposed to pick her up on a prearranged corner. As the car approached, she waved at him. He simply waved back and kept on going. Mrs. Langmuir, however, doesn't remember the incident. There is even an oft-told tale to the effect that Langmuir was once walking down a flight of stairs, and when the lady in front of him fell on the stairway, he simply stepped over her and continued down the how he had got there. Well, Langmuir was by no means in this stairs!

Some would have you believe that Langmuir was the archetype of all absentminded professors, a veritable latter-day Cesare Lombroso. Lombroso, the celebrated criminologist, used to arrive in strange cities and, forgetting what hotel he was staying at, would wander the streets all night. He was always getting on the wrong trains, losing wallets, luggage, tickets, and important papers. Someone was always having to go rescue him from some out-of-the-way place he had wound up, penniless, without knowing category, or anywhere close to it. His lapses were few and far between. He dressed neatly, seldom lost anything — including himself, and most of the stories about him in this vein are very amusing — and they never happened.

Langmuir had a nice sense of humor but not a very sophisticated one. It took him, for example, a long time to see why everyone was chuckling over one of his papers on electron discharge in vacuum tubes. The mathematics involved contained three variables, x, e (the charge on the electron), and S; and in one instance Langmuir had them all on one side of the equation in the following order: $S\ e\ x$.

At home, Langmuir had great fun being an amateur chef. He had enjoyed cooking ever since he had learned, in self-defense, while living with Arthur and Alice in Brooklyn back in the days when he went to Pratt. He nearly always cooked solid, homely dishes — like sausage and eggs for breakfast; but he could whip up a fancy item like baked Alaska when friends dropped by. He loved Chinese food and French cooking, was fond of pork tenderloin and roast goose, and was a great consumer of ice cream and candy. He smoked on and off over the years, never very heavily. He did not drink until he was nearly forty. Then he drank only wine for a while. When he did begin to appreciate stronger alcoholic beverages, he indulged quite moderately, usually satisfying himself with one drink. He did like to sample new kinds of drinks, for the fun of it. And on a rare occasion, like a Christmas egg-nog party, he might even get slightly inebriated. When he did, he would be quite garrulous, and Marion would say, "Irving, you've had too much to drink." And he would say, "Of course I have!"

He had always liked classical music and the opera, but he also learned to enjoy lighter music — never jazz, but light classics and popular ballads. He would often whistle, say, Jerome Kern tunes — but you might also catch him whistling, "I Can't Give You Anything But Love, Baby." He liked the movies — especially musical films starring Fred Astaire and Ginger Rogers. He liked Wallace Beery, Marie Dressler, Maurice Chevalier, Greta Garbo, and Will Rogers (whom he once met). His taste in television and radio programs was corny: "Circus Boy" (he loved the circus), "Portia Faces Life" (the soapiest of soap operas), "Father Knows Best" and the prize-fights.

He really did not like to play cards very much, not caring for competitive sport, either indoors or outdoors. His favorite games were Russian Bank and canasta. When he did play, though, he often made his own rules — and was a poor loser.

He didn't have time to read much fiction — an occasional mystery story, perhaps, or one of Upton Sinclair's Lanny Budd books. He hugely enjoyed following the comic strips, especially Li'l Abner and Little Orphan Annie. This lighter side had always been part of Langmuir's nature. Mrs. Langmuir remembers a time in Brussels when they were having coffee at a sidewalk cafe. A parade was going by — a procession having something to do with a celebration of streetcar conductors. There was music and dancing, and Langmuir simply jumped up, joined the parade, and danced along with the streetcar conductors.

Langmuir was an inveterate art-gallerygoer, too. His tastes in art were quite conventional. He preferred representational art, and admired the old masters. As for abstraction — he understood it in science, but not in art.

He had very little acquaintance with classical philosophers, though one summer, with David, he read Will Durant's *Story of Philosophy*. But he was a profound philosopher in his own right, and was particularly cognizant of the philosophical implications of modern science — especially relativity and quantum mechanics. Nor was he unaware of the implications of his ideas in other fields. In working out his ideas about convergent and divergent phenomena, for example, he pointed out that "In human affairs, we have to deal largely with divergent phenomena, which are not determined by definite relations of cause and effect." And, carrying the idea a bit further: "The average philosopher bases too much on cause and effect. I believe that it is impossible to predict the future because so many small things may influence the men who make history — things like their health — the way they might feel at a certain time." Historians like Hegel, Marx, Spengler and Toynbee would not have cared much for Langmuir's philosophy of history. (It should be noted that, in addition to helping him recognize the limitations of history, his philosophy also helped him recognize the limitations of science.)

As for religion, Langmuir had none. Not in the formal sense, at least. If pressed, he might have answered as Laplace is supposed to have answered when Napoleon asked why he had omitted a Creator from his system: "I had no need of that hypothesis."

Yet he had a peculiar affinity that can only be called mystical for the natural universe and everything in it. He was quite interested in theological ideas, though he never accepted any as his own beliefs. He always told his nephews, "Never believe anything that can't be proved" — a bit of advice which his sister-in-law, Mrs. Charles Herbert Langmuir, a churchgoing lady, never appreciated (though she did appreciate his interest in her sons and his lasting influence on their characters and careers). Langmuir never mocked the religious ideas of anyone else, and often avoided discussing religion — because if he did discuss it, he would be honest, and might therefore give offense. Once he felt safe in talking about religion, he was eager to talk about it.

On one occasion, Kenneth brought an Army friend with him to spend the weekend at Lake George. On Sunday morning there was a great to-do about getting his friend off the island and onto the mainland in time to go to mass, then another flurry about getting him back on the island after mass was over. Later, on the beach, Langmuir asked the young man abruptly, "Why are you a Catholic, anyway?" When he saw that there was no offense taken, he asked some more questions, and they had a long, enjoyable discussion, in which neither convinced the other of anything.

Langmuir liked to tell the story about the time, in 1946, when he was to appear on the American Forum of the Air to discuss atomic energy with some other prominent people — among them Clare Boothe Luce, who was at the time a representative from the state of Connecticut. Before the broadcast, the conversation turned to the scientific method and such matters. "I was sounding off," said Langmuir, "about how a person shouldn't believe anything he couldn't prove. Someone else said that not all true statements were provable, and I challenged him to name one. Mrs. Luce volunteered an answer for him: 'God is love,' she said. She sure had me there."

In politics, Langmuir was, during most of his life, strongly conservative. He was never as conservative as his brother, Arthur, but was frequently more so than either Herbert or Dean. He was a Socialist in his early days at the GE laboratory, but that was a passing phase. He saw in the General Electric Company the exemplar of enlightened capitalism, and soon felt strongly that this was the most viable political system possible. He was very much influenced by his brothers, too, and made quite a bit of money in investments, thanks largely to their astute advice. (Yet Langmuir was basically uninterested in money. He turned down any number of opportunities for better-paying positions, opportunities to head laboratories of his own, opportunities to make considerable sums of money — and was often urged by other members of the family, especially Mama, to accept them. But he was too happy at GE to consider any other offers. He was doing exactly what he liked, and had all the money he needed — why change?) Through most of his adult life, Langmuir voted the straight Republican ticket.

At only one point in his life — for a brief period after the stock-market crash in the early thirties — was he somewhat disgruntled. He had lost quite a bit of money in the market, and General Electric — hard hit by the depression, like everyone else — had cut his salary. On the way back from his Nobel Prize tour, he read, on the boat, H. Pratt Fisher's *Profits or Prosperity* and was much impressed by it, "altho I don't agree with his conclusion that profits are wholly bad or impossible," he noted in his diary, "nor with his attitude of accepting a static society. I want progress. Control of production by hours of labor to avoid unemployment." He worked out some rather unorthodox economic ideas, and was prepared to expound them in a series of public speeches after he returned from Europe. But his brothers talked him out of it. At first he was not to be dissuaded, but Herbert remembered that Irving had recently said — in reference to scientists who got involved in religion and made speeches about it — that scientists should "stay on their own reservation." Herbert repeated this back to him now, and Irving promptly canceled a speaking date he had made in Brooklyn for the following evening.

For a while Langmuir even looked with favor on the New Deal, though he had been fond of Calvin Coolidge and had voted for Herbert Hoover. His essential conservatism soon reasserted itself, however, and he never again toyed with the notion of voting anything but the straight Republican ticket. Just to give the feel of his sympathies, here is his diary entry of November 6, 1944, during World War II: "A disgraceful hourlong Democratic Party program with a prayer offered for the reelection of Roosevelt. Dewey gives a magnificent dignified powerful address at 11 pm, followed by the National Anthem. Hope he is elected." Or again, in a public speech: "There is too much regimentation. Socialized medicine is a manifestation of this trend. I like free enterprise. People should have great incentive to do great things. Business, which is constantly being harassed by government, alone has the means to handle great research. The desire to help the underdog is being carried to such extremes that initiative is being throttled." One evening he was quite shocked when Alex, fresh from college where he had been president of the Harvard Liberal Club, not only had many good words to say for Roosevelt and the New Deal but was even firmly critical — in the face of arguments from himself and Arthur — of big-corporation power interests. No rift resulted from the argument — but the relationship between Alex and Uncle Irving was never quite the same again.

Only the naive expect scientists to be rational at all times — even about science. On his various sorties into the realm of pathological science, Langmuir frequently found scientists distorting their data for purely irrational reasons. Yet, for all his awareness of the symptoms of pathological science, Langmuir himself was frequently taken in by medical theories — and medicine is at least semi-scientific. He was fond of trying out medical fads, experimenting on himself, and sometimes on the family. He was quite convinced, for example, that radium-water treatments — which he did not administer, by the way — had cured his mother's arthritis. For a while he was on an ultraviolet kick, and treated everyone to daily whole-body exposure to ultraviolet light. He was sure it made him feel better; moreover, it made Kenneth behave remarkably well. Poor Kenneth was the guinea pig more than once, even after he became quite a big boy.

For a while, in the early thirties, some of the GE lab people had developed a theory that high fevers would cure a cold; and someone had even worked out a method for inducing a high fever artificially. Just about a week before they were all about to leave on their Nobel Prize tour, in November of 1932, Langmuir wrote the following in his diary: "To cure a cold, I gave Kenneth a hot bath, 108–106°. His temp rose in 10 min to 102.5°. Pulse 138. I cooled water to 105° and kept him in this for 5 min more. Pulse dropped to 130 but temp still 102.5°. He complained of discomfort. I got him in to bed and he said that he felt faint. Pulse dropped quickly to 60. He lost all color and was almost unconscious for 2 min. Then with temp at 101.5, his pulse rose again and color came back. After 25 min: Temp 100° and pulse 108." Despite the ministrations of Irving Langmuir, M.D., Kenneth got better in time for the trip.

These foibles and idiosyncrasies merely serve to show that Irving Langmuir was human. Without them he would have been too perfect a man to be believable.

Chapter 25

"I warmed both hands before the fire of life,
It sinks, and I am ready to depart."

WALTER SAVAGE LANDOR

INEVITABLY, the time arrives when even an Irving Langmuir must finally begin to slow down. It is hard to say when it actually began happening. At Lake George one day, Robert's wife, Lee, noticed that Uncle Irving's step did not seem as springy as it used to be. Near Atlanta on another day, Alex was surprised when Uncle Irving was ready to come back down a mountainside, even though they had only climbed halfway up. He didn't even tell the children they were sissies for not wanting to get to the top. And so it went.

Arthur had died, after prolonged heart trouble, back in 1941. The ravages of persistent cancer had finaly killed Herbert in 1944. When Dean died suddenly of a heart attack early in 1950, only four days before Irving's retirement dinner, that left only Irving as the last of the four Langmuir boys.

At the time he was still going strong. His health had been reasonably good, and he remained amazingly active for a man in his seventies. After the 1939 cancer operation, there had been an appendectomy in 1941, but that had been only a minor interruption. Then there were the cataracts on his eyes. The trouble first began early in 1946, and both cataracts were finally removed by operations in 1948 and 1949, which Irving took in his stride; in fact, they even helped improve his vision a bit, since he had always been quite nearsighted. Later in New Mexico, however, he had suffered a separation of the retina and had to fly back East for an emergency "spot welding" operation to save that eye. But that had come off quite successfully too.

The first real slowdown probably took place early in 1957 when Langmuir, shoveling snow with his usual vigor, was stricken with a heart attack. Even the children were not told about it, but they heard enough by accident to guess the rest. He recovered nicely from that, too, and proceeded as usual, though at a somewhat decelerated pace.

Part of Langmuir's fun had always been to take a personal hand in the education of his nephews. This often meant sending them, or taking them, on trips. After his nephews had all grown up, Langmuir liked to do the same thing for their children. In the summer of 1957, he took Robert's teen-age son, Allan, on an automobile tour of New York and New England. He had to drive rather carefully, and keep as much as possible to the side roads, since his vision was not as good as it might be. And, to conserve his strength, he let Allan drive quite a bit. In the old days — even in the not-so-old days in the Southwest — Langmuir could drive nonstop for practically twenty-four hours without knowing he was tired.

In New York City Uncle Irving made sure that Allan did things like taking a subway ride to Coney Island and going to the top of the Empire State Building, but Uncle Irving didn't come along for the rides any more.

They toured the countryside, seeing the sights — including, of course, Lake George — and stopped to visit numerous relatives. They also stopped frequently while Uncle Irving talked to some farmer about his crops, or explained some natural phenomenon to Allan. Now and then they stayed up late looking at the sky while Uncle Irving pointed out the various stars and constellations. Traveling a leisurely, devious route, they arrived, one Monday evening in August, at Cape Cod, to spend the night with David. David had been sent to Woods Hole by the Air Force with a summer study group for some research work, and he and his family were living in a tiny cottage right on Falmouth Bay, facing the harbor. As soon as Uncle Irving arrived, he wanted to go down to the boat dock and take some pictures. They all went down with him to enjoy the view of the harbor at sunset. Uncle Irving walked more slowly than was his custom on the way back, but at supper he was as cheerful and as talkative as ever.

For a while before bedtime Uncle Irving played with David's six-year-old boy, Charlie (named Charles Herbert, after Herbert) — but he played carefully, not romping energetically, as usual; and when he held Charlie in his lap, he just held him, he didn't bounce him up and down.

"Uncle Irving," said Charlie, "tell me all about science."

"Your daddy is a scientist, Charlie. Why don't you ask him?"

"Oh, he never has time."

Uncle Irving went over some simple arithmetic problems. Charlie did not seem terribly interested. "Well, that's science too, Charlie," he said. Then he showed him some kitchen tricks in chemistry — like the one where you put together a bit of bicarbonate of soda and a bit of vinegar in a glass, then pour out the heavier-than-air carbon dioxide that results from the mixture into another glass; then light a match, wait until it burns brightly, put the match flame into the invisible carbon dioxide and watch it be snuffed out instantly and mysteriously. Charlie thought that was a lot more fun than arithmetic.

Finally Charlie went off to bed, and Uncle Irving asked David about the research he'd been doing at Woods Hole. Then he and Allan told David and Nancy about the trip they had just been taking, and Uncle Irving complained about Allan's finicky eating habits, how few things he liked, how much food he always left on his plate, how he was afraid to experiment with things he had never tasted. "No sense of adventure," he concluded, knowing of course that Allan was as fond of adventure as he had been himself at that age. After some shoptalk and trading of family news, they all finally went to bed, David and Nancy sleeping downstairs while Allan and Uncle Irving went upstairs.

About six o'clock the next morning, Tuesday, Allan woke up suddenly in his cot, and realized that Uncle Irving had thrown a pillow at his head from his own cot nearby.

When he saw that Allan was awake, Langmuir said, in a rather subdued voice, "You'd better call David. I think I need a doctor."

Allan shouted to David from the head of the stairs, and the two met about midway on the staircase. "Uncle Irving doesn't feel very well," Allan told him. "He's calm and quiet, but his face sure looks gray."

When David got upstairs, Langmuir said, "You'd better call a doctor, David. I think I've had a heart attack. My temperature and pulse" — which he had already taken — "are way down. Better tell him to bring some oxygen, too." He spoke quite matter-of-factly, as though he were a doctor discussing some other patient. Langmuir had always taken an objective interest in his own illnesses — even in his cancer operation. During his eye troubles, he had made an intensive study of the human eye, and the oculist had grumbled more than once that Langmuir knew more about it all than he did.

David and Nancy had not been at Woods Hole long. They had no idea where to get a doctor, especially at six o'clock in the morning. Nancy finally called the head of the summer study group. He didn't know of any doctors, either. But he told her there was a central medical service that could be called in emergencies. She got the number from the operator and called them. Then, after what seemed like a long time but was probably not more than ten minutes, a Dr. Burwell called back. David told him the story. The doctor, responding to Langmuir's name, asked a few more questions and said he would be right over. The doctor, a young Harvard Medical School man, soon appeared carrying a portable electrocardiograph machine. As soon as he arrived he called the Falmouth Fire Department for some oxygen, then went to work.

Langmuir, meanwhile, had said it would be nice if Alex could come over. Alex, though he lived and worked in Atlanta as top man for the Public Health Service's Communicable Diseases Center, happened to be nearby, at Martha's Vineyard, where his mother always spent the summer. They called him and he left at once. Nancy took Allan and Charlie with her, met the boat, and sent the boys back to the island with Alex's wife, Sally.

Alex and Dr. Burwell liked one another instantly. Alex didn't interfere. He merely stood by, helping where he could, admiring Dr. Burwell's efficiency and agreeing that he was doing all the right things. Burwell said that Langmuir would need a nurse in constant attendance. There was no nurse to be had in Woods Hole, so Burwell sent the nurse over from his own office to fill in until they could get someone else. Then they started calling all over for a nurse. There were several possibilities, but General Electric came through first, driving a nurse up at once from Schenectady.

Meanwhile Harry, Barbara's husband, flew up from Schenectady with Aunt Marion — who had always hated to fly, unless Irving was at the controls. She slept in the kitchen, Harry stayed at the hotel across the street, and Langmuir was put in the living room with the nurse. He had to be supported in a sitting position in bed a good bit of the time — perhaps out of fear that his lungs might fill with fluid. Though he openly struggled for breath much of the time, he was a spunky patient and talked when he could, often humorously. At one point, after Nancy had been talking on the phone to the Vineyard, she told Uncle Irving, "Sally says Allan has been eating *everything*."

Langmuir took off his oxygen mask and said, "Impossible!"

On Wednesday night he had another heart attack, and Burwell, worried, called a heart specialist in Boston, who came down that same night. The next day, Thursday, Langmuir showed considerable improvement, and the doctors were much encouraged. By Friday morning, after a wonderfully restful night's sleep, Uncle Irving was so perky that everybody felt much better. David, remembering the rugged skipper in the blue serge suit at the helm of a sloop in a tossing sea, drenched with blown spray, munching happily on some biscuit while everyone else was seasick, grinned and thought: you can't keep Uncle Irving down, by golly. He went off to work that morning, and Harry flew back to Schenectady.

A little later, in the somewhat more relaxed atmosphere, Marion was in the kitchen watching the nurse mix an eggnog for Irving. Alex and Nancy were in the living room with Irving. Suddenly there was a shout for the nurse's attention. The patient had just had another heart attack, without warning. They all rushed to his bedside. The color had drained from Langmuir's face, leaving it ashy white. He shuddered once, convulsively, then lay back and died.

Thus, among his own, at the age of seventy-six, on the morning of Friday, August 16, 1957, ended the life — rich in love and joy, and the career — replete with honor and achievement, of the man who was perhaps as great a scientist as has ever been born in America.

List of Principal Sources

ADAM, N. K., memorial essay in Volume 9 of Langmuir's *Collected Works.*

ALBERTO, ALVARO, "Irving Langmuir," *Revista G.E.*, Outobro–Novembro–Dezembro, 1957.

Albuquerque Journal, "Rainmaking Still 'Iffy,' Cloud Seeding Expert Says," July 25, 1952.

BARNES, ROBERT A. (Associated Press), "Final Report: Sky-Milking Value Vague," *Santa Fe New Mexican*, October 14, 1951.

BECKER, J. A., memorial essay in Volume 3 of Langmuir's *Collected Works.*

BELLO, FRANCIS, "Tomorrow's Weather," *Fortune*, May 1953.

BIRR, KENDALL, *Pioneering in Industrial Research*, Public Affairs Press, Washington, 1957.

BLODGETT, KATHARINE B., "Irving Langmuir," *Journal of Chemical Education*, July 1933.

BLODGETT, KATHARINE B., "Irving Langmuir," an unpublished talk, September 4, 1957.

BRIDGMAN, PERCY W., "Some of the Physical Aspects of the Work of Langmuir," Volume 1 and Volume 12 of Langmuir's *Collected Works.*

BURTON, HAL, "Langmuir: Miracle Man of Science," *Coronet*, June 1949.

BYERS, HORACE R., memorial essay in Volume 11 of Langmuir's *Collected Works.*

CANNON, WALTER B., "Gains from Serendipity," in *Great Adventures in Medicine*, Dial Press, New York, 1952.

CARTER, RUTLEDGE E., "Memory Honored—Langmuir Medals Are Presented to GE Lab." *Schenectady Gazette*, December 13, 1958.

COBINE, J. D., memorial essays in Volume 3 and Volume 4 of Langmuir's *Collected Works*.

COHEN, I. BERNARD, *Science, Servant of Man*, Little Brown, Boston, 1948.

COLLINS, GERTRUDE (Mrs.), personal interview.

COOLIDGE, WILLIAM D., "Formative Years of the Laboratory," talk at GE Laboratory Colloquium, December 12, 1951.

COOLIDGE, WILLIAM D., Remarks in "A Tribute to Irving Langmuir," compiled for Langmuir memorial service, August 21, 1957.

COON, DARRYL, personal interview.

Current Biography, Langmuir article, October 1950.

DAVIDSON, CARTER, "Notes on Irving Langmuir as a Man" (unpublished), for Langmuir memorial service, August 21, 1957.

DECOSTA, BENJAMIN F., *Lake George: Its Scenes and Characteristics, with Glimpses of the Olden Times*, Anson D. F. Randolph, New York, 1868.

DUSHMAN, SAUL, "The Spirit of the Research Laboratory," talk at GE Laboratory Colloquium, December 12, 1951.

ECKERT, E. R. G., memorial essay in Volume 2 of Langmuir's *Collected Works*.

Englewood Press, Obituary of Sadie Comings Langmuir, February 12, 1936.

EYRING, HENRY, memorial essay in Volume 8 of Langmuir's *Collected Works*.

FISHER, R. J., "The 'GREAT' of Modern Day Scientists," *The Quadrant*, University of Portland, Winter 1948.

FLEMING, A. P. M., "Irving Langmuir—Pioneer in Research," *Electrical Engineering*, October 1944.

GABOR, DENNIS, personal interviews, correspondence.

GABOR, DENNIS (with E. A. Ash and D. Dracott), "Langmuir's Paradox," *Nature*, November 12, 1955.

GENERAL ELECTRIC LABORATORY, *The Research Laboratory, Past and Present*.

GE Schenectady News, "Dr. Langmuir, GE Scientist, Was World Famous," August 23, 1957.

GIBSON, CHARLES DEWOLF, personal interview.

GRAY, GEORGE W., "A Summer Vacation," *The Atlantic*, December 1933.

HARKER, DAVID, memorial essay in Volume 6 of Langmuir's *Collected Works*.

HARMON, EVELYN (Mrs.), personal interview, correspondence.

HARRISON, GEORGE R., *Atoms in Action*, William Morrow, New York, 1949.

HARROW, BENJAMIN, *The Romance of the Atom*, Boni & Liveright, New York, 1927.

HAWKINS, LAURENCE A., "Willis R. Whitney, Dean of Industrial Research," *G.E. Monogram*, September – October 1950.

HAWKINS, LAURENCE A., *Adventure Into the Unknown*, William Morrow, New York, 1950.

HAWKINS, LAURENCE A., "Research and Dr. Langmuir," *American Heritage*, August 1955.

HENNELLY, EDWARD, personal interview.

HILDEBRAND, JOEL H., "The Humanism of Irving Langmuir," in Volume 12 of Langmuir's *Collected Works*.

HILDEBRAND, JOEL H., "Gilbert Newton Lewis," *Biographical Memoirs*, National Academy of Sciences, 1958.

HUGHES, ALLAN, personal interview.

HULL, ALBERT W., personal interview.

HULL, ALBERT W., "Our Laboratory," talk at GE Laboratory Colloquium, December 12, 1951.

HUXLEY, JULIAN, *Science and Social Needs*, Harper, 1935.

JAFFE, BERNARD, *Crucibles: The Story of Chemistry*, Simon & Schuster, New York, 1951.

JEFFRIES, ZAY, memorial essay in Volume 2 of Langmuir's *Collected Works*.

JUNGK, ROBERT, *Brighter Than a Thousand Suns*, Harcourt Brace, 1958.

KELLOGG, E. W., unpublished Engineering Memorandum, "Visit of Dr. Langmuir and Mr. Stokowski to RCA Victor Laboratory," December 4, 1930.

KENDALL, JAMES, *Great Discoveries of Young Chemists*, Thomas Nelson & Sons, Ltd., London, 1953.

KENT, CHARLES A., "Irving Langmuir," *Oskaloosa Daily Herald*, August 18, 1947.

KINGDON, KENNETH, personal interview.

KINGDON, KENNETH, "Irving Langmuir, 1881 – 1957," unpublished.

KINGDON, KENNETH, "From Submarines to A-Bombs," *GE Review*, Winter 1959 – 1960.

LACHMAN, ARTHUR, *Borderland of the Unknown*, Pageant Press, 1955.

LANGMUIR, ALEXANDER D., personal interview, correspondence.

LANGMUIR, ALEXANDER D., and DAVID LANGMUIR, "Irving Langmuir, 1881 – 1957—A Memorial," remarks read at Langmuir memorial service, August 21, 1957.

LANGMUIR, ALLAN, personal interview.

LANGMUIR, ARTHUR C., diaries, correspondence.

LANGMUIR, ARTHUR C., "My Brother Irving," *Industrial & Engineering Chemistry*, News Edition, 1932.

LANGMUIR, BRUCE, personal interviews.

LANGMUIR, CHARLES, correspondence.

LANGMUIR, CHARLES HERBERT, correspondence.

LANGMUIR, CHARLES HERBERT, "The Winning of the Nobel Prize," unpublished remarks at Englewood, N.J., November 27, 1932.

LANGMUIR, DAVID B., personal interviews, correspondence.

LANGMUIR, DEAN, correspondence, personal diaries, and rough notes for a planned biography of Irving Langmuir.

LANGMUIR, DONALD, personal interview.

LANGMUIR, IRVING, personal acquaintance, correspondence, diaries, laboratory notebooks, congressional testimony.

LANGMUIR, IRVING, *The Collected Works of Irving Langmuir*, Volumes 1–12, Pergamon Press, London, 1961.

LANGMUIR, IRVING, "Theories of Atomic Structure," letter in *Nature*, April 26, 1920.

LANGMUIR, IRVING, *Phenomena, Atoms and Molecules*, Philosophical Library, New York, 1950.

LANGMUIR, IRVING (with Harold E. Stassen, Rep. Clare Boothe Luce and Rep. J. Parnell Thomas), *The American Forum of the Air*, Theodore Granik, Washington, September 10, 1946.

LANGMUIR, KENNETH, personal interviews, correspondence.

LANGMUIR, LAURA (Mrs. John Langmuir), personal interviews, correspondence.

LANGMUIR, LEE (Mrs. Robert V. Langmuir), personal interview.

LANGMUIR, MARION (Mrs. Irving Langmuir), personal interviews, correspondence.

LANGMUIR, NANCY (Mrs. David B. Langmuir), personal interviews.

LANGMUIR, ROBERT V., personal interviews, correspondence.

LANGMUIR, SADIE COMINGS, correspondence, unpublished notes from Memory Book.

LEAR JOHN, "The Thinking Machine That Doesn't Know How to Stop," *Saturday Review*, July 7, 1956.

LEONARD, JONATHAN N., personal interviews.

LEVERENZ, HUMBOLDT, personal interview.

Life, "Solution to Water Shortage?", February 20, 1950.

MARTIN, MILES J., personal interviews, correspondence.

New Mexico Stockman, "Three Quarters of New Mexico Joins in Rain Projects as Krick Firm Assailed by Anderson and McKinney," February 1951.

New York Herald-Tribune, "Dr. Irving Langmuir Finds Magic in Simplest Things," November 21, 1943.

New York Herald-Tribune, "Irving Langmuir Dies; Pioneer in Rain-Making," August 17, 1957.

New York Times, "Pasteur at Notre Dame. Obsequies of the Man of Science Attended by National Homage," October 6, 1895.

New York Times, "Dr. Langmuir Sails to Get Nobel Prize," November 30, 1932.

New York Times, "Langmuir Retires as GE Scientist," January 3, 1950.

New York Times, "Dr. Langmuir Retires" (editorial), January 4, 1950.

New York Times, Langmuir obituary, August 18, 1957.

The Percolator, "The Club Greets Irving Langmuir," Chemists' Club, New York, Christmas 1932.

PFEIFFER, JOHN, "Scientist of Light and Weather," *New York Times Magazine*, January 28, 1951.

RIDEAL, SIR ERIC, unpublished lecture at GE Laboratory, October 15, 1958.

RIDEAL, SIR ERIC, "Dr. Irving Langmuir, For. Mem., R.S.," *Nature*, September 21, 1957.

RIDEAL, SIR ERIC, "Some of the Chemical Aspects of the Work of Langmuir," Volume 1 and Volume 12 of Langmuir's *Collected Works*.

ROESSLE, T. E., *Lake George—A Descriptive and Historical Sketch*, Fort William Henry Hotel, Lake George.

ROGINSKY, S. Z., memorial essay in Volume 1 of Langmuir's *Collected Works*.

Santa Fe New Mexican, "The Rain Makers" (editorial), January 26, 1951.

SCHAAR, BERNARD E., paper on "Serendipity," presented at American Chemical Society meeting, New York, September 10, 1957.

SCHAEFER, VINCENT J., personal interviews.

SCHAEFER, VINCENT J., memorial essay in Volume 10 of Langmuir's *Collected Works*.

SCHAEFER, VINCENT J., unpublished remarks at Langmuir memorial service, August 21, 1957.

SCHAEFER, VINCENT J., "Irving Langmuir, Man of Many Interests," *Science*, May 23, 1958.

Schenectady Gazette, "Dr. Irving Langmuir, 76, Dies at Cape Cod, Nobel Prize Winner," August 17, 1957.

Schenectady Union Star, "Dr. Langmuir Dies; GE Nobel Scientist," August 17, 1957.

Schenectady Union Star, "Langmuir's Scientific Researches Are of Untold Benefit to Mankind," August 17, 1957.

SOBOTKA, HARRY, memorial essay in Volume 7 of Langmuir's *Collected Works*.

STOKOWSKI, LEOPOLD, correspondence.
SUITS, C. G., personal interviews, correspondence.
SUMMERHAYES, BARBARA (Mrs.), personal interview.
SUMMERHAYES, HARRY R., Jr., personal interview.
SZILARD, LEO, personal interview.
TAYLOR, SIR HUGH, "Irving Langmuir—1881–1957," *Biographical Memoirs of Fellows of the Royal Society*, November 1958.
Time, cover story on Langmuir, August 28, 1950.
Time, "Too Much Rainmaking," June 12, 1950.
Time, "Inquisitive Man," January 16, 1950.
VAN DE WATER, RUTH (Mrs.), personal interview, correspondence.
WALKER, C. LESTER, "The Man Who Makes Weather," *Harper's*, January 1950.
WAY, HAROLD E., personal interviews, correspondence.
WHITE, WILLIAM C., personal interview, correspondence.
WHITE, WILLIAM C., "The Naming of Mount Langmuir, Alaska, 1957" (mimeographed).
WHITNEY, WILLIS R., "Langmuir's Work," *Industrial & Engineering Chemistry*, March 1928.
WHITNEY, WILLIS R., "Helpful Thinking," talk at GE Laboratory Colloquium, December 12, 1951.
WHITNEY, WILLIS R., "A Biographical Sketch of the Late Irving Langmuir," unpublished talk, September 18, 1957.
WILSON, MITCHELL, *American Science and Invention*, Simon & Schuster, New York, 1954.
WORKMAN, E. J., personal interviews.
Yonkers Herald-Statesman, "World Traveler Dies at 87; Mother of Famous Chemists," February 12, 1936.

Appendix I

IRVING LANGMUIR — CURRICULUM VITAE

Born

January 31, 1881

Parents

Charles and Sadie Comings Langmuir

Attended

Public Schools, Brooklyn	1887–1892
Boarding School, Suburban Paris	1892–1895
Chestnut Hill Academy, Philadelphia	1895–1896

Graduated

Manual Training High School, Pratt Institute	1898

Received degree

Metallurgical Engineer, Columbia University	1903
Doctor of Philosophy, University of Göttingen	1906

Taught

Stevens Institute of Technology	1906—1909

Married

Marion Mersereau — 1912

Children

Son, Kenneth
Daughter, Mrs. H. R. Summerhayes

Research Scientist

General Electric Research Laboratory	1909–1950
Associate Director	1929–1950
Consultant	1950–1957

Honorary Degrees Awarded

D.Sc.	Northwestern University	1921
LL.D.	Edinburgh University	1921
D.Sc.	Union University	1923
D.Sc.	Columbia University	1925
D.Sc.	Kenyon College	1927
D.Sc.	Princeton University	1929
D.Ing.	Tech. Hochschule, Berlin	1929
D.Sc.	Lehigh University	1934
LL.D.	Union University	1934
LL.D.	John Hopkins University	1936
D.Sc.	Harvard University	1938
D.Sc.	Oxford University	1938
D.Sc.	Rutgers University	1941
D.Sc.	Queen's College (Canada)	1941
LL.D.	University of California	1946

Medals Awarded

Nichols Medal	American Chemical Society	1915
Hughes Medal	Royal Society of London	1918
Rumford Medal	American Association for the Advancement of Science	1920
Nichols Medal	American Chemical Society	1920

Stanislao Cannizzaro Award	Royal National Academy of Linnaeus (Rome)	1925
Perkins Medal	Society Chemical Industry (American Section)	1928
Chandler Medal	Columbia University	1929
Willard Gibbs Medal	American Chemical Society	1930
NOBEL PRIZE	Swedish Academy	1932
Popular Science	Popular Science Monthly	1933
Franklin Medal	Franklin Institute	1934
Holley Medal	American Society of Mechanical Engineers	1934
John Scott Medal	Philadelphia Board of Directors of City Trusts	1937
Faraday Medal	Chemical Society (London)	1938
Egleston Medal	Columbia University Engineering Schools Alumni Association	1939
Modern Pioneer of Industry	National Association of Manufacturers	1940
Silver Beaver	Boy Scouts of America	1942
Faraday Medal	Institution of Electrical Engineers	1943
Medal of Merit	United States Army and Navy	1948
Mascart Medal	Academy des Sciences, Société Française des Electriciens	1948
John J. Carty Medal	National Academy of Sciences	1949
Silver Buffalo	Boy Scouts of America	1950

Died

August 16, 1957

Appendix II

COMPLETE LIST OF PAPERS OF DR. IRVING LANGMUIR AS THEY APPEAR IN THE LANGMUIR MEMORIAL VOLUMES*

VOLUME 1

Low-Pressure Phenomena

Mechanism of Chemical Reactions

1. The Partial Recombination of Dissociated Gases During Cooling. Inaugural dissertation for Doctor's Degree, Göttingen (1906).
2. The Dissociation of Water Vapor and Carbon Dioxide at High Temperatures. JACS, **28**, 1357 (1906).
3. The Velocity of Reactions in Gases Moving Through Heated Vessels and the Effect of Convection and Diffusion. JACS, **30**, 1742 (1908).

---

* Editor's Note: The numbers represent the order in which the papers were published.

8. A Chemically Active Modification of Hydrogen. JACS, **34,** 1310 (1912).
7. The Dissociation of Hydrogen into Atoms. JACS, **34,** 860 (1912).
18. Note on the Heat of Formation of Hydrogen from Hydrogen Atoms. Phil. Mag., **27,** 188 (1914).
22. The Dissociation of Hydrogen into Atoms. (With G. M. J. Mackay). JACS, **36,** 1708 (1914).
25. The Dissociation of Hydrogen into Atoms. II. Calculation of the Degree of Dissociation and the Heat of Formation. JACS, **37,** 417 (1915); Zeit. f. Electrochemie, **23,** 217 (1917).
37. The Dissociation of Hydrogen into Atoms. III. JACS, **38,** 1145 (1916).
9. Chemical Reactions at Very Low Pressures. I. The Clean-up of Oxygen in a Tungsten Lamp. JACS, **35,** 105 (1913).
13. Chemical Reactions at Very Low Pressures. II. The Chemical Clean-up of Nitrogen in a Tungsten Lamp. JACS, **35,** 931 (1913).
27. Chemical Reactions at Low Pressures. JACS, **37,** 1139 (1915).
52. Chemical Reactions at Low Pressures. IV. The Clean-up of Nitrogen by a Heated Molybdenum Filament. JACS, **41,** 167 (1919).
66. Radiation as a Factor in Chemical Action. JACS, **42,** 2190 (1920).
72. Chemical Reaction on Surfaces. G. E. Rev., **25,** 445 (1922); Trans. Faraday Soc., **17,** 607 (1921).
73. The Mechanism of the Catalytic Action of Platinum in the Reactions $2CO + O_2 = 2CO_2$ and $2H_2 + O_2 = 2HO$. Trans. Faraday Soc., **17,** 621 (1921).

VOLUME 2

Heat Transfer — Incandescent Tungsten

Part **1** — *Transfer of Heat*

4. Thermal Conduction and Convection in Gases at Extremely High Temperatures. Trans. Amer. Electrochem. Soc., **20**, 225 (1911).
5. Convection and Conduction of Heat in Gases. Phys. Rev., **34**, 401 (1912).
6. Convection and Conduction of Heat in Gases. Proc. AIEE, **31**, 1011 (1912).
10. Laws of Heat Transmission in Electrical Machinery. Proc. AIEE, **32**, 391 (1913).
11. Convection and Radiation of Heat. Trans. Amer. Electrochem. Soc., **23**, 299 (1913).
12. Flow of Heat Through Furnace Walls: the Shape Factor. (With E. Q. Adams and G. S. Meikle). Trans. Amer. Electrochem. Soc., **24**, 53 (1913).
103. Flames of Atomic Hydrogen. Science, **62**, 463 (1925).
104. Flames of Atomic Hydrogen. G. E. Rev., **29**, 153 (1926).
105. Atomic Hydrogen Arc Welding. (With R. A. Weinman). G. E. Rev., **29**, 160 (1926).
110. Flames of Atomic Hydrogen. Ind. and Engrg. Chem., **19**, 667 (1927).

Part **2** — *Incandescent Lamps and Tungsten*

14. Tungsten Lamps of High-efficiency. I. Blackening of Tungsten Lamps and Methods of Preventing it. II. Nitrogen-filled Lamps. (With J. A. Orange). Proc. AIEE, **32**, 1894 (1913); Trans. AIEE, **32**, 1913 (1913); G. E. Rev., **16**, 956 (1913).
20. The Flicker of Incandescent Lamps on Alternating Current Circuits and Stroboscopic Effects. G. E. Rev., **17**, 294 (1914).

26. The Melting Point of Tungsten. Phys. Rev., **6**, 138 (1915).
34. The Characteristics of Tungsten Filaments as Functions of Temperature. Phys. Rev., **7**, 302 (1916).
111. The Characteristics of Tungsten Filaments as Functions of Temperature. (With H. A. Jones). G. E. Rev., **30**, 408; 310; 354 (1927).
126. Effect of End Losses on the Characteristics of Filaments of Tungsten and other Materials. (With S. MacLane and K. B. Blodgett). Phys. Rev., **35**, 478 (1930).
151. The Design of Tungsten Springs to Hold Tungsten Filaments Taut. (With K. B. Blodgett). Rev. Sci. Instru., **5**, 321 (1934).
156. Radiation and Absorption of Energy by Tungsten Filaments at Low Temperatures. (With J. B. Taylor). Jour. Opt. Soc. Amer., **25**, 321 (1935).
159. The Heat Conductivity of Tungsten and the Cooling Effects of Leads upon Filaments at Low Temperatures. (With J. B. Taylor). Phys. Rev., **50**, 68 (1936).

VOLUME 3

Thermionic Phenomena

Part **1** — *Thermionics — Vacuum Pumps*

17. The Effect of Space Charge and Residual Gases on Thermionic Currents in High Vacuum. Phys. Rev., **2**, 450 (1913).
28. The Pure Electron Discharge and its Applications in Radio Telegraphy and Telephony. G. E. Rev., **18**, 327 (1915); Trans. AIRE, **3**, 261 (1915).
65. Fundamental Phenomena in Electron Tubes Having Tungsten Cathodes. (Part I and Part II). G. E. Rev., **23**, 503, 589 (1920).
79. Use of High-power Vacuum Tubes. Electrical World, **80**, 881 (1922).
81. The Effect of Space Charge and Initial Velocities on the

Potential Distribution and Thermionic Current between Parallel Plane Electrodes. Phys. Rev., **21**, 419 (1923).

85. A New Photo-electric Effect Reflection of Electrons Induced by Light. Science, **58**, 398 (1923).
91. Currents Limited by Space Charge between Coaxial Cylinders. (With K. B. Blodgett). Phys. Rev., **22**, 347 (1923).
93. Currents Limited by Space Charge between Concentric Spheres. (With K. B. Blodgett). Phys. Rcv. **23**, 49 (1924).
133. Diffusion of Electrons back to an Emitting Electrode in a Gas. Phys. Rev., **38**, **1656** (1931).
33. A New Vacuum Gage of Extreme Sensitiveness. (Abstract). Phys. Rev., **1**, 337 (1913).
38. A High Vacuum Mercury Vapor Pump of Extreme Speed. Phys. Rev., **8**, 48 (1916).
44. The Condensation Pump: an Improved Form of High Vacuum Pump. G. E. Rev., **19**, 1060 (1916); Jour. Franklin Inst., **182**, 719 (1916).

Part **2** — *Electron Emission and Adsorbed Films*

36. The Relation Between Contact Potentials and Electrochemical Action. Trans. Amer. Electrochem. Soc., **29**, 125 (1916).
80. Thermionic Effects Caused by Alkali Vapors in Vacuum Tubes. (With K. H. Kingdon). Science, **57**, 58 (1923).
83. Removal of Thorium by Positive Ion Bombardment. (With K. H. Kingdon). Phys. Rev., **22**, 148 (1923).
87. Electron Emission From Caesium-covered Filaments. (With K. H. Kingdon). Phys. Rev., **23**, 112 (1923).
90. The Electron Emission From Thoriated Tungsten Filaments. Phys. Rev., **22**, 357 (1923).
100. Thermionic Effects Caused by Vapors of Alkali Metals. (With K. H. Kingdon). Proc. Roy. Soc., A, **107**, 61 (1925).
109. On the Surface Heat of Charging. (With L. Tonks). Phys. Rev., **29**, 524 (1927).

121. Contact Potential Measurements With Adsorbed Films. (With K. H. Kingdon). Phys. Rev., **34**, 129 (1929).
127. Electrochemical Interactions of Tungsten, Thorium, Caesium, and Oxygen. Ind. and Engrg. Chem., **22**, 390 (1930).
129. Oxygen Films of Tungsten. I. A Study of Stability by Means of Electron Emission in Presence of Cesium Vapor. (With D. S. Villars). JACS, **53**, 486 (1931).
130. The Alleged Production of Adsorbed Films on Tungsten by Active Nitrogen. Phys. Rev., **37**, 1006, (1931).
137. Cesium Films on Tungsten. JACS, **54**, 1252 (1932).
139. The Mobility of Caesium Atoms Adsorbed on Tungsten. (With J. B. Taylor). Phys. Rev., **40**, 463 (1932).
144. The Nature of Adsorbed Films of Caesium on Tungsten. I. The Space Charge Sheath and the Image Force. Phys. Rev., **43**, 224 (1933).
145. The Evaporation of Atoms, Ions, and Electrons from Caesium Films on Tungsten. (With J. B. Taylor). Phys. Rev., **44**, 423 (1933).
148. Thoriated Tungsten Filaments. Jour. Franklin Inst., **217**, 543 (1934).
164. Vapor Pressure of Caesium by the Positive Ion Method. (With J. B. Taylor). Phys. Rev., **51**, 753 (1937).

VOLUME 4

Electrical Discharge

Fundamental Phenomena in Electrical Discharges

82. Positive Ion Currents from the Positive Column of Mercury Arcs. Science, **58**, 290 (1923).
84. Positive Ion Currents from the Positive Column of the Mercury Arc. G. E. Rev., **26**, 731 (1923).
92. A Simple Method for Quantitative Studies of Ionization Phenomena in Gases. Science, **59**, 380 (1924).

97. A New Type of Electric Discharge: the Streamer Discharge. Science, **60**, 392 (1924).

94.
95.
96.
98.
99. } Studies of Electric Discharges in Gases at Low Pressures. (With H. Mott-Smith). G. E. Rev., **27**, 449; 538; 616; 762 (1924).

108. The Theory of Collectors in Gaseous Discharges. (With H. Mott-Smith). Phys. Rev., **28**, 727 (1926).

114a. Electric Discharges in Gases at Low Pressures. Estratto Dagli Atti del Congresso Internazionale del Fisici, Como (Sept. 1927). English translation.

119. Control of an Arc Discharge by Means of a Grid. (With A. W. Hull). Proc. NAS, **51**, 218 (1929).

141a. Electric Discharges in Gases at Low Pressures. Jour. Franklin Inst., **214**, 275 (1932).

154. Electric Discharges in Vacuum and in Gases at Low Pressures. The Denki-Gakkwai, Iwadare Foundation, Lecture III, Japan (1934).

128. Electrical Discharges in Gases. I. Survey of Fundamental Processes. (With K. T. Compton). Rev. Mod. Phys., **2**, 123 (1930).

132. Electrical Discharges in Gases. II. Fundamental Phenomena in Electrical Discharges. (With K. T. Compton). Rev. Mod. Phys., **3**, 191 (1931).

VOLUME 5

Plasma and Oscillations

Ionized Gases

86. The Pressure Effect and Other Phenomena in Gaseous Discharges. Jour. Franklin Inst., **196**, 751 (1923).

101. Scattering of Electrons in Ionized Gases. Phys. Rev., **26**, 585 (1925).

107. The Flow of Ions Through a Small Orifice in a Charged Plate. (With L. Tonks and H. Mott-Smith). Phys. Rev., **28,** 104 (1926).
116. Collisions Between Electrons and Gas Molecules. (With H. A. Jones). Phys. Rev., **31,** 357 (1928).
117. Oscillations in Ionized Gases. Proc. NAS, **14,** 627 (1928).
117a. Oscillations in an Ionized Gas. (With L. Tonks). Science, **68,** 598 (1928).
118. Oscillations in Ionized Gases. (With L. Tonks). Phys. Rev., **33,** 195 (1929).
120. The Interaction of Electron and Positive Ion Space Charges in Cathode Sheaths. Phys. Rev., **33,** 954 (1929).
122. General Theory of the Plasma of an Arc. (With L. Tonks). Phys. Rev. **34,** 876 (1929).
128a. Metastable Atoms and Electrons Produced by Resonance Radiation in Neon. (With C. G. Found). Phys. Rev., **36,** 604 (1930).
136. Study of a Neon Discharge by Use of Collectors. (With C. G. Found). Phys. Rev., **39,** 237 (1932).

VOLUME 6

Structure of Matter

Part **1** — *Atomic Structure*

59. The Structure of Atoms and the Octet Theory of Valence. Proc. NAS, **5,** 252 (1919).
56. The Arrangement of Electrons in Atoms and Molecules. G. E. Rev., **22,** 505, **587,** 789 (1919); JACS, **41,** 868 (1919).
60. The Octet Theory of Valence and its Applications With Special Reference to Organic Nitrogen Compounds. JACS, **42,** 274 (1920).

61. The Structure of Atoms and its Bearing on Chemical Valence. Jour. Ind. and Engrg. Chem., **12**, 386 (1920).
62. The Charge on the Electron and the Value of Planck's Constant **h.** Jour. Franklin Inst., **189**, 603 (1920).
63. Theories of Atomic Structure. Nature, **105**, 261 (1920).
64. The Structure of the Helium Atom. Science, **51**, 604 (1920).
68. The Structure of the Helium Atom. Phys. Rev., **17**, 339 (1921).
69. The Structure of the Static Atom. Science, **53**, 290 (1921).
71. Types of Valence. Science, **54**, 59 (1921).

Part **2** — *Molecules and Crystalline Structure*

58. Isomorphism, Isosterism, and Covalence. JACS, **41**, 1543 (1919).
64a. The Structures of the Hydrogen Molecule and the Hydrogen Ion. Science, **52**, 433 (1920).
76. The Diffusion Coefficient in Solids and its Temperature Coefficient. (With S. Dushman). Phys. Rev., **20**, 113 (1922).
102. The Distribution and Orientation of Molecules. Colloid Symposium Monograph, **3**, 48 (1925).
106. The Effects of Molecular Dissymmetry on Properties of Matter. Colloid Chemistry, **1**, 525 (1926).
125. Forces Near the Surfaces of Molecules. Chem. Rev., **6**, 451 (1929).
67. The Crystal Structure of the Ammonium Halides Above and Below the Transition Temperatures. (With Guy Barlett). JACS, **43**, 84 (1921).
184. Vector Maps and Crystal Analysis. (With D. M. Wrinch). Nature, **142**, 581 (1938).
186. The Role of Attractive and Repulsive in the Formation of Tactoids, Thixotropic Gels, Protein Crystals, and Coacervates. Jour. Chem. Phys., **6**, 873 (1938).
134. Regions of Reversed Magnetization in Strained Wires. (With K. J. Sixtus). Phys. Rev., **38**, 2072 (1931).

VOLUME 7

Protein Structures

Molecular Structure

163. Built-up Films of Proteins and Their Properties. (With V. J. Schaefer and D. M. Wrinch). Science, **85**, 76 (1937).
168. Multilayers of Sterols and the Adsorption of Digitonin by Deposited Monolayers. (With V. J. Schaefer and H. Sobotka). JACS, **59**, 1751 (1937).
169. Improved Methods of Conditioning Surfaces for Adsorption. (With V. J. Schaefer). JACS, **59**, 1762 (1937).
170. Monolayers and Multilayers of Chlorophyll. (With V. J. Schaefer). JACS. **59**, 2075 (1937).
177. The Adsorption of Proteins at Oil-water Interfaces and Artificial Proteinlipoid Membranes. (With D. F. Waugh). Jour. Gen. Physio., **21**, 745 (1938).
178. Activities of Urease and Pepsin Monolayers. (With V. J. Schaefer). JACS, **60**, 1351 (1938).
183. Salted-out Protein Films. (With V. J. Schaefer). JACS, **60**, 2803 (1938).
182a. The Structure of the Insulin Molecule. (With D. M. Wrinch). JACS, **60**, 2247 (1938).
188. Nature of the Cyclol Bond. (With D. M. Wrinch). Nature, **143**, 49 (1939).
189. The Properties and Structure of Protein Films. Proc. Roy. Inst., **30**, 483 (1938).
191. Properties and Structure of Protein Monolayers. (With V. J. Schaefer). Chem. Rev., **24**, 181 (1939).
192. The Structure of Proteins. Proc. Phys. Soc., London, **51**, 592 (1939).
193. Letter to the Editor on Structure of Proteins. Nature, **143**, 280 (1939).
194. A Note on the Structure of Insulin. (With D. M. Wrinch). Proc. Phys. Soc., London, **51**, 613 (1939).

187. Protein Monolayers. Cold Spring Harbor Symposia on Quantitative Biology, **6**, 171 (1938).
196. Pressure-soluble and Pressure-displaceable Components of Monolayers of Native and Denatured Proteins. (With D. F. Waugh). JACS, **62**, 2771 (1940).

VOLUME 8

PROPERTIES OF MATTER

Part **1** — *Fundamental Properties of Solids and Liquids*

42. The Constitution and Fundamental Properties of Solids and Liquids. JACS, **38**, 2221 (1916).
49. The Constitution and Fundamental Properties of Solids and Liquids. II. Liquids. JACS, **39**, 1848 (1917).

Part **2** — *Interfacial Phenomena*

43. The Constitution of Liquids with Especial Reference to Surface Tension Phenomena. Met. and Chem. Engrg., **15**, 468 (1916).
48. The Shapes of Group Molecules Forming the Surfaces of Liquids. Proc. NAS, **3**, 251 (1917).
54. The Mechanism of the Surface Phenomena of Flotation. Trans. Faraday Soc., **15**, 62 (1920); G. E. Rev., **24**, 1025 (1921).
146. Surface Chemistry. Nobel Lecture Presented in Stockholm on December 14, 1932. Kungl. Boktryckeriet. P. A. Norstedt and Söner, Stockholm (1933).
153. Surface Chemistry. The Denki-Gakkwai, Iwadare Foundation, Lecture II. Japan (1934).
162. Two-dimensional Gases, Liquids and Solids. Science, **84**, 379 (1936).
176. Surface Electrification due to the Recession of Aqueous

Solution from Hydrophobic Surfaces. JACS, **60**, 1190 (1938).
185. Repulsive Forces Between Charged Surfaces in Water and the Cause of the Jones-Ray Effect. Science, **88**, 430 (1938).

VOLUME 9

SURFACE PHENOMENA

Part **1** — *Evaporation, Condensation, Adsorption*

16. The Vapor Pressure of Metallic Tungsten. Phys. Rev., **2**, 329 (1913).
23. The Vapor Pressure of the Metals Platinum and Molybdenum. (With G. M. J. Mackay). Phys. Rev., **4**, 377 (1914).
112. The Rates of Evaporation and the Vapor Pressures of Tungsten, Molybdenum, Platinum, Nickel, Iron, Copper, and Silver. (With G. M. J. Mackay and H. A. Jones). Phys. Rev., **30**, 201 (1927).
41. The Evaporation, Condensation, and Reflection of Molecules and the Mechanism of Adsorption. Phys. Rev., **8**, 149 (1916).
47. The Condensation and Evaporation of Gas Molecules. Proc. NAS, **3**, 141 (1917).
50. The Adsorption of Gases on Plane Surfaces of Glass, Mica, and Platinum. JACS, **40**, 1361 (1918).
138. Accommodation Coefficient of Hydrogen: a Sensitive Detector of Surface Films (With K. B. Blodgett). Phys. Rev., **40**, 78 (1932).
140. Vapor Pressures, Evaporation, Condensation, and Adsorption, JACS, **54**, 2798 (1932).
142. A Film Which Adsorbs Atomic H and Does Not Adsorb H_2. (With K. B. Blodgett). JACS, **54**, 3781 (1932).
143. An Extension of the Phase Rule for Adsorption Under Equilibrium and Non-equilibrium Conditions. Jour. Chem. Phys., **1**, 3 (1933).

Part **2** — *Monomolecular Films*

131. Experiments With Oil on Water. Jour. Chem. Education, **8**, 850 (1931).
147. Oil Lenses on Water and the Nature of Monomolecular Expanded Films. Jour. Chem. Phys., **1**, 756 (1933).
150. Mechanical Properties of Monomolecular Films. Jour. Franklin Inst., **218**, 143 (1934). Franklin Medal Speech on May 16, 1934.
157. A New Method of Investigating Monomolecular Films. (With K. B. Blodgett). Kolloid-Zeitschrift, **73**, 257 (1935).
158. Composition of Fatty Acid Films on Water Containing Calcium or Barium Salts. (With V. J. Schaefer). JACS, **58**, 284 (1936).
165. Built-up Films of Barium Stearate and Their Optical Properties. (With K. B. Blodgett). Phys. Rev., **51**, 964 (1937).
167. Optical Measurement of the Thickness of a Film Absorbed from a Solution. (With V. J. Schaefer). JACS, **59**, 1406 (1937).
179a. Overturning and Anchoring of Monolayers. Science, **87**, 493 (1938).
172. The Effect of Dissolved Salts on Insoluble Monolayers. (With V. J. Schaefer). JACS, **59**, 2400 (1937).
181. Effect of X-rays on Surface Potentials of Multilayers. (With F. J. Norton). JACS, **60**, 1513 (1938).
190. Molecular Layers. Pilgrim Trust Lecture. Proc. Roy. Soc., London, A, **170**, 1 (1939).
195. Monolayers on Solids. (Seventeenth Faraday Lecture). Jour. Chem. Soc., London, 511 (1940).
113. The Effect of Monomolecular Films on the Evaporation of Ether Solutions. (With D. B. Langmuir). Jour. Phys. Chem., **31**, 1719 (1927).
207. Molecular Films in Chemistry and Biology. Rutgers University Press, 27 (1942).

VOLUME 10

ATMOSPHERIC PHENOMENA

Part **1** — *Aviation, Weather, Cloud Seeding*

51. The Evaporation of Small Spheres. Phys. Rev., **12,** 368 (1918).
77. Radial Flow in Rotating Liquids. (With H. Mott-Smith). [Abstract]. Phys. Rev., **20,** 95 (1922).
135. A Study of Light Signals in Aviation and Navigation. (With W. F. Westendorp). Physics, **1,** 273 (1931).
160. Airplane Tracks in the Surface of Stratus Clouds. (With A. Forbes). Jour. Aeronautical Sci., **3,** 385 (1936).
173. Air Traffic Regulations as Applied to Private Aviation. The Sportsman Pilot, **18,** 8 (1937).
175. Surface Motion of Water Induced by Wind. Science, **87,** 119 (1938).
198. Rates of Evaporation of Water Through Compressed Monolayers on Water. (With V. J. Schaefer). Jour. Franklin Inst., **235,** 119 (1943).
209. The Production of Rain by a Chain Reaction in Cumulus Clouds at Temperatures Above Freezing. Jour. Met., **5,** 175 (1948).
210. The Growth of Particles in Smokes and Clouds and the Production of Snow from Supercooled Clouds. Proc. Amer. Phil. Soc., **92,** 167 (1948).
213. Control of Precipitation from Cumulus Clouds by Various Seeding Techniques. Science, **112,** 35 (1950).
219. A Seven-day Periodicity in Weather in United States during April, 1950. Bull. Amer. Met. Soc., **31,** 386 (1950).
220. Cloud Seeding by Means of Dry Ice, Silver Iodide, and Sodium Chloride. Trans. N.Y. Acad. Sci., **14,** 40 (1951).

Part **2** *— Smoke Filters — Cloud Droplets (Unpublished)*

225. Super-cooled Water Droplets in Rising Currents of Cold Saturated Air. Report No. RL-223. Parts I and II. October 1943–August 1944. (Re-issued June 1949).
226. Mathematical Investigation of Water Droplet Trajectories. Report No. RL-224. January 1945. (Re-issued June 1949).
227. Mathematical Investigation of Water Droplet Trajectories. Report No. RL-225, December 1944–July 1945. (Re-issued June 1949).
228. Report on Smokes and Filters.

VOLUME 11

CLOUD NUCLEATION

Part **1** *— Nucleation of Clouds with Dry Ice (Unpublished)*

211. Summary of Results Thus Far Obtained in Artificial Nucleation of Clouds. Project Cirrus Report on Meteorological Research (July, 1947).
212. Studies of the Effects Produced by Dry Ice Seeding of Stratus Clouds. Project Cirrus Final Report (December 31, 1948).
214. Progress in Cloud Modification by Project Cirrus. Occasional Report No. 21, Project Cirrus. (April 15, 1950).
215. Cause and Effect Versus Probability in Shower Production. Occasional Report No. 22, Project Cirrus. (July 15, 1950).
216. A Gamma Pattern Seeding of Stratus Clouds, Flight 52, and a Racetrack Pattern Seeding of Stratus Clouds, Flight 53. (With C. A. Woodman). Occasional Report No. 23, Project Cirrus. (June 1, 1950).
217. Results of the Seeding of Cumulus Clouds in New Mexico. Occasional Report No. 24, Project Cirrus. (June 1, 1950).
218. Studies of Tropical Clouds. Occasional Report No. 25, Project Cirrus. (July 1, 1950).

*Part **2** – Nucleation of Clouds with Silver Iodide (Unpublished)*

222. Final Report, Project Cirrus. Part II. Analysis of the Effects of Periodic Seeding of the Atmosphere with Silver Iodide. 340 pages. (May 1953).
229. Widespread Control of Weather by Silver Iodide Seeding. 55-RL-1263. July 1955.

VOLUME 12

LANGMUIR, THE MAN AND THE SCIENTIST

*Part **1** — A Biography*

*Part **2** – Philosophy of Science*

70. Future Developments of Theoretical Chemistry. Chem. and Met. Engrg., **24**, 533 (1921).
115. Atomic Hydrogen as an Aid to Industrial Research. Science, **57** (February 24, 1928). Printed again in Scientific Monthly, **70**, 3 (1950).
123. Address of Presentation of Priestley Medal Award. Ind. and Engrg. Chem. **21**, 896 (1929).
124. Modern Concepts in Physics and Their Relation to Chemistry. JACS, **51**, 2847 (1929). [President's Address].

126a Selecting the Chemist-elect. Jour. Chem. Education, **7** (March, 1930). [Address delivered at dedication of Francis P. Garvan Chair of Chemical Education at Johns Hopkins, October 11, 1929].

149. Science as a Guide in Life. G.E. Rev., **37**, 312 (1934).
155. Mechanical Properties of Matter. Mch. Engrg., **57**, 486 (1935).
166. Chemical Research. Ind. and Engrg. Chem., **15**, 188 (1937).

[Address delivered at the dedication of the new building of Mellon Institute, May 5–9, 1937].

171a. Fundamental Research and its Human Value. G.E. Rev., **40**, 569 (1937).

180. The Speed of the Deer Fly. Science, **87**, 233 (1938).

190a. A chapter "Simple Experiments in Science" on page 3 of book: "Excursions in Science", edited by Neil G. Reynolds and Ellis L. Manning, McGraw-Hill Book Company (1939).

197. Science, Common Sense, and Decency. Science, **97**, 1 (1943). [Retiring President's Address from AAAS].

199. Unforeseeable Results of Research. U.S. Rubber Company Broadcast. (January 21, 1945).

200. Electronics of Tomorrow. N.Y. Herald Tribune Forum. (November 17, 1943).

201. Discussion on Science Legislation. Joint Hearings on Science Bills before Senate Military Affairs and Commerce Committees. (October 1945).

202. Testimony on Atomic Energy Control. Senate Hearings on Atomic Energy. (November 30, 1945).

203. World Control of Atomic Energy. Proc. Amer. Phil. Soc., **90**, No. 1 (1946). [Read November 16, 1945 in the Symposium on Atomic Energy and Its Implications].

204. My Trip to Russia. Chem. and Engrg. News, **24**, 759 (1946).

205. Science and Incentives in Russia. Scientific Monthly, **63**, 85 (1946).

206. Faraday Medalist: Response by I. Langmuir to Presentation Address by A. P. M. Fleming. Elec. Engrg., **63**, 463 (1944).

221. Planning for Progress: Two Alternatives. Columbia University Engineering Center News, **1**, 2 (1951). [Talk presented at Columbia University Engineering Center Dinner on November 7, 1951].

223. Saul Dushman — A Human Catalyst. Vacuum, **3**, 112 (1954).

224. Freedom — The Opportunity to Profit from the Unexpected. Res. Lab. Bulletin, Fall 1956.

Index

ABBOTT, EDWIN 285
ABETTI, GEORGIO 218
Absolute zero 94
Academy of Lagado 117
Academy of Music 220
Academy of Sciences, Copenhagen 195
Academy of Sciences of the U.S.S.R. 280, 283
ADAM, N. K. 231
ADAMS, MISS 223
Adoptions 162, 176
Adsorption 229 et seq.
AEG Laboratories 196
Aircraft icing 275
Air Force Icing Research Laboratory 277
Airplane, riding and flying 208, 210, 214
ALEXANDERSON, E. F. W. 153, 211
ALLEN, H. S. 190
Allison effect 313
American Aristotype Company 110
American Association for the Advancement of Science 187, 199
American Chemical Society 123, 153, 165, 174, 187, 259, 312
American Forum of the Air 320
American Meteorological Society 297, 304, 306
American Physical Society 165, 168, 173, 191
Angkor Vat 251
Anti-submarine research 156, 272
Appendectomy, 1941 324
APPERSON, JOHN S. 143, 198, 203, 260, 274
Argon, isolation of 63, 97
ARMSTRONG, EDWIN 21
Artificial fever 323
Artificial fog 265, 266, 269
Artificial rain 298
Artificial snow 20, 297
Art-gallerygoer 319
ASTAIRE, FRED 318
Atlantic Monthly 107, 235
Atmospheric studies 294
Atomic bomb 18, 279, 293
Atomic energy 18, 293, 294, 320
Atomic hydrogen 20, 126, 127, 129, 170, 187

Atomic hydrogen welding 20, 97 129, 170, 187
Atomic numbers, table of 171
Atomic theory 97
Atom structure 20, 152, 164, 187
Atom's electrical charge 171
AUNT ANNA 257
AUNT DOLLY BURGE 35
AUNT FANNIE 144
AUNT TILLIE 62
Awkwardness with women 138
Aylesworth 218, 219

B–17 flying laboratory 305
BADEN-POWELL, SIR ROBERT 141
Baekeland 123
Bathythermographs 205
BEARD, DANIEL CARTER 141
BECKER, JOSEPH 191
BEERY, WALLACE 318
BELL TELEPHONE LABORATORIES 160, 191, 222
BELLO, FRANCIS 307, 308
BENNETT, HUGH 199
BENNETT, PROFESSOR JOHN IRA 154
Berchtesgaden 82
BERG, PROFESSOR 243, 245
BERLIN, IRVING 253
BERZELIUS, BARON 166, 171
Binaural sound 158, 217, 270
Binaural stethoscope 160
Biographical Memoirs of Fellows of the Royal Society 15
BIRR, KENDALL 110, 114
BLACKETT, P. M. S. 91
Blind man tests 158
BLODGETT, KATHERINE 201, 226, 234, 254, 260
Blumenbach's famous collection of skulls 90
Bohr Institute for Theoretical Physics, Copenhagen 240
BOHR, NIELS 165, 167, 173, 188, 193, 194, 195, 245
Bolton Landing, Lake George 60
BORN, MAX 188, 194
BOW, CLARA 239
BOWEN, HAROLD 212, 216
Boy scouts 141, 294
BRAGG, W. H. 164, 194
BREENE, CAPTAIN 210
BRIDGMAN, P. W. 95, 105, 174
BRIER, GLENN W. 314
BRILLOUIN, L. 194
BROOKE, RUPERT 171
BROOKS, CHARLES F. 215
BROWN, MISS 144
BURWELL, DR. 327, 328
Business Week 124
BUTLER, J. O. 203
BUTLER, NICHOLAS MURRAY 188
BUTLER, SAMUEL 136
BUTTON, MAJOR 210
BYERS, HORACE R. 308, 309

Camp Columbia 69
Camping 139
Cancer operations 259, 324
CANNINE, GEORGE 77
Cannizzaro Award 187
Carnegie Hall 223
CARNEGIE, HATTIE 239
Carnegie Institute 98
Carnegie Research Assistantships 99
CAROTHERS, W. H. 21
Cataracts, eye 324
Cavendish Laboratory 195
CECILE, CROWN PRINCESS 154
Chain reaction, atmosphere 302, 303, 304
Chandler Award 187

CHAPMAN 255, 257
Charter League 257
Chemical and engineering news 280
Chemical warfare service 269
Chemisorption 233
Chemists' Club 27, 29, 60, 228
Chestnut Hill Academy 31, 57, 60, 62
CHEVALIER, MAURICE 318
Chlorine gas smelling 49
CHRISTIE, MARY 317
City College of New York 168
CLARK, VICTOR 276
Classical music and the opera 318
CLEMENT, JOHN 80
Cloud dodging 215
Cloud seeders, commercial 307
Cloud seeding 17, 20, 216, 297, 298, 299, 303, 305, 313
Cloud studies 278
Clouds, subcooled 277
COLLINS, DAN 144
COLLINS, MRS. GERTRUDE 10, 23
Columbia's School of Mines 67, 76
Columbia University 38, 67, 93, 120, 168, 187, 191
Comic strips 319
COMINGS, DR. ISAAC MILLER 35, 36, 46
COMINGS, SADIE 34
COMPTON, A. H. 153, 166, 194
CONANT, J. B. 259
Concentration, powers of 179
Conservation 143, 198, 260
Convection 96
COOLIDGE, CALVIN 322
COOLIDGE, W. D. 116, 117, 135, 137, 138, 140, 157, 270, 313
Cottage Park 255
COYLE, AUBREY 215
Cross-fertilization of ideas 222
Crown Island 200
CROWTHER, J. G. 233
CRUM, BOBBY 217, 218, 219
CRUM, MRS. R. P. 217
Cryogenics 94
Crystalline lattice 231
CURIE, MADAME 194, 195
CURTIS, MISS 145

DALTON, JOHN 203
Dancing lessons 139
DANIELS, JOSEPHUS 156
DARWIN, C. G. 169, 170, 190
DAVIS, A. G. 109, 218, 239
Davis-Barnes effect 313
DAVY, SIR HUMPHREY 225, 261
DAY, CLARENCE 31
DEAN, ALICE 63, 97
DEAN, DR. and MRS. HORACE 28, 64
Death in 1957 329
Deaths, family 223, 258, 324
DEBROBLIE, L. V. 194
DEBYE 193, 194, 196
DE COSTA, BENJAMIN FRANKLIN 198
DE-DONDER, T. H. 194
Deep-sea tests on Malay 161
Deer fly speed 311
DE FOREST, LEE 154
DEWAR, SIR JAMES 228, 229
DICKENS, CHARLES 282
DIESEL, RUDOLF 21
DIRAC, P. A. M. 194
Direction, sense of 159
Dissociation in gases 95, 96, 226
Divergent phenomena 130, 302, 319
Double-channel listening system 221

DOUGHTY, PROFESSOR HOWARD 188
Dramatics 139, 146
DRESSLER, MARIE 318
Dry-ice substitute 301, 302
DUCIE, COUSIN 144
Ductile tungsten 118
Dufresne Brothers 55
Duke University 312
DURANT, WILL 319
DUSHMAN, SAUL 15, 108, 153
Dynamics of gases at high temperatures and low pressures 129

Eastman Kodak 110
Echo location for the blind 160
ECKENER, DR. HUGO 214
École Alsacienne 53
École Jeanne d'Arc 55
École Mange 55
EDISON, THOMAS A. 94, 130, 135, 156
Edison General Electric Company 109
EHRENFEST, P. 194
EHRENHAFT, PROF., Vienna 248
EINSTEIN, ALBERT 113, 194, 196
Einstein formula for mass-energy equivalence 18
EISENHOWER, GENERAL 287
ELECTOR GEORGE AUGUSTUS 89
Electroacoustics 94
Electrochemical interactions of tungsten, thorium, caesium and oxygen 187
Electrostatic precipitation 273, 275
Emerald Buddha 251
Englewood Press 45
Erie Canal boat 28
EVELITH, C. E. 157
Extra-Sensory Perception (ESP) Laboratory 312
Eye trouble 30, 304, 325

FALCONER, RAYMOND 307
FARADAY 225, 228, 230, 261
Faraday medal 294
FAUGHT, FRANCIS and ALBERT 61
Feedback between science and technology 113
FERGUSON, VAUGHN 211, 270, 271
FERMI 193
Fever, artificial 323
FINK, COLIN G. 107, 137, 140, 230
FISHER, H. PRATT 321
Flying saucers 312
Fog, artificial 265, 266, 269
FONDA, GORDON 147, 316
FOWLER, R. H. 194
FRANKLAND, SIR EDWARD 167
FRANKLIN, BENJAMIN 208, 228, 233
FRANKLIN, E. C. 173
Franklin Institute 253
Free enterprise 322
Fresh Air Club 70, 71
FRODSHAM 137, 140
Fujiyama 251

GABOR, DENNIS 15, 21, 186, 247, 311
GALSWORTHY, JOHN 241, 242
GALVANI 123
GANDINI, ANGELO 194
GARBO, GRETA 318
Gas from lamp glass 121
Gases, thermal effects 152

Gases, velocity of reactions 105
GAUSS, KARL FRIEDRICH 80
General Electric Company 10, 13, 94, 109
General Electric Research Laboratory 10, 15, 16, 21, 22, 107
General Electric Review 228
Geophone 160
Geophysics, advances in 310
Georgia Augusta University at Gottingen 86, 89
Gibbs law 230
Gibbs medal 78, 187
GIBBS, WILLARD 229
GIBSON, BURDETTE 141
GIBSON, CHARLES DANA 41
GIBSON, DEWOLF 141, 142, 206
GIBSON, LANGDON 18, 141
GIBSON (family) 154
GILMARTIN, MAJOR GENERAL 210
GODDEN, RUMER 121
Gottingen 86, 89, 93, 100, 106, 192
Graduate work in Germany 77
Graduated optical interference colors 236
Graeco-Schenectady 154
Graff Zeppelin 214
GRAY, GEORGE W. 235
Grid control arc with A. W. Hull 20
GUEST, EDGAR 114
GUYE, E. 194
GUYRE, JOHN 140

H.R.H. HERTIGEN AN SODERMANLAND 243
H.R.H. PRINCE WILHELM 241
HAHN 18, 280
Half-life of radioactive elements 233
Haleys comet 146
HALSTEAD, MAURICE H. 303
HARDY, PROF. (electric organ) 223
HARKER, DAVID 169, 173
HARKINS, W. D. 231
HARMON, EVELYN 10, 281
HARRIMAN, AMBASSADOR 290
HARRIS, CLYDE 308
HARRIS, FRANK 311
Harvard Club 168, 285, 322
Harvard Medical School 327
HAVEN, OTIS 257
HAWKINS, LAURENCE A. 15, 110, 115, 163
HAYWARD, NATHAN 253
Heart attacks 325, 327, 328, 329
Heat loss 126
Heat transfer 96
HEGEL 320
Heidelberg 38
HEISENBERG 193, 194
Helium, liquefaction of 293
HENNELLY, EDWARD F. 10, 16, 159, 270, 271
HENRIOT, E. 194
HENRY, JOSEPH 124
High-temperature low-pressure chemistry 152
High vacuum 20, 118, 122
Hiking 78, 139
HILBERT, DAVID 80, 90
HILDERBAND, JOEL 171
Hitchcock lectures 16
HITLER, ADOLF 247
HOFMAN, JOSEF 223
HOLMES, OLIVER WENDELL, JR. 23
HOOVER, HERBERT 188, 322
Hotel Bellevue 54
Hotel Belmont 57
Hotel de l'Athenée 52
Hotel des Salines 54

HOUGHTON, HENRY 308
Housekeeping habits 65
Hughes medal 163, 187
HULL, ALBERT W. 10, 16, 153, 157, 226, 316
HUMPHREYS, PRES., Stevens Tech. 103, 105
Hungarian Royal Family 248
Hurricane-seeding 300
HUXLEY, ALDOUS 13
Hydrodynamics 204
Hydrogen, atomic 20, 126, 127, 170, 187

Ice crystals 295, 296
Ice nuclei 276
Icing phenomena 275, 277
Illness, final 326
Incandescent lamp gases, behavior of 129
Independent surface action principle 235
Industrial and engineering chemistry 27
INGERSOLL, RAYMOND 199
Insects, live in a vacuum? 115
Interfaces 229
International General Electric 251
Iodide of nitrogen, early experiments with 50
Ionization 94
IRVING, AMELLIUS 29
Irving Institute 49
Iwadare lectures 250

JAFFE, BERNARD 46, 117, 175
Japanese Institute of Electrical Engineers 251
JEFFRIES, DR. ZAY 131, 134
JEWETT, FRANK F. 89
Johns Hopkins 170
JOHNSTON, ERIC 283
Johnstown, Pennsylvania, Flood 32
JONES, H. A. 226
JONES, L. W. 174
Journal of Chemical Education 201
Journal of the Society of Motion Picture Engineers 221
JUST and HANAMAN 135

Kaiser Wilhelm Gesellschaft 196
KATZENBACH, EMERY 51
KC tube 271
KEATS 22
KELLOGG, E. W. 158, 220
KELVIN, LORD 68, 120
KETTERING, CHARLES 116, 188, 316
KING ALBERT 195
King and Royal Family (Sweden) 241, 244
KINGDON, KENNETH H. 10, 15, 96, 205, 225, 226, 234
KING ERNEST AUGUSTUS OF HANOVER 89
KING OF CAMBODIA 252
KLEIN, PROFESSOR FELIX 80, 90, 94, 95
KNAPP, W. J. 199
KNOX, JOHN 34
KNUDSEN, M. 194
KOSSEL, ALBRECHT 167, 169
KRAMERS, H. A. 194
KUHFUSS, FRAULEIN MARTHA 87

Laboratory diaries 137
LACKMAN, ARTHUR 170
LAFAYETTE, MARQUIS DE 34
LAGERLOF, SELMA 244

Lake George 17, 143, 197, 204, 205
Lake George Protective Association 199, 294
Lake Sacandaga 200
LAMB, HORACE 204, 239
Lamp bulb blackening 132
Lamp, electric 94, 95, 97, 131, 228
Lamp, evacuation 129
Lamp filament 95, 231
Lamp, gas-filled 20, 134, 187
LANDOR, WALTER SAVAGE 324
LANGEVIN, D. 194
LANGMUIR, ALEXANDER 10, 17, 257, 259, 322
LANGMUIR, ALICE (DEAN) 63, 97, 254
LANGMUIR, ARTHUR 24, 60, 63, 97, 144, 207, 254, 258, 276
LANGMUIR, BARBARA 176, 179, 227, 238, 254, 258
LANGMUIR, CHARLES HERBERT 24
LANGMUIR, MRS. CHARLES HERBERT 320
LANGMUIR, CHARLES, DR. 26, 28, 30, 31, 32, 34, 35, 37, 46
Langmuir correction factor 314
LANGMUIR, DAVID 10, 191, 202, 254, 255, 257
LANGMUIR, DEAN 22, 24, 34, 70, 101, 144, 239, 254, 276, 281 et seq., 292
LANGMUIR, EDITH 238, 254, 256, 257
Langmuir film balance 234
LANGMUIR, HERBERT 74, 98, 144, 238, 254, 256, 257, 258, 322
Langmuir isotherm 233
LANGMUIR, JOHN D. 276
LANGMUIR, KENNETH 11, 176, 227, 238, 254, 257, 279, 320, 323
Langmuir legend 316, 317
LANGMUIR, MAMA 151
LANGMUIR, MARION 227, 279; *see also* Mersereau
Langmuir Mountain 315
LANGMUIR, MRS. EDITH 10
LANGMUIR, MRS. LAURA 10
LANGMUIR, MRS. MARION 11
Langmuir paradox 247
Langmuir probe 20
LANGMUIR, ROBERT 10, 162, 258
LANGMUIR, SADIE 64
Langmuir–Schaefer smoke generator 270
Langmuir–Stokowski visit 221
Langmuir trough 234
LAPLACE 320
Leibnitz 169
Leipzig 116
LEOPOLD, LUNA B. 303
LEVERRIER 169
LEVI-CIVITA 193
LEWIS, GEORGE C. 228
LEWIS, GILBERT NEWTON 166, 167
Lewis–Langmuir atom 168
Library of Congress 10
Light scattering 213
LINDBERGH, CHARLES 187, 210, 213, 221
LISZT 169
Literary Society 139
LITTLE, ARTHUR D. 111
LOMBROSO, CESARE 317
Lorentzes 195
LUCE, CLARE BOOTHE 320, 321
LUNDBERGH, H. 227
LUNT, SARAH ANN 34
Lycée Carnot 57, 192
LYSENKO, T. D. 293

MACADAM 255, 257
Manhattan Hotel 39

MANN, HORACE 123
MARCONI, ANGLIELMO 188
Marriage 150
MARTIN, MILES J. 10
MARX 320
MARY QUEEN OF SCOTS 35
Massachusetts Institute of Technology 110, 116, 202
Matterhorn, climbing 13, 189
Mayflower 26, 34
MCCALL, JOHN A. 37, 59
MCDONALD, JAMES E. 310
MCLEOD, CHARLIE 54
MEITNER, LISE 196, 280
MENDELEYEV 172
Mercury pump, condensation 20
MERSEREAU, DOROTHY 148, 200, 203, 240, 241, 258
MERSEREAU, MARION 22, 144, 147, 172, 200; *see also* Langmuir
MILLER, MARILYN 239
MILLIKAN, ROBERT ANDREWS 153, 166
MILTON, JOHN 22, 238
MINKOWSKI, HERMANN 80, 90
Mitogenetic rays 313
Molecular physics 187
Molybdenum, ductile 107
Monatomic films 129
Monolayers 230, 233, 261
Monomolecular films 233, 234, 235
MONTAIGNE, MICHEL DE 59
MOREHEAD, AMBASSADOR 241
MOSELEY, HENRY 171
Motion picture engineers 221
Motor trip, 1957 325
MOTT-SMITH, HAROLD 204, 247
Mountain climbing 54, 139
Mount Sinai Hospital 16
Mount Washington 274 et seq., 279
Multicylinder method 277
MUNSTERBERG, HUGO 98
Museum of Natural History 304
Museum of Science and Industry 45
Music 318
MUSSOLINI 193
Mutual Life Insurance Company 36

Nakant Research Station 157
NAPOLEON 320
National Academy of Sciences 163, 199, 264, 302
National Broadcasting Co. 218, 228
National Defense Research Committee 262
NERNST, DR. WALTHER 80, 93, 95, 97, 187, 196, 246
New Mexico experimental range 305
New Mexico School of Mines 17, 305
NEWTON, ISAAC 311
New York Life Insurance Company 25, 32, 37, 38, 52, 58, 74, 144
New York Public Library 10
New York Times 239
New Yorker 295
NEWTON, SIR ISAAC 169, 232
Nichols medal 153, 174, 187
NICHOLSON, J. W. 190
Nitrate supply committee 161
Nitrogen and mercury vapor studies 133
Nitrogen fixation 161
NOBEL, ALFRED 123, 242
Nobel Foundation 241
Nobel prize 21, 26, 60, 62, 94, 97, 100, 107, 129, 175, 187, 201, 207, 225, 226, 227, 228, 235, 238, 241, 242, 244, 246

Nobel prize tour 250, 321, 323
Non-reflecting films 20
Northwestern University 187
NOTTINGHAM, PROFESSOR WAYNE, M.I.T. 202, 213
NOVICOV, N. 282
NOYES, PROF. A. A. 110, 209
N-rays 312, 313
Nude swimming 201

Oberlin College 89
Observatorio Arcetri 218
Octet theory of atom 230
Opera, love of 53, 318
OPPENHEIMER 21
Order of the Rising Sun 251
Organic monolayers 236
OSBORNE, MISS 149
Osmotic pressure 94
OSWALD, WILHELM 114
Overseeding to prevent rain 299
OVID 250
Oxygen in blast furnaces 293
Oxygen jag 217

Panic of 1893 109
Paris 38
PARKHURST, MISS 223
PASTEUR 58, 123, 124
PAULI, W. S. 153, 173, 194
PEALE, REVEREND NORMAN VINCENT 114
Benobscot Bay seals 19
Pergamon Press 9
Periodic seeding 307
Peripatetic school of Aristotle and Theophrastus 86
PERKIN 123
Perkin medal 119, 121, 187
PFEIFFER, G. A. 191
PFEIFFER, JOHN 212
Philadelphia Orchestra 217
Philosophy of history 230
Phonetic spelling 137
Piano-plunking 88
Pianola 178
Picasso's blue period 14
PICCARD, AUGUST 194
Pilot's license 214
PLANCK, M. 194, 196
Planet Neptune 169
Plasmas 15, 20, 129
Playhouse 200
PLUTARCH 186
POCKELS, MISS 233
POINCARÉ, HENRI 197
Politics, interest and activity 143, 257, 321
POLLINGER, ALOIS 189
POND, DR. (Stevens Tech.) 102, 105, 106
Poulenc Frères 52
Pratt Institute 39, 49, 62, 68
Precipitation ice static 273, 275
PRINCE CARL, Sweden 243
PRINCESS SYBILLA, Sweden 243
Princeton University 187
Proceedings of the National Academy of Sciences 247
Proceedings of the Royal Society 247
Project Cirrus 299, 300, 301, 305, 316
Project Manhattan 280
Propagation of sound 160
Protein monolayers 20
Public Health Services Communicable Diseases Center 328
Public School No. 11 51
Pyramids 251

Quantitative analysis of gas 124
Quantum theory 173

RABI, I. I. 46
Rain, artificial 298
Radar 222
Radio research 154
Radio talk, NBC 239
Radium-water treatments 323
RAYLEIGH, LORD 97, 190, 228, 233, 265
Rayleigh–Pockels–Devaux–Marcelin technique 234
RCA Victor 158, 160, 218, 220
Reading 319
REED, DR. FREDERICK 57, 62
Reeds Academy 61
Reform Medical College 35
Reichelderfer (weather bureau) 306
Reichstag Fire 248
Religious ideas 320
Republican ticket 321, 322
Resources for the Future, Inc. 310
Retirement dinner 324
REX, COMMANDER DANIEL F. 300
REYNOLDS, STEVE 306
RHINE, J. D. and ESP 312, 313
RICE, E. W., JR. 109, 156
RICHARDSON, B. H. 191, 194
RIDEAL, SIR EDWARD 195, 228, 236
ROGERS, DR. OSCAR H. 32
ROGERS, GINGER 318
ROGERS, WILL 114, 319
ROOSEVELT, ELEANOR 199
Royal National Academy of Lincie (Rome) 187
Royal Society of London 163, 187
ROYCE, JOSIAH 124
ROZENDAAL, DR. HANS 258
RUDEBACH, BARON and BARONESS 241
Rumford Medal 187
RUSKIN, JOHN 273
RUSSELL, BERTRAND 176
Russia, invitation to 282
Russian Academy 292
RUTH, BABE 250
RUTHERFORD, SIR ERNEST 153, 166, 173, 188, 193, 195, 227

SABIN 137, 140
Sargasso Sea 204
SCHAAR, BERNARD E. 123
SCHAEFER, VINCENT J. 10, 17, 204, 205, 213, 215, 216, 234, 260, 262 et seq., 294, 295, 297, 301, 304, 305
Schenectady Golf Club 316
Schoharie Valley 267, 268
SCHRODINGER, E. 194
SCHWEITZER, ALBERT 93
Science 303
Science and Resources 310
Scientific Monthly 280
Seals, Penobscot Bay 19
SEATON, MARY 34
Seaweed, windrows 204
Serendipity 122, 124, 263, 264, 270
SETON, ERNEST THOMPSON 141
SHAKESPEARE 169
SHEARER, NORMA 295
SHERRINGTON 241, 242
SIEMENS, ALEXANDER 134
Siemens Laboratory 196, 247
Silver iodide 270, 301, 302
SINCLAIR, UPTON 319
Skating 139, 141
Skiing 84, 139
SMITH, EDGAR F. 89
Smoke-filter program 20, 264, 265, 278
Smoke-filtration study 262

Smoke generator 20, 264 et seq., 302
Snow, artificial 20, 297
SNOW, C. P. 147
SOBOTAKA, HARRY 16, 236
Society of Chemical Industry 187
SÖDERBAUM, PROFESSOR, Swedish Academy 227
Sound-directed torpedo 157
Space charge 20, 129, 154
SPILHAUS, DR. ATHELSTAN 205
Sputnik I 293
STALIN 290
Standard Oil Company 267
Stanford University 173
STAPP, COL. JOHN PAUL 164
STEINMETZ, C. P. 22, 110, 113, 146
Stereophonic sound 160
Stereophotography 276
STEVENS, EDWIN AUGUST 100
Stevens Institute of Technology 96, 100, 105, 113
STEVENSON, ALEX 211
STIEGLITZ, JULIUS OSCAR 78
STILLMAN, DR. THOMAS 100, 102, 105, 106
STOKOWSKI, LEOPOLD 88, 158, 160, 188, 217, 219, 220, 222, 223
Storms, manmade 60
STRASSMAN 18, 280
STRAUSS, NATHAN 199
Strontium nitrate red fire 65
Submarine detection 20, 160
SUITS, C. G. 10
SUMMERHAYES, HARRY, JR. 10, 181, 258
SUMMERHAYES, MRS. HARRY, JR. 11
Supercooled water droplets 274, 275
Surface chemistry 14, 20, 175, 225, 227, 228, 237, 239, 261, 278
Surface films 271
Surface lattice 231
Surface phenomena 233
Surface tension 229, 230, 290
Swedish Academy of Sciences 227, 237, 242
SWEETSER, SAMUEL PARTRIDGE 137, 225, 226, 261
Swimming 139
SWOPE, GERARD 239
SZILARD, LEO 247, 248

Taj Mahal 251
TAYLOR, DEEMS 223
TAYLOR, J. B. 226
TAYLOR, SIR HUGH 15, 105, 204
Technische Hochschule 187
Television and radio programs 319
Tennessee Valley Authority 163
Tennis 139
Theory-first-then-experiment school 263
Thermal conduction 96
Thermionic emission 129, 152, 187, 231
Thermodynamics, second law 91
Thickness gauge 236
THOMSON, ELIHU 110, 160, 195
Thomson–Houston Company 109
THOMSON, J. J. 119, 165, 188, 225
THOREAU, HENRY DAVIS 224
Thoriated tungsten filament 20
Thunderstorm, unusual type 298
TILDSDALE, MISS 144
Time 305, 315
Time-lapse camera 268
Time-Life 308
Tongue Mountain 200

TONKS, LEWI 226
Toronto Exposition of 1896 62
Toronto Indian Reservation 28
Torpedo, sound-directed 157
TOULOUSE-LAUTREC 22
Toilet paper experiment 203
Traditional attitude, physicists and chemists 232
Tropical hurricanc 256
TRUMAN, PRESIDENT HARRY 287
Tufts 83
Tungsten contacts for automobile ignition 116
Tungsten filaments 117, 122, 230
Tungsten gas problem 118

Ultramicro determination of nitrogen by absorption spectroscopy 16
Ultraviolet kick 323
Uncertainty principle 174
UNCLE MATT 62
Union College 10
United States Public Health Service 17
United States Weather Bureau 83
University of California 16
University of Colorado 98
University of Edinburgh 26, 187
University of Gottingen 79, 83
University of Illinois 174
University of Leipzig 114
University of London 247
University of North Carolina 312
University of Pennsylvania 89
Uranium fission 18

Vacuum pump 266
Vacuum tube, travel in 316
Valence, mystery of 166
VAN BRUNT 137, 140
VAN DE WATER, RUTH 10, 281, 282, 288
VERSCHAFFELT, R. 194
VON BRAUN, WERNHER 295
VON HINDENBURG, German President 247
VONNEGUT, BERNARD 298, 301, 302, 305
VOSE, MAJ. GEN. JOSEPH 34
Vroman's Nose 267, 268

WAGNER, RICHARD 60
WALPOLE, HORACE 123
Water droplet trajectories 277
Water, making 127
Water-seeding experiments 304
Wave studies 15
Wave theory of plasmas 247
WAY, HAROLD E. 10
Weather bureau 301, 306
Weather study 60, 175, 203, 277
WEBER, WILHELM EDWARD 89
Welding, atomic hydrogen 20, 170, 187
Western Electric Company 144, 157, 166
WHITE, WILLIAM C. 10, 108, 153
WHITNEY, DR. WILLIS R. 108, 110, 112, 122, 124, 130, 134, 137, 140, 156, 192, 209, 211, 221, 263, 317
WHITON, MR. and MRS. CORBETT 62
WHITTAKER, PROFESSOR E. T. 190
Wiener–Khintchin Theorem 247
Williams College 144

WILSON, C. R. 194, 195, 199
Wilson cloud chamber 303
WILSON, MITCHELL 23
Wind tunnel 267
Winnie Mae 214
WOHLER, FRIEDRICH 89
WOLFE, THOMAS 23
WOLFGANG, PAUL I. 166
WOOD, PROFESSOR, R. W. 170
WOODWARD, DR. R. S. 68, 120
Worcester College 35
WORKMAN, E. J. 10, 17, 305, 306, 308, 309, 314, 315
World War I 154
World War II 259
WRINCH, DOROTHY M. 236, 314
WRIGHT, ORVILLE 188

X-ray crystallography 230
X-ray spectra of the elements 172

YATES, MISS 144
Yonkers *Herald-Statesman* 45

ZIMBALIST, MRS. (née Alma Gluck) 223

Printed in Great Britain